Health
Education

Health Education

A Guide for Teachers and a Text for Teacher Education

project of Joint Committee on Health Problems in Education of the National Education Association and the American Medical Association with the co-operation of contributors and consultants

edited by BERNICE R. MOSS, Ed.D.

Professor of Health Education
University of Utah, *Editor*

WARREN H. SOUTHWORTH, Dr. P.H.

Professor of Health Education
University of Wisconsin, *Associate Editor*

JOHN LESTER REICHERT, M.D.

Chicago, Illinois, *Associate Editor*

Fifth Edition *Completely Rewritten, 1961*

published by NATIONAL EDUCATION ASSOCIATION
OF THE UNITED STATES
1201 Sixteenth Street, N.W.
Washington 6, D.C.

Preface

The Joint Committee on Health Problems in Education of the National Education Association and the American Medical Association is happy to present this fifth edition of a pioneering venture in health education which it first presented in 1924.

Health education for the improvement of our children's health involves organized health teaching, co-ordination of health learnings and experience, counseling and guidance. Health education is closely related to physical education and recreation and recognizes the importance of these programs for improved health of children and youth. The full potential of health education can be realized only when school, home, and community are interrelated.

With these goals in mind, *Health Education* has been completely rewritten with the hope that it will not only serve as a source book for teachers in the schools and as a text for teacher education, but will also be a valuable reference for physicians, nurses, and members of other professions related to the school health field.

Health Education is a companion volume of *School Health Services and Healthful School Living,* first published in 1953 and 1957, respectively. These volumes offer a comprehensive view of the total school health program—education, service, and environment—and will assist in answering most of the health problems in education. This fifth edition of *Health Education* is offered in the confident belief that it will serve as a guide in the changing concepts of teaching in the health field, and will further our common goal: better health for the school children and youth of America.

The Joint Committee and its parent organizations, the National Education Association and the American Medical Association, wish to express their grateful appreciation to the Editors, the Sub-Committee on Revision of *Health Education,* and the many consultants and contributors who have worked with them to produce this modern book. Bernice R. Moss, Ed.D., the Editor, served as the education member of the editorial team. She was a member of the Joint Committee in 1944-49. Warren H. Southworth, Dr. P.H., was the Associate Editor concerned with public health. John Lester Reichert, M.D., the Associate Editor for medicine, was appointed to the Joint Committee in 1960. The Chairman of the Sub-Committee on Revision, Robert Yoho, H.S.D., guided the book's development through three difficult years.

DELBERT OBERTEUFFER, Ph.D., *Chairman, 1956-58*
EWALD H. PAWSAT, M. D., *Chairman, 1958-59*
LLOYD S. MICHAEL, Ed.D., *Chairman, 1959-60*
JAY J. JOHNS, M.D., *Chairman, 1960-61*

JOINT COMMITTEE ON HEALTH PROBLEMS IN EDUCATION OF THE NATIONAL EDUCATION ASSOCIATION AND THE AMERICAN MEDICAL ASSOCIATION

Members of the Joint Committee During Preparation of *Health Education*, Fifth Edition

NEA	**AMA**
1953–58 Delbert Oberteuffer, Ph.D. Columbus, Ohio	Carl Wilzbach, M.D. Cincinnati, Ohio
1954–59 H. Austin Snyder, M.Ed. Sayre, Pennsylvania	Herman M. Jahr, M.D. (1949–59) Omaha, Nebraska
1955–60 Lloyd S. Michael, Ed.D. Evanston, Illinois	Ewald H. Pawsat, M.D. Fond du Lac, Wisconsin
1956–61 Robert Yoho, H.S.D. Indianapolis, Indiana	Jay J. Johns, M.D. Taylor, Texas
1957–62 Ruth Abernathy, Ph.D. Los Angeles, California	Donald A. Dukelow, M.D. Chicago, Illinois
1958–63 Sara Louise Smith, Ed.D. Tallahassee, Florida	John F. Abele, M.D. Portland, Oregon
1959–64 Kenneth E. Oberholtzer, Ph.D. Denver, Colorado	Granville W. Larimore, M.D. Albany, New York
1960–65 Cliff Robinson, Ed.D. Klamath Falls, Oregon	John Lester Reichert, M.D. Chicago, Illinois

Sub-Committee on Revision of *Health Education*

Members

Robert Yoho, H.S.D. (Chairman)
Lloyd S. Michael, Ed.D.
Ewald H. Pawsat, M.D.
Jay J. Johns, M.D.
Donald A. Dukelow, M.D.

Elizabeth Avery Wilson, Ph.D. (Consultant)
Fred V. Hein, Ph.D. (Consultant)
William H. Creswell, Jr., Ed.D. (Consultant)

Editors

Bernice R. Moss, Ed.D.
Warren H. Southworth, Dr. P.H.   John Lester Reichert, M.D.

Acknowledgments

The Fifth Edition of *Health Education* is the product of the combined professional competence of many individuals. Persons from a variety of professional and academic disciplines joined with the Joint Committee on Health Problems in Education of the National Education Association and the American Medical Association and the Editors in developing the manuscript.

Major credit goes to the contributors listed on page ix for preparation of the basic manuscripts from which the book was developed. Some of the manuscripts represented the work of one author. Others were produced by two contributors working together. All contributors gave freely of their time and talents to the undertaking.

The consultants listed on pages 409-10 gave valuable assistance, each reviewing at least one chapter of the manuscript and submitting suggestions for modification, additions, and deletions. These suggestions proved to be most helpful in the development of the final copy.

Appreciation is expressed to the many individuals and organizations which permitted the use of quotations from their publications. Special credit goes to staff members of the National Office of Vital Statistics of the U.S. Public Health Service for the careful checking of statistical information contained in Chapter Two.

Members of the Joint Committee devoted many hours to review of the manuscript and discussion of its content. The Editorial Committee and particularly its Chairman, Robert Yoho, exhibited excellent leadership in guiding the undertaking from inception to completion.

Finally, appreciation is expressed to the staff members of the National Education Association and the American Medical Association who worked closely with the Joint Committee and the Editors at every stage of development. Special thanks go to

the Publications Division of the National Education Association
for final preparation of the manuscript for printing.

Health Education is truly an interprofessional production.
Many disciplines have joined to develop this book so that it may
be helpful to all concerned with health education in the school.

BERNICE R. MOSS, Ed.D., *Editor*
WARREN H. SOUTHWORTH, Dr. P.H., *Associate Editor*
JOHN LESTER REICHERT, M.D., *Associate Editor*

Contributors

The Joint Committee is indebted to the following persons who gave generously of their time and talents to help produce this publication. While assuming full responsibility for the viewpoints expressed, the Committee expresses thanks for valuable and constructive help received from contributors.

W. W. Bauer, M.D.
Director of Health Education
American Medical Association
Chicago, Illinois

Ethel T. Bell
Associate Supervisor, Health
    Education
University of California
Los Angeles, California

Catherine K. Campbell
Assistant Professor, Health
    Education
Wayne State University
Detroit, Michigan

Marjorie L. Craig
Director, School Health Bureau
Metropolitan Life Insurance
    Company
New York, New York

Wesley P. Cushman
Professor of Health Education
The Ohio State University
Columbus, Ohio

Katherine E. D'Evelyn
Chief Psychologist and Coordinator
    of Psychological Services
Great Neck Public Schools
Great Neck, New York

J. Roswell Gallagher, M.D.
Chief, The Adolescent Unit,
    Children's Hospital and
    Lecturer on Pediatrics
Harvard Medical School
Boston, Massachusetts

Marie A. Hinrichs, M.D.
Lecturer, Health Education
Roosevelt University
Chicago, Illinois

Edward B. Johns
Professor, School Health Education
University of California
Los Angeles, California

Dorothy La Salle
Professor, Health and Physical
    Education
Wayne State University
Detroit, Michigan

Howard Leventhal
Assistant Professor, Psychology
Yale University
New Haven, Connecticut

J. Keogh Rash
Chairman, Department of Health
    and Safety
Indiana University
Bloomington, Indiana

Robert D. Russell
Assistant Professor of Health
    Education
Department of Health Education
Stanford University
Stanford, California

Heyworth N. Sanford, M.D.
Professor and Head, Department
    of Pediatrics
University of Illinois, College of
    Medicine
Chicago, Illinois

John H. Shaw
Professor of Health and Physical
    Education
Syracuse University
Syracuse, New York

Elena M. Sliepcevich
Professor of Health Education
The Ohio State University
Columbus, Ohio

Sara Louise Smith
Professor and Head, Health
  Education Department
Florida State University
Tallahassee, Florida

Mary E. Spencer
Director of School Health
Malden Public Schools
Malden, Massachusetts

C. Harold Veenker
Assistant Professor of Health
  Education
Purdue University
West Lafayette, Indiana

George M. Wheatley, M.D.
Third Vice President, Health
  and Welfare
Metropolitan Life Insurance
  Company
New York, New York

Charles C. Wilson, M.D.
Professor, Education and Public
  Health
Yale University
New Haven, Connecticut

Sylvia Yellen
Consultant in Health Education
Los Angeles County Schools
Los Angeles, California

W. W. Bolten, M.D.
American Medical Association
Chicago, Illinois

Contents

Chapter 1

Health and Education

Why teach about health? Is education an adequate means for improving individual and community health? How can teachers develop and conduct programs to increase pupil understanding of health? What are the content and methods of health teaching? What are the ways of building and strengthening desirable health attitudes and behavior? How is health education geared to the interests and needs of growing boys and girls? What is the "fire power" for health education? These are a few of the significant questions answered in this book.

The World Health Organization defines health as "a state of complete physical, mental, and social well-being, not merely the absence of disease or infirmity." On the other hand, it may be defined as a condition in which the individual is able to mobilize all of his resources—intellectual, emotional, and physical—for optimum living. In these and other definitions health is a highly valued asset, but one that is often taken for granted and sometimes not fully appreciated until it is lost. Health influences one's way of life, it improves personal efficiency, it facilitates the attainment of personal goals.

Good teachers are sincerely and enthusiastically interested in children and youth, and want to see them grow and develop into healthy, well-adjusted men and women. This interest, coupled with knowledge of health problems and with ability and skill in helping pupils to understand themselves and to learn ways of solving health problems, can be a vital force in improving the health of present and future generations.

In this chapter, development of a viewpoint on modern health education is preceded by consideration of certain other matters to give the reader an appreciation of the purpose of education for health. It is necessary, for example, to have a clear picture of the total school health program and of the relationships between the health responsibilities and efforts of school personnel and those of other people who are concerned about the health of

1

boys and girls. It is also helpful to enumerate the primary forces
that affect health, and to show how education is related to each.
Furthermore, with attention to the foundations for health progress, health education may be viewed in broad perspective and in
relation to other items which are conducive to health improvement. These, and a brief summary of the historical background
of school health education, comprise the main topics in this
chapter.

SCHOOL RESPONSIBILITY FOR HEALTH

School health efforts must be consistent with the purposes of
schools and with educational objectives. Furthermore, the activities in a school health program need to be co-ordinated with the
health efforts of home and community.

Goals of Education

School interest in pupil health has changed over the years,
partly because of greater recognition of health as an important
ingredient of successful living, and partly because of changing
concepts of education. Schools have become increasingly concerned with the full lives of boys and girls and with the environment in which they live, grow, play, and learn.

Groups of teachers have been particularly active in stating
the aims of education in terms of behavioral outcomes. One of
the most influential of the early statements is the 1918 report
by the Commission on the Reorganization of Secondary Education appointed by the National Education Association.[1] The
report stipulates health as one of seven cardinal principles or
outcomes of education. The complete list includes: (a) health;
(b) command of fundamental processes; (c) worthy home-
membership; (d) vocation; (e) citizenship; (f) worthy use of
leisure time; and (g) ethical character. In this pioneer statement health is given a distinct place among the major concerns
of education.

The Educational Policies Commission [2] in its classic statement
of 1938, *The Purposes of Education in American Democracy,*

[1] U.S. Department of the Interior, Bureau of Education. *Cardinal Principles of
Secondary Education.* Bulletin 1918, No. 35. Washington, D.C.: Superintendent of
Documents, Government Printing Office, 1918. 32 p.

[2] National Education Association and American Association of School Administrators, Educational Policies Commission. *The Purposes of Education in American
Democracy.* Washington, D.C.: the Commission, 1938. 157 p.

describes desired pupil outcomes in each of four groups of educational objectives: (a) self-realization; (b) human relationships; (c) economic efficiency; and (d) civic responsibility. In discussing education for self-realization, the Commission says that the health-educated person is characterized as follows:

1. *The educated person understands the basic facts concerning health and disease.* Health is a factor which conditions our success in all our undertakings, personal and social. For that reason schools properly place great emphasis on health as an outcome of education.

2. *The educated person protects his own health and that of his dependents.* Knowing what is necessary for maintaining health in body and mind, the educated person so conducts his life as to respect these great rules of the game. He tries to secure competent medical advice and treatment for himself and his family, with special attention to the early discovery and treatment of remediable defects and a systematic plan of health inventory and illness prevention.

3. *The educated person works to improve the health of the community.* The interests of the educated person in the field of health are comprehensive. That which he desires for himself in this field, the educated person desires also for others, knowing that health is one commodity which is increased in proportion as it is shared. Especially in a democracy, the educated person will cherish a sincere interest in maintaining the health standards of the entire community.

More recently, the Educational Policies Commission[3] in *An Essay on Quality in Public Education* states that the elementary curriculum, among other things, ". . . teaches the essentials of safety and personal health and promotes physical co-ordination and skill." It continues, "The programs of all secondary-school students should include English, social studies, science, mathematics, and fine arts, as well as physical and health education."

Another statement about the objectives of schools is found in *A Design for General Education*, prepared by the American Council on Education.[4] In this report the health objective, first in the list, is expressed as follows:

[3] National Education Assocation and American Association of School Administrators, Educational Policies Commission. *An Essay on Quality in Public Education.* Washington, D.C.: the Commission, 1959. 31 p.

[4] American Council on Education. *A Design for General Education.* (Edited by T. R. McConnell.) Washington, D.C.: the Council, 1944. 186 p.

In the committee's judgment, general education should lead the student: To improve and maintain his own health and take his share of responsibility for protecting the health of others.

In 1955, a White House Conference on Education was held in Washington. It was attended by representatives of many walks of life, including education and medicine, from all of the states and territories. In answer to the question "What should our schools accomplish?" the Conference Report[5] states that schools should continue to help each pupil develop

1. The fundamental skills of communication—reading, writing, spelling, as well as other elements of effective oral and written expression; the arithmetical and mathematical skills, including problem solving

2. Appreciation for our democratic heritage

3. Understanding of civic rights and responsibilities and knowledge of American institutions

4. Respect and appreciation for human values and for the beliefs of others

5. Ability to think and evaluate constructively and creatively

6. Effective work habits and self-discipline

7. Social competence as a contributing member of his family and community

8. Ethical behavior based on a sense of moral and spiritual values

9. Intellectual curiosity and eagerness for life-long learning

10. Esthetic appreciation and self-expression in the arts

11. Physical and mental health

12. Wise use of time, including constructive leisure pursuits

13. Understanding of the physical world and man's relation to it as represented through basic knowledge of the sciences

14. An awareness of our relationships with the world community.

All these reports include health as a desired outcome of education. All have had significant bearing on educational philosophy and on health education. They present realistic attainable goals. Using them as guides, local school systems and individual schools may formulate statements of their specific purposes, preferably

[5] The Committee for the White House Conference on Education. *A Report to the President*. Washington, D.C.: Superintendent of Documents, Government Printing Office, 1956. 126 p.

following discussion by all school personnel and representatives of the community. In turn, each teacher needs to have clearly in mind his objectives in teaching and their relevance to the total school program. The latter includes health among its objectives.

Interlocking Responsibilities

The fact that health is an objective of education means that the schools share responsibility for protecting and promoting the health of pupils. Parents have basic responsibility for the health care and supervision of children, and for supplying such important health needs as food, shelter, medical care, clothing, and the satisfaction of human relationships. In each community, governmental or private social agencies help to care for children whose parents cannot or do not provide them with the necessities of life. School efforts to promote pupil health are designed to assist parents in fulfilling their child care responsibilities, not to relieve parents of their obligations.

Practicing physicians and dentists contribute much to the health of pupils through both preventive and curative services. They possess the professional skills to provide periodic health examinations, counseling on medical and dental problems, immunization against disease, and medical and dental care. Such procedures do not belong in the realm of school responsibility, but communication and co-operation between medical and dental advisers, parents, and school personnel are nevertheless important.

Local medical, dental, and other professional societies are interested in school health education and services, and in recent years many of them have formed school health committees to help schools improve their programs. Resource people from these organizations can assist in special areas of health instruction, such as home nursing, recognition of quackery, and sex education. Representatives from these groups can be helpful in the scientific evaluation of health education materials and as members of the school health council.

Local health departments perform numerous services from which pupils, as well as all other members of the community, benefit. They direct communicable disease control measures, supervise community sanitation, and give leadership to a variety of activities for improving community health. The extent to which the local health department enters into the school health program varies greatly in different localities.

The voluntary community health agencies provide education and service as part of their programs. Each is concerned with special health problems. They raise money for research and experimental programs, and work very closely with official health agencies. A major objective of these organizations is the education of the community about certain specific health needs. They serve schools by furnishing teaching aids, helping in the preparation of teachers guides, assisting with short-term projects, advancing the in-service education of teachers, providing speakers and consultants for pupils and teachers, and participating on school health committees.

The preceding statements point out the need to relate school health efforts to those of the home and community. Schools supplement, but do not supplant, the health activities of parents, of practitioners of medicine and dentistry, of health departments, and of other agencies in the community. This concept becomes clearer as the scope and content of a modern school health program are described.

The School Health Program

During recent years it has become customary to divide the school health program into three interrelated parts, namely, *healthful school living, school health services,* and *health education.*

The phrase "healthful school living" embraces all efforts to provide conditions at school which are beneficial to the health and safety of pupils. From the physical point of view this requires attention to selection of school site, construction of buildings, provision of safe equipment, and fire prevention, as well as to sanitary factors such as water supply, sewage disposal, illumination, ventilation, heating, and care of food supplies. Healthful living, from the social and emotional viewpoints, involves adapting programs to pupils' abilities, developing constructive interpersonal relationships, organizing the school day to avoid undue fatigue, and consideration of the health implications of such school procedures as examinations, homework assignments, and standards for pupil progress from grade to grade. A description of this part of the school program and suggestions for procedures to be used are contained in another publication of the Joint Committee.[6]

[6] National Education Association and American Medical Association, Joint Committee on Health Problems in Education. *Healthful School Living.* Washington, D.C. and Chicago: the Associations, 1957. 323 p.

Provision for healthful school living is an important responsibility of schools. Health officials (in addition to their legal obligations), parents, physicians, and others may offer suggestions and recommendations for this part of the school health program, but its actual conduct is in the hands of teachers, custodians, school administrators, and other school employees. Schools contribute to the health of children and youth through making it possible for them to live healthfully while they are in school.

"School health services," the second facet of a school health program, includes arrangement of procedures for

1. Appraising the health status of pupils and school personnel

2. Counseling pupils, parents, and others concerning appraisal findings

3. Encouraging the correction of remediable defects and the proper adjustment to those identified as not remediable

4. Assisting in the identification and education of handicapped pupils

5. Helping to prevent and control disease

6. Providing emergency service for injury or sudden illness.

[School health services require teamwork among teachers, physicians, nurses, psychologists, social workers, and others. Such co-operation is instrumental in helping pupils obtain needed medical and dental services, in adapting school programs to the needs of the individual pupil, and in providing emergency care when a pupil is injured or sick while at school.] Detailed suggestions for planning and conducting school health services are presented in another publication of the Joint Committee.[7]

The third area of a school health program is called "health education." It may be defined as *the process of providing learning experiences which favorably influence understandings, attitudes, and conduct in regard to individual and community health.* This definition recognizes that pupils learn from their experiences and that this learning may include pupil knowledge, attitudes, and behavior. The fact that health education is a process indicates that it needs to be planned, and that it cannot be merely the result of incidental occurrences. This book suggests ways of incorporating health education into the curriculums of elemen-

[7] National Education Association and American Medical Association, Joint Committee on Health Problems in Education. *School Health Services.* Washington, D.C. and Chicago: the Associations, 1953. 486 p.

tary schools, junior high schools, senior high schools, and colleges.

EDUCATION FOR HEALTH

The interrelationships between education and health are close, definite, and extensive. These interrelationships can be best clarified by analyzing the forces which affect an individual's health and by considering how education leads to improved health.

Except that it is a quality of life itself, there is nothing mysterious or magical about health. Scientific investigation has increased man's knowledge of the factors which are conducive to health and those which tend to destroy it. These determinants are complex and interdependent, but expressed simply, the most important ones are heredity, environment (including prenatal environment), and ways of living.

Heredity

What each person is and can be depends in part on his inherited endowments. Some of these endowments cannot be altered after the moment of conception. The life task of each individual is to develop fully the mental and physical capacities with which he is endowed. Fortunately, most diseases are not inherited.*

Knowledge about the exact interaction between heredity and health is incomplete, but it is sufficient to lend additional emphasis to the need for considering each person as a unique individual. Each boy or girl has particular physical, mental, and emotional characteristics because of differences in inherited factors. Learning experiences can be provided, at appropriate grade levels, to help pupils understand and accept the influence of heredity on their size, growth, and physical and mental capacities.

Environment

What an individual is or becomes, within the limits set by his native endowments, is determined primarily by the environment in which he lives. There is little doubt that factors in the environment play a major role in health and disease. Even the prenatal environment of the individual is important.†

In general, environment is the aggregate of all external condi-

---

*For a discussion of the relationship between heredity and disease, see Chapter Three.

†See Chapter Three.

tions and circumstances which affect the development and life of an individual. As such, it is comprised of four closely allied parts: physical, biological, social, and economic.

The physical environment embraces climate, season, weather, geography, water, air, soil, buildings, and machinery. These physical surroundings of man have direct and indirect effects upon his health. So does *the biological component* of the environment which consists of all living things—plants and animals—that surround man. It is this component which includes food and the microorganisms of disease.

The social component of the environment is made up of people, and of the customs, ideals, and values of society. It is a web of forces, some favorable and some inimical to emotional health. Some of these forces are: (a) the family, especially the emotional interactions among its members; (b) associates, including groups and intimate friends; (c) the church and other organized religious experiences; (d) the school and other avenues of education; (e) clubs and recreational groups; and (f) the mass media of communication, including radio, television, movies, newspapers, and magazines. The feelings which an individual develops in response to the situations and people who make up a vital part of his social environment affect his mental and physical health.

The social and *economic* components of the environment are mutually dependent. There is evidence that, with important exceptions, the lower the socioeconomic status, the higher the prevalence of overt disease. The association is two-way in that low economic status promotes disease, and disease, particularly when it is chronic, is a significant factor in causing reduced socioeconomic status. On the other hand, there are differences in economic status among persons of the same social gradation. It is also true that high economic status does not necessarily assure good health, since some people with ample income may purchase goods and services which impair health and fail to purchase those that nurture it. Further, they may neglect sensible health practices.

Health education can acquaint pupils with their total environment, and with some of the problems of adjusting to the environment in which they live. It can help them to understand that health, both mental and physical, is influenced for good or bad, depending upon the extent and manner in which control over the environment is exercised. Likewise, it can help them to appreciate the fact that environment affects the degree to which one succeeds in realizing his inherited potentialities. Satisfactory adjustment to environmental conditions promotes feelings of security, of being needed, and of achievement.

Health education can help pupils learn ways of coping with, adjusting to, and controlling various phases of the environment. The environment of the school itself can be utilized as a laboratory to provide boys and girls with a series of meaningful experiences for learning about their environment and ways of solving environmental problems.

Ways of Living

An individual's way of living may help him to use fully his potentialities for living. Health education plays a significant part in helping to establish healthful ways of living. Among other things, through health education pupils can learn to select suitable meals, work and play with others, engage in a variety of recreational activities, alternate periods of work and rest, care for personal appearance and body cleanliness, and appreciate the structure and functioning of their bodies. Through health education, too, pupils can learn to live satisfying and productive lives with handicaps of vision or hearing, or with other physical limitations. Health education can give pupils insight into their own behavior as well as that of others. It can teach pupils about the safeguards and hazards to emotional health, and about the interrelatedness of emotional and physical disturbances. Information about mental illness can foster positive attitudes toward the mentally sick. Study of the health problems in family living can give pupils desirable patterns for action in protecting the health of their own families.

The maintenance of individual and community health requires intelligent application of up-to-date knowledge about the causes of disease, the ways diseases are spread, and available methods for controlling or preventing them. These are appropriate topics for health education when adapted to the capacity of the learners. Pupils need such information about disease as will help them to do whatever is necessary to protect themselves and others. Similarly, health education can give pupils an understanding of the magnitude and seriousness of accident problems. Most accidents are preventable. Foresight and forethought implanted by education can prevent a large percentage of accidents.

Full and intelligent use of professional services is important in the promotion of health. Not many years ago the services and ministrations of physicians, nurses, dentists, and other professional persons were considered necessary only in cases of emergency and distress. This is no longer true, for members of the health professions also perform important preventive services. The physician immunizes, makes periodic health examinations, and provides medical guidance. The dentist encourages patients to make regular visits to his office because periodic dental care is more adequate than any other single procedure in helping individuals maintain dental health. The nurse serving the school gives many practical suggestions for maintaining and improving health and for the prevention of sickness.

At some time, each person finds himself in need of the professional services of a physician, dentist, or nurse; sometimes hospitalization is required. Health education acquaints pupils with the qualifications of various medical and dental personnel, and with the way hospitals are organized and financed. Therefore, consideration of insurance programs for physician services, hospital care, and indemnity for sickness are also included in health education.

The outcomes listed here are not all that can be achieved through health education. However, they do illustrate that by providing the facts of health and by developing concomitant attitudes and appreciations, health education can help children and youth to establish healthful ways of living.

Health and Learning

[Health education is related to each of the forces that affect health—heredity, environment, and ways of living. It is a means of developing understanding about health and how it may be sustained and improved, and of translating health knowledge into desirable health behavior. What a pupil learns can influence his health, and his health can influence his ability to learn. The pupil with poor vision, poor nutrition, or impaired hearing will not learn as readily or easily as one without these defects. Learning is retarded in the tense, anxious, frustrated, or depressed pupil. As the health of pupils is improved, so is their ability to learn. Education and health go hand in hand.] This alignment between health and education can help fortify the teacher's interest in health. He can feel confident that his achievements in improving pupil health will eventually be reflected in increased effectiveness of the total school program.

FOUNDATIONS OF HEALTH PROGRESS

Progress in improving the nation's health, including the health of school children and youth, is dependent upon several basic requisites of which health education is but one. Analysis of progress made in the past indicates that the foundations for health progress are research, health education, and the availability of health services. Since these three essentials will also affect all future efforts to improve health, each is discussed briefly in this chapter.

Research

Regardless of strong desires to prevent or eliminate disease and to improve health, definite accomplishments result only when action is guided by accurate facts. Research was fundamental to the successful attacks on diphtheria and to the marked decrease in infant and maternal mortality made in the past 50 years. It was necessary for progress in combating typhoid fever, tuberculosis, poliomyelitis, smallpox, and many other diseases. Research made possible the formulation of dietary standards and the almost complete eradication of such deficiency diseases as rickets, scurvy, and pellagra.

The solution of many current health problems awaits the results of research. At present, many forms of cancer cannot be prevented; all the knowledge and techniques for doing so are not yet available. Similarly, specific measures for preventing colds, mental deficiency, mental illness, certain types of heart disease, and numerous other ills must await the results of further scientific research.

In time, extensive research will lead to the conquest of health problems which are today unsolved. Everyone in the field of science agrees that research is the key to progress. Within the past few years research grants from governmental appropriations, voluntary health agencies, and private foundations have more than trebled.

Health Education

By encouraging widespread acceptance of scientific knowledge, health education decreases the time lag between a discovery and its practical application. Health education rests on the premise that a scientific fact does not exert its fullest impact on health progress until it has been widely disseminated and people have been motivated to use it. For example, the fact that bottles used in infant feedings need to be sterilized did not contribute to a reduction in infant mortality until that fact became known to mothers, and they applied it in caring for their infants. Discovery of methods to prevent diphtheria did not produce a reduction in diphtheria cases and deaths until education brought this information to parents and favorably influenced their attitudes toward immunization. The same is true of knowledge about the prevention of such illnesses as tetanus, poliomyelitis, and whooping cough.

Health education is not concerned only with new discoveries; it presents, at the appropriate time and in a suitable way, the knowledge about health and disease which has accumulated during the years, and attempts to motivate persons into action. The process of health improvement begins with the discovery and establishment of scientific knowledge and is furthered by health education. Education is the means of securing intelligent utilization of health knowledge.

Health Services and Facilities

Neither research nor health education, singly or combined, is sufficient. In addition, health progress requires that the necessities for health be available to all. The knowledge that between a pint and a quart of milk is needed daily by most school-age boys and girls has little practical value for children whose parents do not have the money to buy milk. Nor does the fact that speech-reading is of value to children with impaired hearing help such children unless this specialized teaching is available in their communities. Medical care and dental treatment are necessary for health and need to be made available if complete health progress is the goal. One of the great practical objectives of health education is to teach people to budget carefully for their health needs, and to use advantageously the available legitimate health services and facilities.

Through co-ordination of research, health education, and health services for all individuals, the health of the nation can be promoted. This book details the schools' part in the total effort toward better health for better living.

HISTORICAL BACKGROUNDS

In 1842, Horace Mann, the father of public schools in the United States, suggested that health be taught in schools, but the idea was not well received. A full history of how health education did eventually develop has not been written, but it is known that the teaching of simplified anatomy and physiology was common in the elementary grades during the last decade or two of the nineteenth century, and that many secondary schools required courses in physiology. The instruction was quite formal, with emphasis on memorizing technical terms and with little attention to improving ways of living. Undoubtedly, the instruction had value in helping young people understand how their bodies were made and how different organs functioned, but how much this type of instruction significantly helped pupils improve their health or health practices is questionable.

In the early years of the present century, the teaching of anatomy and physiology was augmented and to some extent replaced by instruction in hygiene and prevention of contagious disease. This change reflected a desire to make teaching more meaningful and to place emphasis on health rather than solely on the structure and functions of the body.

During the 1920's further steps were taken to improve the teaching of hygiene. Formal rules for health behavior were developed, rules which each child or youth was expected to apply day by day at home and at school. This was the period of personified foods, health fairies, jingles, and songs. Instruction was still quite academic with comparatively little attention to pupil interest or to individual differences.

Modern programs of health education have evolved from earlier programs through increased understanding of the factors that influence health and learning, and with improved methods of teaching. Today health education is potentially interesting, challenging, and stimulating, in contrast to the dull, unimaginative teaching of hygiene to which many members of earlier generations were subjected. These shifts in school health education came about through advances in health science; progress in the modern public health movement; changes in educational philosophy; instruction in allied subjects; the advent of school health services; pioneer conferences, projects, and programs sponsored by a variety of governmental, professional, voluntary, and business groups. Only a brief review is presented here.

Advances in Health Science

The work of Louis Pasteur, Robert Koch, and others during the 1860's and 1870's in discovering the role of microorganisms in disease opened up a whole new era in health science. From their work on the causative agents of disease new procedures in sanitation emerged to assure clean water supplies, pure foods, and adequate sewage disposal. They also laid the foundations for development of immunological weapons against disease— vaccines, antitoxins, antiserums, and toxoids. For the first time man had tools for controlling many of the epidemic diseases which had plagued mankind for centuries, bringing with them misery and death. In addition to their use by the medical profession, some kind of community organization—a public health program—was needed to use these tools for the benefit of mankind.

Progress in Public Health

The year 1850 marks the beginning of public health as an organized movement in the United States. During that year plans for a comprehensive public health program, including a program of health education, were published in the *Report of the Sanitary Commission of Massachusetts*,[8] prepared by Lemuel Shattuck. In addition to describing much of what is included in a modern program of public health, the report contained suggestions for health education.

City governments were the first to respond to the proposals in the Shattuck Report. Many established new health departments or reinforced the activities of local boards of health which earlier had been created to cope with an immediate emergency and later permitted to atrophy. By 1885, each state had enacted a law creating a state board of health or its equivalent. At the national level, the United States Public Health Service (so named in 1912) grew out of the Marine Hospital Service which had been established by Congress in 1798. The work of these agencies at the national, state, and local levels was directed to the prevention and cure of disease, and particularly to the control of epidemics. While the public health movement gained momentum, the need for health education as a means of securing co-operation and broader application of health science became more and more apparent. Elisha Harris,[9] at the initial meeting of the American Public Health Association in 1873, said:

[8] Shattuck, Lemuel. *Report of the Sanitary Commission of Massachusetts, 1850.* Facsimile edition. Cambridge, Mass.: Harvard University Press, 1948. 321 p.

[9] Smillie, Wilson G. *Public Health Administration in the United States.* New York: Macmillan Co., 1947. 637 p.

In the United States, the permanent value and success of any method or system of sanitary government will depend upon the degree to which people are generally enlightened, concerned, and made responsible in regard to sanitary duties.

Many years later this same principle was expressed more explicitly in *Building America's Health*,[10] a report to the President:

The individual effort of an informed person will do more for his health and that of his family than all the things which can be done for them. In the past, measures for health maintenance demanded individual responsibility only to a limited degree. The development of pure water supplies, pasteurization of milk, and other sanitary accomplishments were achieved through social action in which the individual may have participated as a citizen, but was required to take no further individual responsibility.

Future accomplishments, however, depend to an even greater degree upon the individual's assumption of responsibility for his own health. It is the individual who must consult his physician for early care, avoid obesity and alcoholism, and drive his automobile safely. These things can not be done for him. They require both information and motivation. Personal health practices which are determined by the individual's knowledge, attitude and decision have now become of paramount importance in gaining health. Effort by each person to improve his own health can be expected to pay great returns.

This means that there must be an educational process which leads the individual and the group to adopt and practice the methods of maintaining personal and community health.

Changes in Educational Philosophy

Concurrently with the growth of health science and the expansion of public health programs, changes were taking place in the philosophy of education. Before 1900, teachers and school administrators as a group worked mostly with the intellectual development of the pupil and the subject matter he could acquire. They felt little, if any, responsibility for his growth, hearing, vision, or nutrition. However, the child study movement, which was started in the 1890's by G. Stanley Hall, Felix Adler, William H. Burnham, and others, sought to understand child needs and to meet these needs through suitable educational methods. This work on child development brought the mental, emotional, social, and physical needs of pupils into the focus of attention. Teachers gradually became interested and concerned with the total development of the pupil, including his health. In turn,

---

[10] The President's Commission on the Health Needs of the Nation. *Building America's Health*. A Report to the President. Washington, D.C.: Superintendent of Documents, Government Printing Office, 1951. Vol. 1, 80 p.

the school program became less subject-centered and more pupil-centered.

Instruction in Allied Subjects

The Temperance Movement was a definite stimulus to health education. Between 1880 and 1890 every state had enacted legislation requiring instruction about the effects of alcohol and narcotics. In 40 states these laws specified that the instruction be part of a broader program of teaching physiology and hygiene. At about the same time physical education, as an outcome of the Turnvereins (German-American Gymnastic Societies), made its appearance in some schools. The early classes stressed calisthenics to counteract the effects of sedentary life and to develop physical efficiency. In 1890, Ohio enacted the first state law requiring physical education in the school curriculum. By 1910, legislation to include physical education in schools became widespread. Many of the laws mentioned the teaching of health habits. Home economics, another related subject, had its introduction into public schools for the first time in 1885 and, with the subsequent beginning of school lunches, emphasized nutrition education as a part of total health education. All three, the Temperance Movement, physical education, and home economics gave impetus to health instruction in schools.

Advent of School Health Services

Another influence on the development of school health education came with the introduction of school health services. The first public school medical officer in the United States was appointed by the City of New York in 1892.[11] The first system of daily medical inspections was initiated in Boston in 1894. In that year, following epidemics of diphtheria and scarlet fever, the Commissioner of Health appointed 50 school physicians as medical visitors, one to each of the 50 school districts. They visited the schools daily and examined all children thought by their teachers to be ailing. In 1899, Connecticut enacted legislation which required periodic vision testing of all public-school pupils. By 1905, nurses were included in the school health services. In 1903, the first school dentist was appointed in Reading, Pennsylvania. Later, in 1914, 10 dental hygienists were employed in Bridgeport, Connecticut, to conduct a school dental clinic and an

[11] Ravenel, M. P., editor. *A Half Century of Public Health.* Jubilee Historical Volume of the American Public Health Association. New York: American Public Health Association, 1921. 461 p.

educational program. As school health services expanded, it gradually became apparent that participation in the school health services could be an educational experience for boys and girls, particularly if this phase of the services were planned carefully by health specialists and teachers.

Pioneer Conferences, Projects, and Programs

The White House Conference on Child Health and Protection, convened in 1910, was the first of a series of conferences which have influenced all phases of school health, including health instruction. Two organizations in particular did much of the pioneering for improved health teaching. In 1915, the National Tuberculosis Association developed the "Modern Health Crusade." It was based upon advancement toward "knighthood" as a reward for pupils who had followed certain health practices. Such devices as stories, plays, posters, ceremonies, and routines were used to arouse pupil interest in health. In 1918, the Child Health Organization was created to help awaken the nation to the need for health education. It was at a conference called by the Child Health Organization that the term "health education" was formally used for the first time.

Through the co-operative efforts of private, professional, governmental, and industry-sponsored organizations, several school health projects were conducted to demonstrate that health education can change behavior and improve child health. Sometimes college and university personnel were responsible for these studies.

The Joint Committee on Health Problems in Education (established in 1911) of the National Education Association and the American Medical Association issued its first report, *Health Education,* in 1924. Ever since then this book, and its revised editions, has been a standard reference and an authoritative guide in school health education. It has exerted a major influence on school health programs throughout the country.

Space does not permit a further recounting of the specific contributions which have been made by dedicated groups and tireless pioneers in nurturing health education. With the help of many outstanding leaders; the co-operation of parents, teachers, health specialists, and school administrators; and the resources of official, voluntary, professional, and industry-sponsored organizations, health education has made great strides in helping to put health knowledge to work in the lives of people.

A MODERN APPROACH

Present-day health education is a far cry from the hygiene of a generation ago. Attention is now given to the interests and needs of pupils; attractive textbooks arouse interest and present significant information in a meaningful way; teaching methods emphasize pupil participation; instruction is based upon the real problems of real people; and the content deals with all aspects of living. These are some of the characteristics of school health education; others will be described in subsequent chapters.

The present and future health of the nation depends in part on the understanding of individual and community health problems by the public at large, and on intelligent health behavior. Here is the goal toward which health education is directed. This book indicates ways by which further progress can be made toward this important goal.

SELECTED REFERENCES

AMERICAN ASSOCIATION FOR HEALTH, PHYSICAL EDUCATION, AND RECREATION. *Fit To Teach*. Washington, D.C.: the Association, a department of the National Education Association, 1957. 249 p.

AMERICAN ASSOCIATION OF SCHOOL ADMINISTRATORS. *Health in Schools*. Revised edition. Twentieth Yearbook. Washington, D.C.: the Association, a department of the National Education Association, 1951. 477 p.

COMMITTEE ON THE SCHOOL CHILD, WHITE HOUSE CONFERENCE ON CHILD HEALTH AND PROTECTION. *The School Health Program*. New York: Century Co., 1932. 400 p.

GROUT, RUTH E. "Health Education Today in the Light of Yesterday." *Yale Journal of Biology and Medicine* 19: 573-80; March 1947.

HEIN, FRED V. "Health Education." *Encyclopedia of Educational Research*. Revised edition. (Edited by Chester W. Harris.) New York: Macmillan Co., 1960. 1564 p.

IRWIN, LESLIE W. "Basic Needs in Health Education." *Boston University Journal of Education* 141: 1-77; April 1959.

JEAN, SALLY LUCAS. "The Development of Health Education in the U. S. A." *Health Education Journal* 27: 36-48; March 1959.

LEAVELL, HUGH R., and OTHERS. *Textbook of Preventive Medicine*. New York: McGraw-Hill Book Co., 1958. 629 p.

MAXCY, KENNETH F., editor. *Resenau's Preventive Medicine and Public Health*. Eighth edition. New York: Appleton-Century-Crofts, 1956. 1465 p.

NATIONAL CONFERENCE FOR COOPERATION IN HEALTH EDUCATION, COMMITTEE ON SCHOOL HEALTH POLICIES. *Suggested School Health Policies*. Third edition. Washington, D.C. and Chicago: National Education Association and American Medical Association, 1956. 40 p.

NATIONAL EDUCATION ASSOCIATION AND AMERICAN ASSOCIATION OF SCHOOL ADMINISTRATORS, EDUCATIONAL POLICIES COMMISSION. *Policies for Education in American Democracy*. Washington, D.C.: the Commission, 1946. 277 p.

NATIONAL EDUCATION ASSOCIATION AND AMERICAN MEDICAL ASSOCIATION, JOINT COMMITTEE ON HEALTH PROBLEMS IN EDUCATION. *Healthful School Living*. Washington, D.C. and Chicago: the Associations, 1957. 323 p.

NATIONAL EDUCATION ASSOCIATION AND AMERICAN MEDICAL ASSOCIATION, JOINT COMMITTEE ON HEALTH PROBLEMS IN EDUCATION. *School Health Services*. Washington, D.C. and Chicago: the Associations, 1953. 486 p.

SLIEPCEVICH, ELENA M. "Echoes from the Past." *Journal of School Health* 30: 205-11; May 1960.

SOUTHWORTH, WARREN H., and DAVIS, ARTHUR F. *Meredith's Science of Health*. Third edition. New York: McGraw-Hill Book Co., 1957. 492 p.

TRUMP, J. LLOYD. *New Directions to Quality Education*. Washington, D.C.: Commission on the Experimental Study of the Utilization of the Staff in the Secondary School, National Association of Secondary-School Principals, NEA, 1960. 16 p.

U.S. DEPARTMENT OF HEALTH, EDUCATION, AND WELFARE. *School Health Program, an Outline*. Revised edition. Washington, D.C.: Superintendent of Documents, Government Printing Office, 1959. 1 folded page.

PROGRESS
DECLINING DEATH RATE
PROBLEMS PERSIST
HEART DISEASE
CANCER
ACCIDENTS
EMOTIONAL DISORDERS
DENTAL PROBLEMS
NUTRITIONAL PROBLEMS

Progress and Problems

For centuries the sciences progressed at a walking pace. Change came slowly and people had years, often generations, to absorb it. But suddenly, toward the end of the 1800's the pace of research and discovery began to increase with spectacular rapidity. Before the twentieth century was half over, science and applied technology had catapulted the country from a comparatively simple life into the atomic and jet age, profoundly changing the entire world's political, economic, and sociological future, as well as its health problems. Most of the changes have helped to improve health and increase the average length of life in many countries throughout the world.

In the United States, tremendous strides have been made toward better health and longer life within the last six decades. Many of the ancient enemies are near defeat although serious health problems must still be faced. Once comparatively minor causes of death have moved forward to greater prominence and certain new threats to life and health have appeared. The modern teacher needs to be familiar with both the progress made and the problems remaining.

Much information comes from vital statistics—records of births, deaths, and illness. These statistics tell the story of progress and give warning of new dangers. They are also an invaluable tool in health education, because they suggest places of needed emphasis and indicate at which points teaching efforts will bring the greatest return. Other indications of the health status of children and youth come from medical and dental examinations, illness and absence records, facts of growth and development, and observations of appearance and behavior. Although many disorders are not major causes of death and disability, they hinder growth and development and affect the child's ability to reach his individual potentialities. The goal for each child today is a high quality of health—the kind of vital, vigorous, and wholesome health that will enable him to become what he is capable of becoming. This greater insight into the meaning of good health and a better understanding of the many factors involved make health education today more challenging than ever.

THE STORY OF PROGRESS

Health improvement may be presented in terms of shrinking death rates, or in terms of gains in life expectancy. Such figures have been carefully and systematically kept for many years. The regular annual collection of such records was begun by the Bureau of the Census in 1900 and is now carried on by the National Office of Vital Statistics of the United States Public Health Service.

The term "death rate," as ordinarily used, means a crude death rate. It is the ratio of deaths in a year to the average population for that year. The death rate from all causes combined is usually expressed as the number of deaths per 1000 population. For specific causes of death, it is stated in terms of the number of deaths from a particular disease per 100,000 population. The infant mortality rate is the number of deaths of children under one year of age per 1000 live births.

To compare death rates of one community with another or death rates at one period of time with another, it is usually necessary to adjust the death rates to allow for differences in the age and sex composition of the two populations. This is necessary because one community may have a high proportion of babies or elderly people, and death rates are normally greater at the extremes of life than among young adults or the middle-aged. Furthermore, the proportions of persons of different ages may change over the years.

Americans Are Living Longer

The crude death rate for the United States has fallen steadily since 1900 (Table 1). By 1959, it had dropped to almost half the 1900 rate for white Americans and to less than half the 1900 rate for the nonwhite population.

The falling death rate is an indication of the remarkable progress made since 1900 in lengthening the average duration of life (expectation of life at birth) in the United States. In 1958, the average exceeded by 2.2 years the figure for 1948 and by about 20 years that at the turn of the century.

TABLE 1
AMERICA'S FALLING DEATH RATE
Deaths per 1000 Population in the United States for Selected Years Since 1900

Year	Deaths	
	White	Nonwhite
1900	17.0	25.0
1910	14.5	21.7
1920	12.6	17.7
1930	10.8	16.3
1940	10.4	13.8
1950	9.5	11.2
1955	9.2	10.0
1956	9.3	10.1
1957	9.5	10.4
1958	9.4	10.2
1959	9.3	9.9

Source:
National Office of Vital Statistics, U.S. Public Health Service. *Vital Statistics of the United States.* Washington, D.C.: Superintendent of Documents, Government Printing Office, 1900-59.

Under mortality conditions which prevailed around 1900, one-fourth of the newborn would fail to reach their twenty-fifth birthday; now only 5 percent are not likely to attain that age. Similarly, half the children born at the turn of the century could expect to survive to age 58; today that proportion may reach age 73.

In 1958 expectation of life at time of birth for white females was 73.7 years. As Table 2 shows, 70.5 years of life remain for white girls at age five, about 60 years for those at age 16, and about 50 years for those at age 26.

For white males, the average length of life in 1958 was 67.2 years, or 6.5 years less than that for white females. The sex differences with respect to longevity lessen with advance in age; they decrease from six years at age 10 to five years at age 44 and to four years at age 56. The differences between the sexes were considerably smaller around 1900; namely, less than three years at birth and only about one year at age 56.

Among nonwhite persons the expectation of life at birth in 1958 was 60.6 years for males and 65.5 years for females. Although the recent gains in longevity have been greater for the nonwhite than for the white population, the average length of life for the nonwhite population still lags considerably behind

TABLE 2

EXPECTATION OF LIFE AT SELECTED YEARS OF AGE

By Race and Sex, United States, 1958

Age (years)	Expectation of Life in Years				
	Total Persons	White		Nonwhite	
		Male	Female	Male	Female
0	69.4	67.2	73.7	60.6	65.5
5	66.7	64.3	70.5	59.3	63.8
10	61.8	59.5	65.6	54.5	59.0
20	52.2	50.0	55.9	45.0	49.3
30	42.8	40.7	46.2	36.3	40.1
40	33.6	31.5	36.7	28.0	31.5
50	24.9	22.9	27.6	20.5	23.7
60	17.3	15.7	19.2	14.5	17.4

Source:

National Office of Vital Statistics, U.S. Public Health Service. *Vital Statistics of the United States.* Washington, D.C.: Superintendent of Documents, Government Printing Office, 1958. Section 5, "Abridged Life Tables."

that for the whites. The difference amounts to as much as 8.2 years for females and to 6.6 years for males.

By revealing such sex and race differences these statistics show not only areas where progress has been made but also where current problems lie.

The improvement in mortality rates and longevity has been greatest for children and young adults. Thus, since 1900-1902 the expectation of life has increased 11.7 years at age five and 8.4 years at age 25. Although the gains have been much smaller past mid-life, even at age 65 the average remaining lifetime has been increased 2.1 years.

Control of Infectious Diseases

The major reason for the extraordinary reduction in the death rates and the gain in life expectancy within a comparatively short time is the increasing mastery of infectious diseases. As Table 3 shows, in 1900-1904 tuberculosis and the combination of pneumonia and influenza each had a death rate of over 184 per 100,000 population, and each accounted for one-ninth of all deaths in the United States. By 1959, the respective death rates were only 6.5 and 31.2 per 100,000 and their proportions of all deaths were about 1 percent and 3 percent. Striking decreases will also be noted for diarrhea and enteritis, the

TABLE 3

AVERAGE ANNUAL DEATH RATES PER 100,000 FROM CAUSES NOW LARGELY UNDER CONTROL

United States, 1900-59

Cause of Death	Death Rate per 100,000				Percent Distribution of Deaths	
	1900-1904	1920-24	1940-44	1959	1900-1904	1959
Tuberculosis	184.8	97.1	43.4	6.5	11.4	0.7
Pneumonia and influenza	184.4	141.0	63.7	31.2[a]	11.4	3.3[a]
Diarrhea and enteritis	115.6	43.2	9.8	4.4	7.1	0.5
Communicable diseases of childhood[b]	65.3	34.0	4.6	0.4	4.0	0.0
Typhoid fever	26.8	7.4	0.6	0.0	1.6	0.0
Syphilis	12.9	17.5	12.6	1.7	0.8	0.2
Appendicitis	9.3	14.0	7.3	1.0	0.6	0.1

Source:
National Office of Vital Statistics, U.S. Public Health Service. *Vital Statistics of the United States.* Washington, D.C.: Superintendent of Documents, Government Printing Office, 1959. (See especially, Vol. 7, No. 13, July 22, 1959.)
Note: Because of a change in the procedures of reporting and classifying detailed causes of death, some of the figures for 1959 are not strictly comparable with those for earlier years.
[a] Excludes newborn.
[b] Measles, scarlet fever, whooping cough, and diphtheria.

communicable diseases of childhood, typhoid fever, and syphilis, which jointly accounted for 13.6 percent of all deaths in 1900-1904, but for less than 1 percent in 1959. Appendicitis, at one time prominent among the causes of death, is now largely controlled.

Decline in Infant Mortality

The achievements in the prevention of infant deaths are clearly reflected in Table 4. Although annual infant mortality rates on a national basis are available only since 1915, these data indicate a steady downward trend. In that year, the infant mortality rate was 99.9 per 1000 live births; by 1959 it had declined to 26.4 per 1000.

Many factors have contributed to this marked reduction. Pasteurization of milk, protection of water supplies, immunization procedures and, more recently, new chemical and biological drugs have been instrumental in reducing mortality from infectious diseases. Better and more widespread prenatal, obstetrical,

TABLE 4
DEATH RATE OF INFANTS UNDER ONE YEAR[a] PER 1000 LIVE BIRTHS
United States, 1915-59

Year	Death Rate per 1000
1915	99.9
1920	85.8
1925	71.7
1930	64.6
1935	55.7
1940	47.0
1945	38.3
1950	29.2
1955	26.4
1956	26.0
1957	26.3
1958	27.1
1959	26.4

Source:
National Office of Vital Statistics, U.S. Public Health Service. *Vital Statistics of the United States.* Washington, D.C.: Superintendent of Documents, Government Printing Office, 1915-59. (See especially, Vol. 8, No. 13, April 25, 1960.) Figures for 1959 are estimated from the Monthly Vital Statistics Report, *Annual Summary for 1959, Part 2.*
[a] Excludes fetal deaths.

and infant care have also contributed to the number of healthy infants and children. Health education, which has helped to put these advances to work, has been an important factor in this achievement, and emphasis on the health practices of young mothers has proved to be of particular importance. Other factors, such as the rise in standard of living and the application of the newer knowledge of nutrition, have also helped considerably. It is impossible to assess the exact contribution of the various factors.

While infant mortality rates have been reduced everywhere in the United States, there are still marked geographical differences. Today, babies born in the large cities have the best chance of survival. The chances are less favorable in rural areas, villages, and moderate-sized cities. The favorable position of the large cities is due, in part at least, to better medical services and hospital facilities and to organized activities in behalf of infant and child health.

TABLE 5

MATERNAL DEATH RATE PER 10,000 LIVE BIRTHS

United States, 1915-59

Year	Death Rate per 10,000
1915	60.8
1920	79.9
1925	64.7
1930	67.3
1935	58.2
1940	4.1
1945	4.1
1950	3.8
1955	3.7
1956	37.6
1957	20.7
1958	8.3
1959	4.7

Source:
National Office of Vital Statistics, U.S. Public Health Service. *Vital Statistics of the United States.* Washington, D.C.: Superintendent of Documents, Government Printing Office, 1915-58. The 1959 figure is estimated.

Reduction in Maternal Mortality

Recent years have witnessed remarkable progress in safeguarding maternity (Table 5). For the country as a whole, there were less than four maternal deaths per 10,000 births in 1958, whereas in 1935 the rate was 58 per 10,000. This rapid progress has been due in large measure to the reduction in death from puerperal (period of confinement after labor) infections. These tragedies have been prevented or successfully treated by hospital delivery, better obstetrical techniques, use of the sulfonamides and of a variety of antibiotics. Leaders in medicine and public health organized continuing studies in their communities to determine responsibility for maternal deaths. The results of their findings, translated into action, continue to reduce maternal death rates each year. The improvement has been so great that in order to avoid the use of fractions in expressing the rates, it was necessary to change the baseline from 1000 to 10,000 live births in figuring maternal death rates.

Death Rates Among Children

The downward trend in mortality has been very sharp in the childhood ages. Since 1900 the death rate in the preschool group,

TABLE 6

DEATH RATES PER 1000 FROM ALL CAUSES, AGES ONE TO FOURTEEN YEARS

United States, 1900-59

Year	Rate	
	1-4 Years of Age	5-14 Years of Age
1900	19.8	3.9
1920	9.9	2.6
1930	5.6	1.7
1940	2.9	1.0
1950	1.4	0.6
1957	1.1	0.5
1958	1.1	0.5
1959	1.1	0.5

Source:

National Office of Vital Statistics, U.S. Public Health Service. *Vital Statistics of the United States.* Washington, D.C.: Superintendent of Documents, Government Printing Office, 1900-59. (See especially, Vol. 7, No. 13, July 22, 1959.)

one to four years, has been cut nearly 95 percent; since 1920, by about 89 percent. The reductions have been only slightly less at the elementary-school ages. This is shown in Table 6.

The reduction in the total number of deaths among school children has been brought about by decreases in deaths from many diseases, with maximum declines recorded for the infectious and communicable diseases. The death rate for accidents has also been reduced by a substantial amount. It is notable that this reduction applies even to motor vehicle accidents in this age group, although there has been little change in the motor vehicle accident death rate in the population as a whole.

ELIMINATION OF EPIDEMICS

Today it is difficult to believe that the United States ever experienced terrifying epidemics of yellow fever, cholera, typhoid fever, smallpox, and diphtheria. It is customary now to associate these plagues with backward countries or with devastated lands. But epidemics of these diseases did occur here and took a dreadful toll of lives, young and old.

Cholera, Epidemic Typhus Fever, and Yellow Fever

In 1793, yellow fever killed 10 percent of the people in Philadelphia; and in 1853, 8000 people died from this disease in New Orleans. In the epidemic of 1849, there were more than 5000 deaths from Asiatic cholera in New York City alone. Epidemic typhus was present from time to time in the United States prior to 1890; in 1893 there were 200 deaths in New York City.

By careful study of the causes and manner of spread, and the application of proper protective measures for these diseases, they have been eliminated almost completely in the United States. Victory came from vigorous attacks on insect vectors: the *Aedes aegypti* mosquito in yellow fever and the body louse in epidemic typhus; by measures to assure pure drinking water in the case of Asiatic cholera.

Typhoid Fever

The reduction in mortality from typhoid fever illustrates another dramatic and brilliant victory won by medical science and public health, including health education. Since the turn of the century this disease has declined from its position as a major cause of death to one of negligible numerical importance. In 1900, the death rate from typhoid fever in the United States was in excess of 30 per 100,000. Today the rate has dropped almost to the vanishing point.

Prime factors in the conquest of typhoid fever are the protection of water and milk supplies, the installation of sewer systems, the use of antityphoid vaccine, and the control of typhoid carriers. The latter are people who, after having recovered from the disease, continue to carry and spread the germs.

Smallpox—A Preventable Disease

Smallpox has been almost eradicated in the United States, but unfortunately there are large numbers of unvaccinated persons in all areas of the country. The introduction of smallpox could bring about a serious outbreak. The present low level of smallpox incidence is no reason for complacency, because so long as reservoirs of infection are permitted to remain, they will continue to be potential foci of smallpox epidemics, not only for the local residents, but also, because of modern transportation facilities, for the people of other areas as well.

Diphtheria at Low Level

At the beginning of the twentieth century, the death rate from diphtheria was 40.3 per 100,000 in the United States; by

1940 the rate had fallen to 1.1 per 100,000. Despite the disrupting influences of war and the large increase in the number of young children, among whom the disease most commonly occurs, the diphtheria death rate has been kept down near this low figure. The reduction in mortality from this disease has been due, first, to the discovery of diphtheria antitoxin in 1890 and to its administration to people with diphtheria or to those exposed to a patient with the disease; second, to the development of safe and convenient immunizing substances, at first toxin-antitoxin and more recently toxoid, with which individuals may be protected in advance against the disease; and third, to the development in 1913 of the Schick test, which shows whether or not an individual is susceptible to diphtheria.

It would be a mistake to ignore or discount diphtheria as a fatal disease. It has lost none of its power to strike with devastating force when control measures are relaxed. This is shown by widespread epidemics in Europe during World War II. At the wartime peak, the prevalence of the disease in Europe was comparable to that of a generation ago, before immunization began to be practiced on a wide scale.

In the United States, too, there has been a recent rise in the number of cases and reports of death in many states with outbreaks in some others. With a rapidly rising birth rate, the child population has increased greatly in recent years, and the rise in diphtheria is not disproportionate to this increase. Nevertheless, the situation calls for greater efforts to protect children, particularly young children, from this entirely preventable disease. Initial immunizations should ordinarily be given during the first six months of life and periodically thereafter at about three-year intervals up to and during the school years. Unfortunately, booster shots for diphtheria are seldom continued throughout the grade-school and high-school years and immunity is greatly reduced by the time adulthood is reached. Unless immunity is maintained, diphtheria incidence may be transferred to the adult group instead of being controlled or eliminated.

PROGRESS AGAINST TUBERCULOSIS

During the first decade of the present century, tuberculosis appeared as either first or second in the list of important causes of death in the United States. Today it no longer appears in the first 10 important causes of death. Deaths from this disease

TABLE 7
AGE-ADJUSTED DEATH RATES^a FOR TUBERCULOSIS (ALL FORMS) BY COLOR AND SEX
United States, 1950-59

Year	White		Nonwhite	
	Male	Female	Male	Female
1950	23.3	10.2	81.8	53.2
1951	21.1	9.2	73.8	42.9
1952	16.6	6.8	60.0	32.8
1953	13.3	5.0	46.4	24.1
1954	11.2	4.1	36.6	19.3
1955	10.1	3.6	32.9	16.7
1956	9.4	3.2	30.4	15.0
1957	9.0	2.9	28.8	13.1
1958	8.1	2.6	27.9	12.2
1959	7.4	2.4	23.8	11.3

Source:
National Office of Vital Statistics, U.S. Public Health Service. *Vital Statistics of the United States.* Washington, D.C.: Superintendent of Documents, Government Printing Office, 1950-59.
ᵃ Per 100,000.

have decreased steadily through periods of prosperity and depression; in time of war as well as in time of peace. The rate of decline has been accelerated in recent years so that between 1949 and 1959 the age-adjusted rate fell a spectacular 77 percent from 25.5 to 5.9 per 100,000 population, compared with a reduction of 46 percent in the preceding 10-year period.

As Table 7 shows, both white and nonwhite persons have shared in the accelerated downward trend in mortality from the disease. The recent gains have been particularly marked among white females. Their *age-adjusted* death rate from tuberculosis was 2.4 per 100,000 in 1959, a decrease of 81 percent since 1949. For white males the corresponding reduction was about 72 percent. In the nonwhite population, too, the control of tuberculosis has progressed more rapidly among females than males. As a result, mortality from the disease is being increasingly concentrated among males. In 1959 the *crude* death rate for nonwhite males (19.4) was twice that for nonwhite females (9.8) and for white males (8.3) was three times the rate for white females (2.8). It is also apparent from the table that the rate continues to be much higher in the nonwhite than in the white population.

As the number of active cases of tuberculosis has decreased, there has been a diminishing proportion of young people with primary tuberculosis infection, as demonstrated by numerous studies of tuberculin tests of school-age children. The great majority of people in our country now reaching age 20 react negatively to the test. This is a very encouraging development. Primary tuberculosis is a highly contagious disease in childhood. The decrease in incidence of tuberculosis in children suggests that present methods of detection and of prevention of spread are fairly effective, but they must be continued and intensified if tuberculosis is to be eliminated or further reduced.

In spite of the remarkable progress made in the reduction of deaths from tuberculosis it would be foolhardy to underestimate the magnitude of the problem which still exists. The number of persons in the United States with active tuberculosis has been estimated at 150 per 100,000 population. Of this total, only about 60 percent are known to public health authorities, which means that there are unidentified persons with active disease who constitute a major reservoir of infection.

Intensified detection programs need to be continuously emphasized with major emphasis being placed on those groups of the population in which the tuberculosis problem is now largely concentrated: low income groups, including Indians and Spanish-speaking groups in southwestern states, migrant workers, people in institutions, and those known to be exposed to the disease. At the same time, the methods used to control the disease need to be modified in the light of the fact that an increasing proportion of active cases is found among people past mid-life. Some promising results in preventing the disease have come from the use of antituberculosis drugs, but further research is required in this field. The search for still better drugs and more efficient programs of treatment continues.

GROWTH AND PHYSICAL STATUS

Falling death rates are but one statistical measure of health improvement. Records of physical growth and development constitute another evidence of progress toward health made by the current population of children as compared to those of previous generations. Although increase in size is of itself no assurance of improved health, better physical development reflects good nutrition, freedom from debilitating disease, and better living conditions in general.

TABLE 8

AVERAGE HEIGHTS AND WEIGHTS OF SCHOOL-AGE BOYS AND GIRLS

Selected Studies, United States

Age (years)	Boys				Girls			
	Michigan[a] 1954	Michigan[b] 1937-38	United States[b] 1937-38	United States[c] 1922-24	Michigan[a] 1954	Michigan[b] 1937-38	United States[b] 1937-38	United States[c] 1922-24
Height in Inches								
7	48.2	47.5	47.5	47.0	47.5	47.2	47.0	46.7
8	50.2	49.6	49.6	49.3	50.3	49.4	49.2	48.9
9	52.8	51.6	51.7	51.3	52.0	51.3	51.3	50.9
10	54.4	53.6	53.6	53.2	54.8	53.4	53.3	52.9
11	56.8	55.4	55.4	55.1	57.7	55.5	55.6	55.2
12	57.9	57.0	57.3	56.8	59.7	57.3	57.9	57.5
13	60.7	58.8	59.5	59.1	61.3	59.0	60.1	59.9
14	63.6	61.4	61.9	61.2	62.9	60.8	61.6	61.2
Weight in Pounds								
7	53.5	51.1	50.2	48.3	49.8	50.0	49.0	47.4
8	59.8	56.4	55.5	53.6	58.9	56.1	54.3	52.1
9	67.5	62.0	61.3	58.9	64.4	61.8	60.1	58.1
10	74.5	67.8	67.3	64.9	74.0	67.8	67.3	64.1
11	84.3	74.6	73.6	71.2	85.6	75.0	74.5	72.4
12	88.8	80.4	80.9	77.7	95.4	81.7	83.9	81.2
13	98.9	87.8	90.0	86.6	102.2	88.3	94.0	92.3
14	113.7	100.3	101.0	96.5	113.6	97.7	102.5	100.4

Note: Data relate to age at nearest birthday. Measurements are without shoes or clothing.

[a] Edgar, Martin W. *Children's Body Measurements for Planning and Equipping Schools.* U.S. Department of Health, Education, and Welfare, Special Publication No. 4. Washington, D.C.: Superintendent of Documents, Government Printing Office, 1955. (Includes nonwhite children.)

[b] O'Brien, Ruth, and others. *Body Measurements of American Boys and Girls for Garment and Pattern Construction.* U.S. Department of Agriculture, Miscellaneous Publication No. 366. Washington, D.C.: Superintendent of Documents, Government Printing Office, 1941. (White children only.)

[c] Palmer, Carroll E., and Collins, S. D. "Variations in Physique and Growth of Children in Different Geographic Regions of the United States." *Public Health Reports* 50: 335; March 8, 1935. (White children only.)

Children Are Growing Taller

Children today are taller and heavier than those of a generation ago, not only in the United States but also in other countries. The principal interruptions in the long-time trend toward increase in size reflect the effects of war and economic depression, but the impact of these adverse circumstances was ameliorated by special measures, such as the distribution of food surpluses in the United States during the depression of the 1930's and the feeding programs in effect in England and other countries during World War II.

The available data on the long-term increase in the height and weight of children are limited largely because there are no periodic large-scale or representative studies for countries as a whole. The data available for the United States are not strictly comparable with respect to ethnic origin and socioeconomic status, both of which influence average height and weight. Nevertheless, the evidence which does exist is so consistent that it leaves no doubt that today's children are taller and heavier than youngsters of a generation earlier, even though the figures do not give an exact measure of the changes.

Table 8 shows the average height and weight of boys and girls at successive ages from 7 through 14 years, for various calendar periods in the United States. A recent study of a sizable sample relates to measurements in 1954 of 3318 boys and girls from 10 elementary and secondary schools in southern Michigan. For comparison, figures are given for Michigan children included in a study by the Department of Agriculture in 1937-38, as well as data for 16 states and the District of Columbia which were included in that study. Shown also are the results of a survey made in the early 1920's which covered several areas of the country; this study, however, related to third-generation native-born white children, whose average measurements tended to be higher than those for children as a whole at that time.

Both the average heights and weights of the Michigan children in 1954 are consistently higher than those for the other groups shown in the table. Among boys under nine years of age the average heights are greater by a fraction of an inch, and at ages nine and over by an inch or more. Among girls the difference comes to an inch as early as age eight. The increase in the average weight of the Michigan boys between 1937-38 and 1954 ranged from more than 2 pounds at age seven to as much as 13 pounds at age fourteen. Even greater gains were recorded for the older girls. When the recent figures on weight for the two sexes are compared with those for 1922-24, the differences are still wider.

Similar trends are evident from a study of the average heights and weights of elementary-school children residing in or near Eugene, Oregon, according to a comparison of their measurements in 1950-52 with those for comparable groups of children in 1937-38 and in 1920-24.

The acceleration in the rate of growth of school-age children reflects a number of factors. Of major importance are increased knowledge of the principles of good nutrition, the availability of a wide variety of foods, and the rise in living standards. Another contributing factor has been the decreased frequency of debilitating diseases among children. Better knowledge of the factors that affect good health and the application of this knowledge in daily living have also had a salutary influence on the development of school-age children and the marked improvement in their physical status.

PRESENT-DAY HEALTH PROBLEMS

Although encouraging progress has been made in advancing the health of the nation and in reducing death rates, many health problems of great magnitude and significance still exist. Knowledge of these, so essential for effective health education, is provided in part by mortality and morbidity statistics.

Most Frequent Causes of Death

The principal causes of death in the United States in 1959 are shown in Table 9. Heart disease accounts for nearly two-fifths of all deaths in the United States, while the cardiovascular-renal diseases as a group—heart disease, stroke, and diseases of the kidney—account for more than half the total mortality. Cancer, "malignant neoplasms," is second, accounting for approximately 16 percent of all deaths. Together these two groups of conditions now account for nearly 71 percent of all deaths.

Reflecting the increasing concentration of chronic disease in the middle and later years, the proportion of deaths at the higher ages has been rising steadily, as may be seen in Table 10. At the beginning of the century only 24 percent of all deaths were at ages 65 and over; in 1958 the proportion was 58 percent. On the other hand, the proportion of deaths at ages under 20 decreased from 37 percent in 1900 to only 9 percent in 1959. In some degree, these shifts also reflect the increasing proportion of population at the older ages. The proportion of total population at ages 65 and over increased greatly from 1900 to 1959, from 5.1 to 8.7 percent. Over the same period, the proportion of population at ages 45 to 64 rose from 15.7 to 20.3 percent.

TABLE 9
MORTALITY FOR THE TEN LEADING CAUSES OF DEATH
United States, 1959

Rank	Cause of Death	Number of Deaths	Death Rate per 100,000	Percent of Total
	All causes	1,656,814	939.1	100.0
1	Diseases of the heart	641,044	363.4	38.7
2	Malignant neoplasms (cancer)	260,047	147.4	15.7
3	Vascular lesions affecting central nervous system (stroke)	191,376	108.5	11.6
4	Accidents	92,080	52.2	5.6
5	Certain diseases of early infancy	67,934	38.5	4.1
6	Influenza and pneumonia	55,039	31.2	3.3
7	General arteriosclerosis	34,622	19.6	2.1
8	Diabetes mellitus	28,080	15.9	1.7
9	Congenital malformations	21,780	12.3	1.3
10	Cirrhosis of the liver	19,242	10.9	1.2

Source:
National Office of Vital Statistics, U.S. Public Health Service. *Vital Statistics of the United States.* Washington, D.C.: Superintendent of Documents, Government Printing Office, 1959. (See especially, Vol. 7, No. 13, July 22, 1959.)

Fatalities due to violence increased in relative importance in the mortality picture since the beginning of the century. In the early years (1900-1904) this category of deaths, which includes accidents, suicide, and homicide, accounted for 5.6 percent of all deaths. By 1939-41 this had increased to 8.8 percent. Although the ratio had dropped to only 7.2 percent by 1959, it is still significantly above the figure at the start of the century.

Mortality Variations in Childhood Age Groups

The causes of death in infancy, childhood, and early youth are quite different from those for all ages combined. There is also a distinctive pattern for the preschool age groups as compared with the school-age children (Table 11). In infancy, premature birth, congenital defects, and injury at birth account for more than two-thirds of the deaths. Other important causes are pneumonia and accidents.

The problems of prematurity and prenatal mortality (death during 28 weeks of gestation)[1] are receiving an increasing amount of attention. More than half of the 141,000 deaths in

[1] United Nations. *Demographic Yearbook.* Ninth edition. "Mortality Statistics." New York: Statistical Office of the United Nations, 1957.

TABLE 10
PERCENT DISTRIBUTION OF DEATHS BY AGE
United States, 1900-59

Year	Age Group, Years				
	Total	Under 20	20-44	45-64	65 and Over
1900[a]	100.0	37.1	20.4	18.2	24.3
1920[a]	100.0	28.6	21.1	21.4	28.9
1940	100.0	12.7	13.3	28.2	45.7
1959	100.0	9.5	7.1	24.9	58.5

Source:
National Office of Vital Statistics, U.S. Public Health Service. *Vital Statistics of the United States.* Washington, D.C.: Superintendent of Documents, Government Printing Office, 1900-59.
   [a] Expanding death registration states.

1958 in the United States which occurred in the perinatal period (commonly defined as extending from the moment of birth until a few minutes after birth) were among prematures, that is, those weighing 2500 grams (5½ pounds) or less at birth. The mortality among premature births in the first week of life is estimated to be more than 25 times that among mature babies— those weighing more than 2500 grams at birth. The lower the birth weight of prematures, the more unfavorable is their outlook for survival.

The problem of reducing prematurity and its resulting high fetal and infant loss is very complex. There is need for more intensive research on the factors involved in the cause and onset of premature labor. Significant gains can be made by better medical management during pregnancy, particularly for women most likely to experience premature labor. Much can be accomplished by bringing expectant mothers under prenatal care early in pregnancy and by improving their dietary habits. Greater stress on proper prenatal care is needed. More emphasis on fetal and infant survival is indicated in health education in schools and colleges and is particularly important for teaching of high-school girls.

At ages one to four, *accidents* cause more deaths than any other condition. Influenza and pneumonia are second. Congenital defects and malignancies are also among the principal causes of death in this age group. None of the communicable diseases of childhood is now of major importance as a cause of death. Good

TABLE 11
THE FIVE LEADING CAUSES OF DEATH AT VARIOUS AGES FROM INFANCY TO AGE 24
United States, 1959

Cause	Death Rate per 100,000
Under 1 Year	
All causes	2944.5
1. Certain diseases of early infancy: (a) infections of the newborn, (b) other diseases peculiar to early infancy, and immaturity unqualified, (c) birth injuries and postnatal asphyxia and atelectasis	1785.4 990.3 (a & b) 795.1 (c)
2. Congenital malformations	409.5
3. Influenza and pneumonia, except pneumonia of newborn	256.2
4. Accidents	101.4
5. Gastritis, duodenitis, enteritis, and colitis, except diarrhea of newborn	67.0
Ages 1-4	
All causes	107.0
1. Accidents	30.6
2. Influenza and pneumonia	15.3
3. Congenital malformations	12.2
4. Malignancies (including leukemia)	10.6
5. Gastritis and enteritis	3.4
Ages 5-14	
All causes	46.8
1. Accidents	18.5
2. Malignancies	6.9
3. Congenital malformations	3.7
4. Influenza and pneumonia	2.4
5. Diseases of the heart	1.3
Ages 15-24	
All causes	106.5
1. Accidents	55.9
2. Malignancies	8.4
3. Homicide	5.8
4. Suicide	4.9
5. Diseases of the heart	4.3

Source:
National Office of Vital Statistics, U.S. Public Health Service. *Vital Statistics of the United States.* Washington, D.C.: Superintendent of Documents, Government Printing Office, 1959. (See especially, Vol. 7, No. 13, July 22, 1959.)

medical care and more effective health education for parents are important factors in bringing about lower death rates in the preschool group.

At the school ages also, accidents far outdistance all other causes of death. Each year, accidents take the lives of about 6000 children at the school ages from 5 to 14 years; these fatalities account for two-fifths of all deaths in this age range. For the next leading cause of death, cancer, the number of deaths recorded is only about one-third that of accidents.

In 1959, the death rate from accidents among children in the United States at ages 5 to 14 years was 25.9 per 100,000 for boys and 10.9 per 100,000 for girls. Within this period of life the death rate increases for boys but decreases for girls, as shown in Table 12. Thus, the death rate for boys at ages 5 to 9 years, 23.4 per 100,000, is nearly twice that for girls (12.8) of the same ages. The rate for boys rises to 28.7 per 100,000 at ages 10 to 14 years, when it is under three times that for girls (8.7).

Motor vehicle fatalities account for two-fifths of the total number of accidental deaths at these school ages. At ages 5 to 9 years, three of every five motor vehicle deaths are the result of children being run over or hit as they play on or cross streets, highways, and driveways. At ages 10 to 14 years, only one-fourth of the motor vehicle fatalities are among pedestrians. At these ages, deaths of bicyclists in collision with motor vehicles are at their peak.

The home is the place of accident in 18 percent of the fatalities among boys and 31 percent of the fatalities among girls of school age. These proportions tend to decrease as children grow older.

A substantial number of fatalities among school-age children occur in recreational and other outdoor places, about 24 percent for boys and approximately 11 percent for girls. The relative frequency of accidents in such places rises as children grow older and play more often away from home. Only 1 percent of the fatal injuries at ages 5 to 14 years sustained on the street or highway do not involve a motor vehicle.

One-fifth of the accidental deaths among children 5 to 14 years old are due to *drowning*. Boys are the most frequent victims, with the death rate from drowning for boys four times that for girls. In this age group drownings increase in relative importance among both sexes with age. Not only do the older children participate more often in swimming, boating, and other sports, but they are also increasingly permitted to do so on their own.

TABLE 12

MORTALITY FROM ACCIDENTS AMONG SCHOOL-AGE CHILDREN ACCORDING TO
PLACE AND TYPE OF ACCIDENT
United States, 1959

Place and Type of Accident	Ages 5-14			Ages 5-9			Ages 10-14		
	Total	Boys	Girls	Total	Boys	Girls	Total	Boys	Girls
Annual Number									
Number of deaths	6,511	4,644	1,867	3,402	2,232	1,170	3,109	2,412	697
Death rate per 100,000	18.5	25.9	10.9	18.2	23.4	12.8	18.9	28.7	8.7
Percent Distribution by Place of Accident									
All places	100	100	100	100	100	100	100	100	100
Transport	47	45	51	49	49	49	44	41	53
Motor vehicle	42	40	47	46	45	46	38	35	47
Nontransport	53	54	49	50	50	50	56	58	46
Home	22	18	31	25	20	36	18	17	23
Farm	5	7	2	3	4	2	7	9	2
Street and highway	1	1	a	1	1	a	1	1	a
Other specified (inc. recreation)	21	24	11	17	22	9	25	27	16
Unspecified	1	a	1	1	1	1	a	a	1
Percent Distribution by Type of Accident									
All types	100	100	100	100	100	100	100	100	100
Motor vehicle—total	42	40	47	46	45	46	38	35	47
Pedestrian	19	18	20	27	28	26	9	9	10
Other road vehicle	23	22	27	18	17	20	29	26	37
Railroad	1	1	a	1	1	a	1	1	1
Water transportation	2	3	2	2	2	1	3	3	2
Drowning (exc. water transportation)	18	22	10	17	21	9	20	22	13
Fire and explosion	12	7	23	16	9	27	7	4	17
Firearm	7	9	3	4	4	3	10	12	3
Falls	3	3	3	3	3	3	3	3	3
From one level to another	2	2	2	2	2	2	2	2	1
Machinery	2	3	1	1	2	a	3	3	1
Blow from falling object	1	1	1	1	2	1	1	1	1
Electric current	1	1	a	1	1	a	1	1	a
Other and unspecified	11	11	10	9	9	9	13	13	12

Source:
National Office of Vital Statistics, U.S. Public Health Service. *Vital Statistics of the United States.* Washington, D.C.: Superintendent of Documents, Government Printing Office, 1959
a Less than 0.5.

Fires and explosions are responsible for over one-tenth of the total number of accidental deaths among children at ages 5 to 14 years. Among girls at ages 5 to 9 years this cause ranks second only to motor vehicle accidents. A considerable number of casualties are due to firearm accidents, particularly among the older school-age boys. Thus, at ages 10 to 14 years, 12 percent of the accidental fatalities among boys result from the careless use of firearms. Although *falls* are an important cause of non-fatal injury among children, they account for only 3 percent of the fatal injuries.

The toll of accidental deaths also includes a wide variety of other types of mishaps, such as those involving machinery, falling objects, electric current, and railroad trains.

Parents, teachers, and others concerned with the welfare of children and youth have the responsibility to help growing boys and girls develop safe living practices and for providing adequate supervision when necessary. Co-operative action is needed in programs of safety sponsored by educative, medical, public health, and community organizations. Good medical care, effective health education for parents and children, and sound school and community health programs can help to fight other important causes of death among elementary and junior high school youngsters.

In the high-school and college-age group (15 to 24), accidents, particularly motor vehicle fatalities, take an even higher toll than at the 5 to 14 year group, with malignancies in second place and homicide third. Suicide and diseases of the heart are the fourth and fifth principal causes of death in this age group. These figures have many implications for those working with young people. Suitable medical care, better understanding of the emotional requirements of teen-agers and young adults, the encouragement through health education of better skills, attitudes, and practices in healthful and safe living, and more adequate health and recreation facilities are a few of the ways to further reduce deaths in this group.

Most Frequent Causes of Illness Among Adults

Some conditions that cause an enormous amount of disability or chronic illness are not included in the list of important fatal diseases. Relatively few people die from arthritis, mental illness, or colds, but millions suffer from them. Unfortunately, data concerning the prevalence of disability caused by these and other usually nonfatal conditions are fragmentary.

The rheumatic diseases far outrank every other chronic disease in frequency. It is estimated that more than 10 million adults in our country have some form of rheumatism or arthritis. These diseases include a wide variety of conditions which may directly involve not merely the joints in one or more parts of the body but also the muscles or other tissues.

Progress has been made in treatment of the rheumatic diseases, even though the gains cannot compare with the brilliant achievements in many other branches of medicine. Interest in these diseases has grown rapidly in recent years, and research has been stimulated by the discovery of ACTH, cortisone, and other substances now used in treatment, although the first enthusiasm for some of these drugs has been moderated. Much work is being done in the field of rehabilitation of arthritis victims. Those crippled by the disease have been enabled to walk again, and some formerly unemployable persons are able to work following intensive rehabilitation procedures.

The wide variety of the rheumatic disorders and the many factors in their etiology make progress in this field difficult, but the outlook for further gains is promising. The control of these diseases rests largely on development of new knowledge through research.

Mental illness continues to be a serious problem in terms of frequency of illness and prolonged disability as well as family and social disruption. However, recent advances in the management and treatment of mental disorders promise to improve measurably the outlook for patients with such conditions. These developments have already had an impact on the hospitalization of mental patients in the United States. In 1956, for the first time in many years, there was a *decrease* in the number of resident patients in state and county hospitals for the long-term care of mental patients. Further reductions were recorded in 1957 and in 1958.

The introduction of the new tranquilizing drugs, which are of greatest use in the treatment of schizophrenia and other functional psychoses, has been a major factor in shortening the average hospital stay of patients with mental disturbances. The use of tranquilizers has also effected a marked change in the type of therapy employed in hospitals. Figures for the Veterans Administration hospitals show that only half as many patients were given shock therapy in 1956 as in the year before, while the number receiving individual and group psychotherapy increased markedly. At the same time, many more patients than in past years are being given greater freedom in the hospital, and increasing numbers are being released on trial visits to their homes. The tranquilizing drugs have also made it feasible for many more patients to be treated outside of hospitals. However, in assessing the value of these drugs, it should be noted that they do not cure patients but only make them more amenable to psychiatric treatment.

Although recent developments are encouraging, bed capacity in hospitals for the mentally ill, while increasing, falls far short of needs. The acuteness of the situation is indicated by the large waiting lists that exist and by the rapidity with which new hospitals are filled. The number of admissions has continued upward almost everywhere.

Efforts to provide more adequate hospital care for mental patients are hindered also by the serious shortage of professional personnel. According to the minimum standards of the American Psychiatric Association, physicians employed in state and county mental hospitals for long-term patient care in 1956 numbered less than half the total needed. Numbers of hospital personnel— psychologists, nurses, attendants, and psychiatric social workers —likewise fell far short of requirements. The shortage of social workers tends to reduce the number of patients who can be released on trial visits to their homes, since hospitals have the responsibility for supervising such patients until they are discharged from care.

Vocational rehabilitation for patients discharged from mental hospitals is another badly neglected aspect of the problem. Unless former patients are helped to find suitable employment, much of the gain from modern therapy is negated.

Blindness is another social and economic problem of considerable size. Although the exact number of blind persons in the United States is not known, the National Society for the Prevention of Blindness estimates that there are 345,000 persons who are either totally blind or who have impairment of vision sufficiently great to prevent the conduct of normal activities. This number is equivalent to a rate of 2 per 1000 population. The annual number of new cases of blindness, so defined, is estimated at nearly 30,000, or 17 per 100,000 population.

Blindness is more prevalent among older persons and reflects the fact that the most frequent causes of blindness generally have their onset in middle and later life. These include specific conditions of unknown etiology, particularly glaucoma and cataract, and general disorders, such as arteriosclerosis, high blood pressure, nephritis, and diabetes. Glaucoma and cataract account for nearly one-third of all cases of blindness, and degenerative disorders and diabetes for about one-seventh of the total. Prenatal and hereditary disorders, the most common causes of blindness occurring in infancy and childhood, are responsible for about one-eighth, and infectious diseases for one-tenth, respectively, of all cases. Accidents account for about one-twentieth of the total.

Additional research obviously is needed in this field, but even in the present state of knowledge, much can be done to prevent blindness. A study in Baltimore showed that half the cases of blindness could have been prevented. Early diagnosis and treatment of pathological eye conditions are the best available means to conserve sight. Periodic health checks, particularly for people past mid-life, should include examination of the eyes for glaucoma and cataract as well as for changes due to degenerative vascular diseases.

There are many other disabling conditions which affect large numbers of the population. Some of these, such as the common cold, await further findings from research while others, such as dental caries, poor nutrition, and some skin conditions, could be partially prevented or corrected by applying known health facts. Hearing difficulties and orthopedic handicaps are partially or totally disabling to many people and highlight the importance of adequate medical and health services for prevention, treatment, and rehabilitation.

Major Causes of Disability Among School Children

Many school children today have physical or emotional disorders which, although not a threat to life, affect their state of health and their daily activities. Some of these may not become a source of difficulty until later years.

One source of national data on child health problems is the series of publications from the National Health Survey, conducted by the United States Public Health Service from July 1957 to June 1958. Information was collected from 36,000 households. During this period, children 6 to 16 years of age averaged

8.4 school days lost. Respiratory conditions represented 71 percent; and injuries and their effects, 5 percent of causes for
absence. Boys averaged 8.0 days lost; girls, 8.9 days lost. The
urban rate of school days lost was higher than the rural farm
rate; children of families with incomes over $4000 lost more
days than children from poorer families.

Children 5 to 14 years averaged 3.5 acute conditions during
the year; young persons 15 to 24 years old averaged only 2.7
such conditions. Girls of these ages had slightly more acute conditions than boys.

Chronic impairments occurred at a rate of 41.0 per 1000
for the group from birth to 14 years and at a rate of 82.8 for
those 15 to 24 years. Visual impairments, including blindness,
accounted for 8 percent of the impairments in each of the two
age groups, while hearing impairments, including deafness, accounted for an additional 15 percent of each group. Speech
impairments accounted for 26 percent of the impairments of
the younger group and 8 percent of the impairments in the older
group. Orthopedic defects were relatively more important in
the older group.

Several volumes of data have been published on this survey,
some of which refer to children and youth of school age.
Unfortunately, the data are based on the unconfirmed statements of nonmedical people discussing their families and themselves.

A number of local studies have been published which give
some indication of the scope of child health problems. A 1955
survey of physicians in private practice in the state of Washington [2] showed that a respiratory disorder, usually a condition
of the tonsils and adenoids or the common cold, was the primary
complaint among children at ages 5 to 14 years in about one-
fourth of home or office visits. Accidental injuries, principally
lacerations of the face and fractures of the upper limbs, ranked
next in frequency, and accounted for 15 percent of the visits.
Sizable proportions of the cases were reported for eye and
ear disorders and for the allergies, mainly hay fever and
asthma. It is noteworthy that health checkups and immunizations accounted for 7 percent of all physician visits for children
between 5 and 14 years old.

[2] Standish, Seymour, Jr., and others. *Why Patients See Doctors*. Seattle: University of Washington Press, 1955. 94 p.

A measure of the impairments found among school children is contained in a report on medical examinations given to first-graders in Rochester, New York, in 1952-53.[3] Over one-fifth of the children were found to have a condition affecting health adversely; economic status of the family had little influence on the ratio. The most frequent impairments, in the order named, were: orthopedic conditions; allergies; emotional problems; ear, nose, and throat disorders; and nutritional disturbances. The study excluded such impairments as those of vision or hearing, dental defects, and minor skin disorders.

Dental Health Problems

Dental health problems are the most prevalent of all health defects among children of school age, with dental caries or tooth decay the most common dental disease of children and youth. A national survey [4] conducted in 1952 showed that 80 percent of all dental patients under 20 years of age had teeth needing fillings. The average number of teeth needing fillings increased with age from about 3 teeth for patients under five years of age to 3.5 teeth for patients five to nine years of age, 4 teeth for patients 10 to 14 years of age, and more than 5 teeth for patients 15 to 19 years of age. A survey of dental caries experience of 14- and 15-year-old pupils in Utah schools in 1955 revealed that the DMF rate (decayed, missing, and filled teeth per individual) varied from 14.4 in the highest county to 3.97 in the lowest.[5] Variations in rates are related to several factors including fluoride content of water supplies, per capita consumption of sugar, individual dental health practices, and utilization of prophylactic and remedial dental services. Other dental problems affecting children include malocclusion (teeth that do not come together properly), gingivitis (inflammation of the gums), and fractures of the teeth resulting from accidents or from participation in sports. Health education has a significant role to play in the prevention and treatment of dental problems.

[3] Yankauer, A., and Lawrence, R. A. "A Study of Periodic School Medical Examinations. 1. Methodology and Initial Findings." *American Journal of Public Health* 45: 71-78; January 1955.

[4] Bureau of Economic Research and Statistics, American Dental Association. *Survey of Needs for Dental Care.* Chicago: the Association, 1952. Tables 10 and 11.

[5] Utah State Department of Health. *Biennial Report.* Salt Lake City: the Department, 1954-56.

Morbidity Among Children

An insight into morbidity, both acute and chronic, among 5- to 14-year-old children, is available from a survey made in New York City in the spring of 1952, covering 4200 households in which there were about 2100 children.[6] According to respondents, the frequency of illness reported, based on the prevalence of medical conditions on the day preceding the interview, was 15.6 percent. During the eight-week period preceding, those interviewed reported that 40 percent of the children experienced illnesses, of which half were respiratory diseases, chiefly colds, and about one-fifth were other infections, including sore throat and the communicable diseases. Other reported illnesses affecting 2 percent or more of the children according to respondents were, in order of rank, allergies, skin disorders, and diseases of the bones and organs of locomotion. Injuries were reported for just under 2 percent of the children. Within the eight-week period a physician saw 62 percent of the children with acute conditions and 42 percent of those with chronic diseases.*

Information concerning child health is least adequate with regard to mental and emotional disorders and nutrition. It is difficult to estimate the number of children who have emotional disturbances. There are undoubtedly a considerable number with emotional problems of such significance as to constitute a handicap not only to their school progress but also to their careers and adjustment in adult life. Obesity is one of the more frequent nutritional problems in children which may hamper them as they grow older and which primarily reflects poor food and eating habits, and sometimes emotional disturbance.

These difficulties, and many others from which children suffer, require early detection and correction lest they become deeply rooted. Regardless of the number of sufferers, any condition which adversely affects the health and growth of a child is important to him and should be prevented, alleviated, or compensated for, if possible. It is important that all those who work with children be alert to the nature and importance of early signs of deviation from good health and know where and how to obtain proper help when necessary.

---

[6] Committee for the Specific Research Project in the Health Insurance Plan of Greater New York. *Health and Medical Care in New York City*. Cambridge, Mass.: Harvard University Press, 1957.

* NOTE: Information obtained from interviews of this type is subject to the inaccuracy of "lay diagnosis" of medical conditions.

GOALS IN CHILD HEALTH

The rapidly increasing child population makes it necessary to intensify efforts to improve child health through preventive and remedial measures. Special attention should be directed to giving children a sound foundation with which to meet the health problems of later years.

The goal today is a high level of health, not merely the prevention of disease and defects. Schools are more competent than ever to teach children responsibility for their own health and safety; understanding of some basic principles of disease; factors affecting healthy growth and development; appreciation of the value of early detection and treatment of disease or disorders; and the need for good medical and dental services. Lastly, children and youth are becoming ever more familiar with the role of the home, the school, the official and voluntary community agencies, as well as that of the physician, the hospital, and other medical services in promoting individual and public health.

SELECTED REFERENCES

COMMITTEE FOR THE SPECIFIC RESEARCH PROJECT IN THE HEALTH INSURANCE PLAN OF GREATER NEW YORK. *Health and Medical Care in New York City.* Cambridge, Mass.: Harvard University Press, 1957.

DEPARTMENT OF HEALTH, EDUCATION, AND WELFARE, U.S. PUBLIC HEALTH SERVICE. *Health Statistics from the U.S. National Health Survey.* Washington, D.C.: Superintendent of Documents, Government Printing Office, July 1957-June 1958. (Several publications issued in 1958 and since.)

METROPOLITAN LIFE INSURANCE COMPANY. *Statistical Bulletin.* New York: the Company, issued monthly.

NATIONAL OFFICE OF VITAL STATISTICS, U.S. PUBLIC HEALTH SERVICE. *Vital Statistics of the United States.* Washington, D.C.: Superintendent of Documents, Government Printing Office, issued regularly.

SPIEGELMAN, M. "Mortality Prospects and Their Implications." *Annals of the American Academy of Political and Social Science* 316: 25-33; March 1958.

STANDISH, S., JR., and OTHERS. *Why Patients See Doctors.* Seattle: University of Washington Press, 1955. 94 p.

WINSLOW, C.-E. A. *The Conquest of Epidemic Disease.* Princeton, N.J.: Princeton University Press, 1943. 411 p.

YANKAUER, A., and LAWRENCE, R. A. "A Study of Periodic School Medical Examinations. 1. Methodology and Initial Findings." *American Journal of Public Health* 45: 71-78; January 1955.

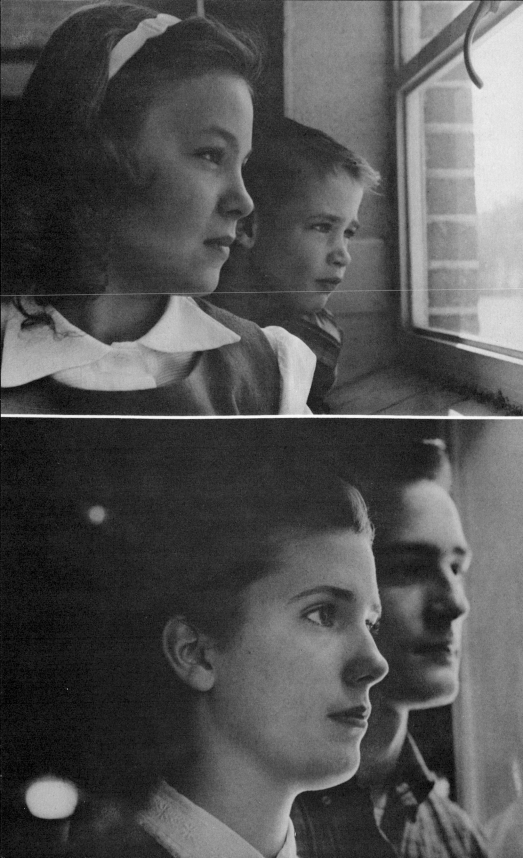

Characteristics of
Children and Adolescents

The teacher must know his pupil as well as his subject. The teacher's knowledge of a child's level of physical and emotional maturity and a recognition of any special health problems are essential for achieving sufficient understanding for educational purposes. Since the educator is interested in these aspects of a child's functioning and since the physician, too, is interested in growth and development, which includes school experiences, there is a large area of mutual concern. Inevitably, a close degree of co-operation between teachers, physicians, nurses, and parents will work to the benefit of the school child. Today, the representatives of education and medicine work together with a considerable degree of understanding and toward a single goal of understanding children and promoting their health and their education. With a policy of continuing interprofessional co-operation, an optimal school program and health education program can be developed based on an understanding of the special characteristics and special needs of all pupils.

Children are like nothing but children. They are made up of an infinite variety of attributes based on a few fundamental similarities. The purpose of this chapter is to outline the similarities and to indicate the scope of and the reasons for the variation. We must know these things if we are to give children individualized, effective guidance according to their individual endowment and potential.

WHY CHILDREN ARE LIKE THEY ARE

One of the most fundamental similarities among all children is that they are not small adults. From birth through adolescence the child's thinking, his reactions to his environment, and his physical, mental, and emotional needs differ from those of the adult. Since he is constantly and individually changing and growing, his need and his reactions are constantly changing.

The failure of adults to appreciate the wide variations of normal growth and what constitutes normal behavior for a given developmental level is an important cause for the emergence of undesirable behavior patterns in children.

What the teacher sees in a child when he enters kindergarten for the first time is the net result of his heredity and of all the environmental influences which have played upon him since he was a single-celled embryo. If we are to greet him as more than a complete stranger, we must know something of what has made him what he is, and what we can expect of him.

Hereditary Factors

The mental and physical traits of every human being are to some extent determined by the nature of his genes.[1] Research is bringing to light an increasing number of conditions which are of genetic origin. They include a number of forms of mental retardation, some types of diabetes and other errors of metabolism, a number of diseases of the blood, some types of epilepsy, albinism, as well as an increasing list of bone, eye, and muscle abnormalities and malformations. In addition to these diseases and abnormalities, heredity plays a dominant role in a person's body build, the color of his eyes and hair, whether or not he is right-eyed or right-handed, and to some extent, his mental capacity and temperament. Genetic factors cannot be changed once the ovum is fertilized, but if they are properly evaluated in the study of the child, they can be influenced to a degree by environmental factors. If the environment is favorable to the individual, he can make full use of the physical and mental capacities he has inherited, and to some extent modify or adjust to unfavorable attributes.

Environmental Factors Following Conception

It has been said that every normal fertilized human ovum is a potential superman. That the embryo does not always reach its optimum stage of development is due to the environmental insults which it may suffer from the moment of conception.

Prenatal influences are of great importance in determining what the child will be like. High on the list is the mother's diet.

---

[1] Nelson, W. E. *Textbook of Pediatrics.* Seventh edition. Philadelphia: W. B. Saunders Co., 1959. p. 234-85.

An exhaustive study by Burke [2] indicated that mothers on a superior diet had four times as many superior babies as did mothers on an average diet; mothers on a deficient diet had one-twentieth as many normal babies as mothers on an average diet. Excessive exposure to radiation through repeated x-rays of the mother constitutes another insult to the fetus. The same applies to drugs given to the mothers and to certain maternal infections. These dangers are especially great during the early weeks of pregnancy when organ differentiation in the fetus is most active. There are studies that indicate that there can be seven times as much mental retardation and neurologic abnormality in babies born prematurely as in those born at term.[3] Multiple births (twins, triplets, etc.), birth by Caesarean section, and improper resuscitation at birth are a few of the other factors which may affect the development of the child.

In many instances the effect of the deficiency is damage to or underdevelopment of the brain. The more severe insults result in paralysis, idiocy, or other apparent defects. The signs of lesser damage may not be detected until the child starts to school and for the first time faces the demands of formal education and training. School difficulties resulting from mild damage may be subtle in their manifestations. They are usually observed in the area of speech and hearing defects, writing and reading disabilities, memory disturbance, failure in understanding and obeying oral instructions, bizarre behavior, and hyperactivity.[4] When the significance of these manifestations in the child is not appreciated or properly managed, emotional maladjustment and disturbance in socialization often result.[5] A number of studies in this field show the frequency of these disabilities and point out methods for their prevention and management. These methods employ the team approach involving educators, research scientists, clinicians,

[2] Burke, Bertha S., and others. "Nutrition Studies During Pregnancy." *Journal of Nutrition* 38: 453-56; August 1949.

[3] Knoblock, H.; Rider, R.; Harper, P.; and Passamanick, B. "The Neuropsychiatric Sequelae of Prematurity: A Longitudinal Study." *Journal of the American Medical Association* 161: 581; June 16, 1956.

[4] Kawi, A. A., and Passamanick, B. "Association of Factors of Pregnancy with Reading Disorders in Childhood." *Journal of the American Medical Association* 166: 1420; March 22, 1958.

[5] Weir, H. F., and Anderson, R. L. "Organic and Organizational Aspects of School Adjustment Problems." *Journal of the American Medical Association* 166: 1708; April 5, 1958.

and social workers. Encouraging results have been obtained in the prevention and management of these handicaps to learning.[6,7]

Environmental Factors During the Early Years

The effects of favorable or unfavorable physical factors, such as diet, housing, sanitation, rest, and activity, on the growing child are obvious when the child first enters school. More difficult to evaluate are the more subtle factors which relate to family and community relations. The unwanted or unloved child may develop into an insecure, timid individual, or into an aggressive bully whose need for attention or self-expression leads him into antisocial behavior. Parental domination can lead to similar deviations from normal behavior. There is a significant amount of human wastage through these factors. With more understanding some of these children might be leaders in our society.

Equally important to a child's need for love is his need for discipline. Discipline is synonymous with guidance. Guidance is the discipline that children need and want. To many parents discipline means domination and regimentation, which any normal child resents, often violently. The child will not accept a pattern of behavior arbitrarily imposed on him, but if firm and kind guidance is consistently practiced, the child learns to respond to it and to rely on it in developing an acceptable form of behavior. Equally frustrating to the child is lack of consistency and over-permissiveness in his management.

Specific environmental problems and their effect on the child's attitude can be summarized as follows:

Problems

Broken homes

Home conditions which do not motivate a child to learn

Poverty and overcrowded homes

Child neglect

Late hours, inadequate diet, poor hygiene

Barren cultural, intellectual, experiential, or moral background

Unco-operative attitude of parents toward children's problems, defects, and illnesses

---

[6] Thelander, H. E., and others. "Learning Disabilities Associated with Lesser Brain Damage." *Journal of Pediatrics* 53: 405; October 1958.

[7] Oppenheimer, E., and Mandel, M. R. "Behavior Disturbances of School Children in Relation to the Pre-school Period." *American Journal of Public Health* 49: 1537; November 1959.

Foreign language obstacle or poor language patterns
Knowledge of being a member of a minority group
Excessive mobility of residence.

Possible Effects

Physical, mental, and intellectual inferiorities and inadequacies
Social immaturity and emotional disturbance
Poor personal and group habits
Lack of respect for authority
Failure to keep up with age group
Excessive absence from school
Susceptibility to infections
Susceptibility to truancy and delinquency
Failure to recognize democracy in action
Dissatisfaction with self.

GROWTH AND DEVELOPMENT OF SCHOOL-AGE CHILDREN

Fortunately for teachers, the deviations in child behavior and development which have been presented do not significantly affect the majority of school children. Nature is usually kind. Almost any child who has more favorable than unfavorable hereditary attributes, and who has lived in an environment in which desirable physical and emotional health conditions outweigh the undesirable, enters school as a happy, adjusted, teachable pupil. In the light of widely varying genetic and environmental backgrounds we can, then, outline essential attributes and project the general course of growth and development through childhood.

The period of childhood extends from infancy to adolescence. It therefore includes the early school years roughly through the sixth grade, or from the age of 5 or 6 through about the age of 11 years. This is ordinarily the beginning of the initial period of a pupil's formal education and is an appropriate time to plan for new and significant experiences with the outside world, and for his ever growing independence from his parents. This is when he begins to formulate a sense of responsibility about matters that previously have seemed unimportant to him. It is a time for developing a concept of right and wrong. These are the years when the need for companionship brings the child into closely-knit groups, such as clubs or gangs, and when he is confronted by various standards and accomplishments which may resemble those of his former home life, or may be entirely different from those his parents have taught him. It is in this period that his ability to make and judge friendships begins to form as he meets other children whose values and ideas of life reflect the teachings of their own particular environment, either for good or ill.

Individual Differences

Each child has a pattern of growth that is individual and characteristic of himself. In describing norms for children there is the risk of creating a stereotype by attempting to make every child conform to a particular pattern. There is great flexibility and a tremendous range in variation in development within "normal limits." While there are some broad patterns of behavior and of growth which can be referred to as average for different age levels, we must use them as criteria with caution, and then only after taking into consideration other factors such as race, sex, cultural influences, socioeconomic status, and previous state of health before deciding whether "average" means "normal" for that child.

An average weight for a child of five years, for example, is simply a tabulation and mathematical averaging of the weights of large numbers of five-year-old children. Because a particular child is within the range of the majority means that he is of average weight; it does not necessarily mean that he is normal or that this weight represents his optimum. It indicates only what he *is*, not necessarily what he *might be*. A figure for his optimum weight can be reached only by a consideration of the total child, including all of his particular developmental influences. All children go through latent periods and periods of growth spurts in their physical, emotional, and mental development. While a latent period often occurs at about two years and again at about six years, and a growth spurt is common at about 12 years of age, there is great variation in the time, duration, and numbers of these periods of irregular growth in different children. It is apparent, then, that the rigid use of physical, mental, or emotional growth charts, graphs, or patterns can easily lead to errors in the evaluation of a child's status, except as multiple observations on the same child are used to record progress of growth.

Guideposts Needed

On the other hand, some guideposts are necessary along the road of growth and development through the formative years. There are growth and behavior trends which are roughly formed in each period of a child's life. A knowledge and considered use of these can give some basis for observing the growth and maturity level of an individual child. Some of the statistics related to physical growth are discussed in Chapter Two.

We are concerned here with accomplishments and various common behavior patterns of play, eating habits, and relations with other people which are usual at different age levels, remembering always the wide individual normal variations in the performances and accomplishments of each child.

Since the 5-year-old, the 11-year-old, and the adolescent cannot be described simultaneously, they are rather arbitrarily grouped. The phenomena of growth and development, the accomplishments, and the social adjustments are discussed as related to the following periods: (a) kindergarten and the primary grades (early childhood); (b) the intermediate grades (middle childhood and preadolescence); and (c) secondary-school years (adolescence).

There is overlapping between these groups. A child in any group may show attributes of a more or less mature child than one of his chronologic age.

THE CHILD IN KINDERGARTEN AND THE PRIMARY GRADES

The child enters kindergarten at approximately the age of five and completes the third grade by the time he is nine. This four-year period brings many changes, some of which are particularly important in the planning of health education activities.

Physical Growth Characteristics [8]

The gain in *weight* is relatively slow compared with that of infancy. The average annual gain during the early school years is about 5 pounds. Unlike weight, the annual increments in height diminish continually from birth to maturity, except for the short period referred to as the adolescent growth spurt. During the early years the height increments average about

[8] Watson, E. H., and Lowrey, A. H. *Growth and Development of Children*. Third edition. Chicago: Year Book Publishers, 1958. 334 p.

2 inches per year. Whereas height at birth is doubled by the age of four, it is not trebled until about the fourteenth year. Throughout the early school years boys average 1 inch taller and 1 pound heavier than girls of the same age. Conversely, girls tend to be about one year more advanced along the pathway to maturity than boys during this period.

Body proportions change significantly as the arms and legs grow longer in comparison to the body. The spine loses its exaggerated lumbar curve. As a result, the child becomes less potbellied and sway-backed, and assumes more of the posture of the adult. During the transition, postural defects commonly develop. In a healthy child, these defects usually correct themselves as the child grows.

Variations in the normal range for height and weight tend to increase during this period. By the age of eight years, there may be a difference of as much as 50 pounds in weight and 10 inches in height between two children of the same sex. These differences tend to increase throughout the childhood years.

At this period the large muscles are more developed than the small ones. The primary-grade child is therefore more adept in activities involving the body as a whole than in those requiring finer movements and co-ordination. By the end of this period, small-muscle skills and eye-hand co-ordination improve. Left-handedness is almost always apparent when the child enters school. This should not be changed. Domination of the left eye, left ear, and left foot may accompany the left-handedness. They need to be recognized because of their possible effect on the child's learning capacity in the areas of reading, spelling, writing, mathematics, and physical education.

While, in general, fine co-ordination muscles develop from the head down, their growth can be very uneven and sporadic. Awkwardness and poor posture are frequently seen. This is aggravated by long hours in an ill-fitting or inappropriately sized seat, and can lead to permanent structural deformities.

The temporary or deciduous teeth begin to be lost at five or six years, and the first permanent teeth appear. The progressive replacement of deciduous teeth by the permanent set, which continues through and beyond this period, leads to alteration in the shape of the upper and lower jaw, and, consequently, a change in the structure of the face.

The young child is normally farsighted. As the eyeball develops, this farsightedness normally disappears. Nearsightedness, if it develops, usually appears at about the age of eight years or older. Most studies indicate that 20 to 30 percent of elementary-school children have significant visual defects, and that 2 to 5 percent have a hearing loss which is sufficient to interfere with their learning. Visual and hearing defects are often not apparent to the teacher or parent, and are discovered only by appropriate tests. Undetected hearing and visual problems are among the most common causes of learning difficulties.

A tendency to respiratory infections, including middle-ear infections, carries over from the earlier years, but is progressively less marked. This also is true of gastrointestinal upsets which are due not only to infection but also to incompletely developed digestive enzymes and to immature neuromuscular control. Periodic outbreaks of communicable diseases for which immunizing serums are not yet generally available (measles, mumps, chicken pox, German measles) are characteristic in the lower grades.

While the child in this group usually has a good appetite, he often continues to eat poorly at breakfast, and may complain of a stomach ache in the early hours of the school day. Food likes and dislikes are generally strong at this period and children need to be encouraged but not forced to try a variety of foods.

Social and Emotional Characteristics

In kindergarten and the primary grades children develop rapidly toward maturity. The initial shyness and the frequent desire to run away usually disappear within days of starting school. The beginner enjoys routine and planned events, and quickly assumes responsibility. But he often forgets, and needs adult supervision. He shows little abstract thought and learns and plays best through active participation and in concrete situations. His interest centers more in the activity than in the end result. Play habits at first are oriented to a domestic pattern. Sex differences and interests, absent in the early months, gradually become more prominent as he progresses through this period. He grows steadily from interest in the present and the immediate reality to interest in past and future. Similarly, he identifies himself more and more with his peer group. With his growing independence he makes much of "fairness," demanding his own turn, making his own rules, and competing actively with his companions as he identifies himself with his teachers and parents. He shows a constant need for adult approval, and often loses interest in an activity if his participation is not recognized. Toward the end of the period he becomes more concerned with the approval of his peers than that of adults. This is accompanied by a clearer sense of the rights of his companions in the group and the beginning of an abstract sense of right and wrong.

His attention span is short, but gradually lengthens. He has abundant energy, but tires easily. He has periods of restlessness, and is often dreamy and withdrawn. Cleanliness is not important to him. Early in this period he resents being told what to do and accuses adults of being bossy and unfair. As he approaches his ninth year he should be able to accept criticism. Failure of a child in the fourth grade to do so usually indicates a feeling of insecurity or inadequacy.

THE CHILD IN THE INTERMEDIATE GRADES

Children in the fourth, fifth, and sixth grades generally include the 9-, 10-, and 11-year-olds. They are often referred to as preadolescents although some children will have entered adolescence by the time they are 12 years old.

Physical Growth Characteristics

Slow and steady growth in weight and height continues except for the adolescent or preadolescent growth spurt. At times the growth spurt is preceded in the preteen years by a rapid increase in weight, often referred to as physiologic preadolescent obesity. It is of no organic significance but it is often an unnecessary source of worry to the child and his parents. It must, of course, be differentiated from other causes of obesity. While girls usually mature about two years earlier than boys, the variation in the rate of development at this period becomes marked.

Permanent teeth are still erupting and deciduous teeth are being shed. The need for orthodontia may become apparent. The normal farsightedness of the earlier period has disappeared and more close work without eye strain is possible. However, near-sightedness, often familial, may develop at this age.

Motor skills increase rapidly through this period. Eye-hand co-ordination is good. An interest in crafts develops. Attention span lengthens and the child plans ahead. Energy level is high, but children often play to the point of fatigue. The broadening span of interest in both in-school and out-of-school activities often results in too great an activity load. The child in this period needs 10 hours of sleep a day. A mid-day relaxation period is beneficial, and tends to hold down the number of his activities. There is markedly less tendency to respiratory infections and gastrointestinal disturbance, but the enormous appetites which develop toward the end of this period may result in stomach upsets.

Social and Emotional Characteristics

The child in the intermediate grades shows greater responsibility and dependability. Wide individual differences in interest and discrepancies in ability appear, especially as adolescence approaches. Friendships often break up because of diverging interests. The gang spirit is strong and at this age involves one sex only. There is considerable hostility to other groups and to the opposite sex. Gang memberships change rapidly. The gang spirit is stronger in boys than in girls, who more often cling to two or three girl friends.

The child develops perfectionist traits, but rapidly loses interest if his accomplishments are not appreciated, either by himself or by others. He is highly self-critical, often morbidly so. He is acutely aware of his body, and is painfully embarrassed at anything that offends his modesty. In matters of dress he is a conformist. He must dress and act like his friends. Peer recognition is more important to him than adult approval. At the same time he seeks distinction and prestige through attempts at physical or social superiority. He often becomes a show-off; this may take the form of clowning, overexercise, overeating, or other excesses. He is alternately respectful to and resentful of his parents and other adults. He spends much time in discussion and argument. He develops fixed ideas, often highly idealistic or unrealistic. He is often overactive, hurried, and careless. As adolescence approaches, this may be replaced by periods of inactivity beyond his need for rest. Some exasperated parents and teachers have referred to these periods as adolescent hibernation.

His activities and his discussions show that he is reaching for something he cannot quite grasp, a sense of relationship between the past, present, and future, a moral code for the group, a growing sense of his own individual importance which clashes with his feeling of group loyalty, and a sense of loyalty to and pride in country.

In other words, as he approaches adolescence, he is undergoing profound physical, mental, and emotional changes. His body,
his ideas, his interests, his contacts, his horizons are growing
and broadening at a bewildering rate. More than ever before
he needs sympathetic and skillful adult guidance. Ideally, this
guidance should come primarily from his home, aided and com-
plemented by guidance from his school. The child who has had
the benefits of a comprehensive education and health program
throughout his elementary-school years, with adequate individual
attention to meet his specific and recognized needs, has an important advantage in this period of change. He will have the
benefit of guidance to which he is accustomed, and which he
understands and accepts, guidance which has helped carry him
to adolescence with a minimum of maladjustment, and which,
if continued, will help him both in adjusting to his developing
maturity and to the more departmentalized and specialized
atmosphere of the secondary school. Nevertheless, it is unfortunate that the profound personality changes of approaching
adolescence often coincide with a fundamental change in the
type of school living which occurs when the pupil enters secondary school. This change creates more or less serious problems
for pupils enrolling for the first time in the secondary school.

THE ADOLESCENT IN SECONDARY SCHOOL

Elementary school in a sense affords a family type of living.
Secondary school brings the child into new types of relationships,
and with many more people. The single classroom teacher, who
knew the "total child" and who sometimes functioned as an
auxiliary parent, is replaced by a number of teachers, each of
whom is assigned to teach him a particular subject. The change
to a departmentalized school atmosphere occurs at about the
same time that he is breaking away from his parents, when
he still needs an adult's personal interest.

Changing People, Schools, and Relationships

Adolescents are different. They are no longer little children
and they are not yet adults. Many of their illnesses and problems differ either in frequency or characteristics from those
which occur in either younger or older people. As adolescence
brings out new characteristics, attitudes, questions, and worries,

there are changes in their parents' relationships to them, and in their teachers' attitudes, feelings, and behavior toward them. It is a period when expert guidance is especially important.

Understanding Adolescents

The prime requisite for developing a program which will meet the school and the health needs of the individual adolescent is an understanding of adolescents themselves. It is not enough for a physician to know the causes, symptoms, and treatment of a disease, but it is equally important that he know the person who has the disease, and that he really understand this person's characteristics, attitudes, needs, and worries. Similarly, it is important that secondary-school personnel know the pupils. This means that the guidance program must provide the services that will make it possible for teachers to know and understand pupils as persons and also as learners. Desirable as this may be with a student of any age, it is imperative in the educational experience of an adolescent. The adolescent literally insists that he receive attention. This comes about because of one of the adolescent's outstanding personality traits: an unyielding over-concern with himself.

Adolescents' Overconcern with Themselves

Adolescents are so intent on developing their own personalities into a thing of their own, so alert to any effort by adults to force them into a mold, and yet so cool to any adult who does not show an interest in them, that it is impossible to deal effectively with them unless one recognizes these drives and pays some attention to the pupil while one is teaching a subject or dealing with a problem. However, although adolescents are concerned with protecting their own personalities and are intent on running their own lives, they still vacillate in their capacity to be independent and to be themselves, and often behave in a blustering fashion which is characteristic of insecure people at any age. With the inconsistency typical of the adolescent, there are areas in which they are rigid conformists. This is evidenced by fads of dress, hair style, and speech. In dealing with these boys and girls it is important to remember that they are more aware of themselves, and that their developing personalities are more precious to them, than is the case with little children or with adults. They are more susceptible to expressed interest in them, and at the same time less able to yield or to compromise

than is either the adult or the little child. In short, to meet
successfully their overconcern with themselves, adolescents need
to be recognized as persons, as young people trying to be more
adult.

Some of Their Worries

There are many peculiarly adolescent characteristics. One of
these is great interest in their bodies. Their blemishes may not
seem significant to an adult, but the adolescent regards any one
of them quite seriously and he wants other people to do the
same. Things wrong with his body are charged with emotion for
the adolescent. These same defects will be of little concern
either to the child or to the adult. He is not pleased when any
bodily ill is casually shrugged off as inconsequential. An adult
must be prepared to pay attention to conditions which may be
quite minor.

Lack of adequate guidance is at least partially responsible
for the many poor health practices which develop commonly in
the adolescent. Motivated by commercial advertising and by the
writings of faddists, he is an easy victim to the menace of laxa-
tives, diets, pimple removers, "skin purifiers," body builders, and
other nostrums. Often he is not capable of evaluating his need
for rest and his proper activity load. Some adolescents spread
their interests too thinly over too broad an area, feeling the
urge to take part in every possible local project. Others limit
themselves to too few curricular and extracurricular pursuits.

Sex upsets many adolescents. It takes time for them to
reconcile their behavior and their thinking adequately to this
powerful drive and to the customs of their particular community. During the high-school years most girls' sexual drive is
considerably less than boys'. Growing up is frightening to some
girls and they make themselves unattractive by overeating or
by persisting in tomboyish pursuits. At the same time some
boys, doubting their masculinity, will seek to prove it to themselves and behave in unacceptable ways. To add to their confusion, they now recognize the dual standards imposed by the
culture and find it difficult or impossible to reconcile these standards with their developing moral code. This is seriously dis-
turbing to many teen-agers. During this confusing time they
need opportunities to talk about these matters with an understanding adult who listens well, who will take them seriously,
and who will not be too quick to criticize or to advise.

Need for Recognition and Accomplishment

Adolescents need, and perpetually are seeking, prestige and recognition from their contemporaries. They want to be somebody, to win their own place in the sun. They need the confidence in themselves which these will bring. This usually requires activities which are strenuous and which may be in conflict with a prescription of rest. At times rest may be necessary, but it should be less frequently suggested, and only after much more consideration than would be the case when dealing with younger or older people.

No matter can upset young people and their parents more than *their changing relationships to each other*. This is the time when the adolescent is making sporadic and vacillating attempts to achieve independence. When parents are possessive or fearful and allow a son or daughter little responsibility, and when by constant prodding and suggestion and supervision they give tangible evidence that they have little confidence in this young person's ability, there is usually an unhappy period of rebellion which is compounded by the adolescent's lack of confidence in himself. At this time the adolescent's feelings toward each parent are changing, and finding these upsetting, he attempts to solve the situation by pretending that neither parent (or what either parent stands for or believes in) is important. Those adolescents who are most fond of their parents may treat them in the most deprecatory fashion. It is as if only by denying their value can they break away.

School is very commonly the source of an adolescent's anxiety. Just as work can bring satisfaction or worry to an adult, so can school bring these to an adolescent. Schoolwork which is not going well is a common cause of headaches and stomach upsets.

Religious conflict, an upset home, the death of a friend, the misbehavior of fallen heroes, and at times the peculiar behavior of adults also confuse and disturb young people. During adolescence, when they are trying to stand on their own feet and to form their own beliefs, they need some strong ties. They need friends and acceptance. They need strong, stable, warm adults for whom they have respect, in whom they have confidence, and upon whom they can rely, but who will not dominate them. When school does not go well, when their families dominate them, when old beliefs, old friends, or old heroes fail them, they, not yet secure, may flounder badly. They protest that they

can stand alone, but they need to know that there are things
and people upon whom they can rely.

ADOLESCENTS' GROWTH AND DEVELOPMENT

In contrast to small children and to adults, adolescents are
vitally concerned with any suspected abnormality in their own
growth and development. Their height and the degree of their
sexual development are especially important to them. A boy who
is shorter than most of his companions, or has smaller genitalia,
or is less bearded not only dislikes being different from his
friends, but also may become emotionally upset and believe that
he is abnormal. A girl who has little breast development, or has
not yet had her menarche, or who is very tall may have a similar
reaction.

Some of this overconcern with growth and maturation stems
from the adolescents' fear that something is wrong with their
bodies, a thought to which they are especially vulnerable at this
stage of psychosexual development. Some overconcern is due to
the fact that size and maturity are major factors in their athletic
and social success. Some has been developed by their teachers'
and physicians' frequent reference to their growth and its
percent of deviation from average figures. This has made average growth seem disproportionately desirable. In some, anxiety
arises because they mistakenly believe that masturbation may
make them grow in an abnormal way.

*Few adolescents understand that wide variations from the
average figures are compatible with normality.* Most of them
believe that to deviate from what is average is to be abnormal.
They do not recognize the fact that many different states, rates,
and modes of growth and development are normal and that
individuality in growth is the rule, rather than the exception.
There is a usual sequence in which growth and development
phenomena take place, but wide differences in time, extent, and
rate of growth can be compatible with normality. Members of
a group, all of whom are of almost the same chronological age
and all of whom are free from chronic illnesses and from nutritional disturbances, will still show great differences in growth.

The Growth Spurt

An adolescent growth spurt occurs in all boys and girls, but
the age at which it appears and its extent and duration vary

considerably from one individual to another. In boys, the growth spurt usually occurs between 12 and 16 years of age. It may result in an increase of from 4 to 12 inches in height, with an average increase of as much as 4 inches in height within a year. In girls the adolescent growth spurt begins earlier, commonly occurring between the ages of 11 and 14, and usually proceeds at a somewhat slower rate and to a lesser extent than in boys.

All parts of the body, not just height alone, show an adolescent growth spurt, but not all parts of the body grow to the same degree at the same time. Leg length increases first and is usually first to complete its spurt; the hips widen before the shoulders; the increase in trunk length and increase in chest depth come later. The major increase in muscle and weight comes last. Subcutaneous fat, particularly in boys, is apt to show a considerable increase before the height spurt develops. A year or two later this fat is lost and tends to recur only after skeletal growth has subsided. At this time there are also changes in secondary sexual characteristics. In boys there is first a gradual increase in size of genitalia, then the appearance and development of pubic, facial, and axillary hair. In girls there is first a budding of the breasts, next an appearance of pubic hair, and then the menarche.

The fact that the height spurt and other evidences of maturity appear earlier in girls than in boys may account for their preference for older boys and a lack of success of efforts by adults to pair them off with boys of their own grade. Girls do not want to dance with a boy shorter than they are and prefer an upperclassman. Boys do not want to dance with a girl who is taller than they are and will say they still prefer guns and baseball. In the later high-school years boys' height surpasses girls' and their sexual drive is also considerably greater. So again, boys and girls of the same chronological age may have difficulty in adjusting to one another.

Developmental Rather than Chronological Age as a Yardstick

Chronological age is a deceptive yardstick for discussing growth, not only when comparing boys with girls but also when comparing members of the same sex. It is better to think in terms of the boy's or girl's developmental status, that is, how far he (or she) has progressed toward maturity than it is to make an evaluation or prediction on the basis of the number of

years and months he has lived. A developmental age may be estimated on the basis of degree of development of secondary sexual
characteristics, or, more accurately, from x-ray evidence of the
extent of changes at the line of growth (the epiphysis) of such
bones as those of the hand and wrist.

At chronological age 15, for instance, a boy may vary in
developmental age or skeletal age from 13 to 17 years, and, when
compared to a girl of the same age, there may be even more
variation. There is a wide range of size, sexual maturity, and
interests among boys and girls who are held to the same standards and rules just because they all started school at the same
age. Competing with one another can produce difficult problems
even though they are of the same chronological age. This is an
important fact in matching adolescents for competitive sports.

The extent to which a boy or girl will gain in height or weight
is difficult to predict. Height-weight tables vary a good deal,
probably because of differences in the racial and nutritional
backgrounds of those individuals whose measurements made up
the tables. With the remarkable changes which have occurred
in growth in the past 30 years, and which are still occurring,
tables rapidly become obsolete. When these factors are considered, one can select and use the chart which seems most appropriate. Tables designed to predict height have a greater accuracy
when they incorporate developmental age data than when they
depend upon chronological age alone. Such tables indicate the
statistical growth potential and are not predictive. When the
rate of growth has been either very slow or very rapid, or when
the skeletal age varies considerably from the chronological age,
the accuracy of these tables is diminished.

The Adolescent's Capacity for Change

The adolescent is constantly changing. These are his most confusing and most unpredictable years. At times it seems as if it
were the exception for things to proceed in an orderly, normal
fashion. An adult's opinion of an adolescent based upon observations made at a single point in time can be misleading. Two
successive measurements of any factor mean much more; three
are still better. It is the degree of progress which is important,
for adolescence is a process. When changes occur in one aspect
of growth, further changes in another aspect will appear shortly.
Time brings about great changes in growth and development.

The immature become mature, the fat thin out, and the short become tall.

Most young people are normal, most of them have great capacity for change, and most of them *want* to be normal. For adults to imply that they are not normal by constantly trying to change them, or by not accepting them as they are, may accomplish little except to decrease their confidence in themselves and to increase their anxiety. On the other hand, although almost all boys and girls eventually reach a satisfactory and what may be for each of them an ideal adult state, it is well to remember the psychological potentialities of wide differences from the usual, and anticipate the anxieties which are so likely to develop in those adolescents who consider themselves to be different. It is all very well to understand that these differences frequently occur and are within normal limits, but quite another thing to ignore them, to pass them off with a casual comment, or to forget that they can be the source of real anxiety and of a variety of psychosomatic disorders in an adolescent.

Consideration of Individual Differences

Finally, the individual differences which exist among boys and girls, particularly in regard to their academic ability, must be recognized. Young people's insecurity, their need for acceptance, their need for praise, and the importance of their developing self-confidence are involved in this phenomenon. This is one of the hazards of education, a hazard which may become greater as our standards are raised and as the base of education widens further. Many individuals of good character, who would have made a satisfactory adjustment at the time low academic ability was not an insurmountable handicap, now are starved for praise and are subject to what is for many an overwhelming degree of defeat and frustration. We are not all destined to be scholars, but we all have the potential of becoming good citizens. Obviously this calls for full co-operation between parent, educator, psychologist, nurse, counselor, and physician, and demands that a careful appraisal be made (with due regard for adolescents' capacity to change), and that just as much effort be made concurrently in attempting to discover the younger person's assets as is expended in evaluating his deficiencies. Similarly, there is need to be sure that the more able and academically superior pupils are given sufficient challenge, lest boredom and mediocrity be fostered. Of course, much of this will have been done in the earlier years, but there will still be need for re-evaluation as time goes on, and when adolescence has been reached, there is need to think quite realistically in terms of preparation for a job and for adult living.

SELECTED REFERENCES

ALMY, MILLIE. *Child Development*. New York: Henry Holt & Co., 1955. 490 p.

AMERICAN PUBLIC HEALTH ASSOCIATION, SCHOOL HEALTH SECTION. "Suggested Standards for Health Services in Secondary Schools." Report of the Committee on Health Service Programs for the Secondary School. *American Journal of Public Health* 42: 139-47; May 1952.

BAKWIN, H., and BAKWIN, R. *Clinical Management of Behavior Disorders in Children*. Philadelphia: W. B. Saunders Co., 1953. 495 p.

CARMICHAEL, L., editor. *Manual of Child Psychology*. Second edition. New York: John Wiley & Sons, 1954. 1295 p.

CHILDREN'S BUREAU, SOCIAL SECURITY ADMINISTRATION. *Your Child from Six to Twelve*. Publication No. 324. Washington, D.C.: Superintendent of Documents, Government Printing Office, 1949. 139 p.

FAEGRE, MARION L. *The Adolescent in Your Family*. Publication No. 357. Washington, D.C.: Superintendent of Documents, Government Printing Office, 1954. 110 p.

FRANK, MARY, and LAWRENCE, K. *Your Adolescent at Home and in School*. New York: Viking Press, 1956. 336 p.

GALLAGHER, J. ROSWELL. *Understanding Your Son's Adolescence*. Boston: Little, Brown & Co., 1951. 212 p.

GALLAGHER, J. ROSWELL, and HARRIS, HERBERT I. *Emotional Problems of Adolescents*. New York: Oxford University Press, 1958. 174 p.

GESSELL, A., and OTHERS. *The Child from Five to Ten*. New York: Harper & Brothers, 1946. 475 p.

JENKINS, GLADYS G., and OTHERS. *These Are Your Children*. Expanded edition. Chicago: Scott, Foresman & Co., 1953. 320 p.

JOSSELYN, IRENE M. *The Adolescent and His World.* Fourth printing. New York: Family Service Association of America, 1957. 124 p.

MARTIN, WILLIAM E., and STENDLER, CELIA B., editors. *Readings in Child Development.* New York: Harcourt, Brace & Co., 1954. 513 p.

MENNINGER, WILLIAM C. *Understanding Yourself.* Life Adjustment Booklet. Chicago: Science Research Associates, 1948. 52 p.

TANNER, J. M. *Growth at Adolescence.* Springfield, Ill.: Charles C Thomas, 1955. 212 p.

THORNDIKE, A. *Athletic Injuries: Prevention, Diagnosis and Treatment.* Philadelphia: Lea & Febiger, 1949. 243 p.

WHEATLEY, GEORGE M., and HALLOCK, GRACE T. *Health Observation of School Children.* Second edition. New York: McGraw-Hill Book Co., 1956. 488 p.

WOLF, KATHERINE M. *The Controversial Problem of Discipline.* New York: Child Study Association of America, 1953. 35 p.

Its Scope and
Socioscientific Bases

What is health education? What areas of instruction and experience are included in organized programs of health teaching? In short, what is the content around which curricular experiences are organized in order to achieve the goals expressed in better health for individuals and society?

The concept of health as defined in Chapter One is broad and positive in its implications. A multiplicity of factors contributes to the achievement of a state of health. It is important to decide which of the specific goals that contribute to optimum living are provinces of health education and which are more appropriate to include in other areas of curricular experience. For example, learning to spend money wisely may contribute to optimum living, but may not necessarily be considered a legitimate goal of health education. The curricular time available for health teaching and the priority of health needs help to determine the choice of content and experiences. Realistic attention to these two criteria may help to overcome the tendency to interpret the health curriculum as an over-all umbrella under which any goal contributing to general well-being may be justified.

The health curriculum needs to be built around the biological and social facts and principles which relate to man's existence, survival, and adjustment. Health education is conceived as an applied science which rests on solid scientific and social foundations. One root of health education is to be found in the biological and physical sciences and the other in the social and behavioral disciplines.

Health education entered the curriculum as instruction in physiology and hygiene. The change in terminology resulted in part from an effort to change the emphasis from didactic instruction limited to the structure and function of the human body to a broader approach which included the application of knowledge in human living. Facts and principles, drawn from scientific areas or disciplines such as genetics, anatomy, physiology, bacteriology, and psychology, which are applied to human living and human health, are essential. Likewise, those facts and principles arising from sociology, social psychology, anthropology, economics, and political science, known to be significant in understanding health needs and problems and which are important in motivating health behavior, become important in the process of health education.

THE SCOPE OF HEALTH EDUCATION

The content of health education might well include learning experiences selected from the following areas of study:

1. *The human body*—Its origin, structure, function, and control. Young people in particular have need to develop not only an understanding but also an appreciation of the intricacy and wonder of the biological organism and to form concomitant attitudes that give high value to the protection of life and health. The educated person with knowledge of his body and the basic life processes of circulation, respiration, digestion, excretion, metabolism, movement, control, and reproduction is better able to make intelligent choices relative to health behavior. He likewise possesses the information that can help him to evaluate the worth of health products and services by the exercise of critical judgment based on knowledge of the human body and how it works.

2. *Biological needs of the human organism*—Food, air, water, activity, rest, sleep. An analysis of biological needs and healthful ways of meeting them is an important area of the health curriculum and can be related to the understandings and appreciations suggested in the preceding paragraph. Meeting biological needs through adoption of a sensible health regimen and a balanced day in terms of work, study, recreation, and rest is an important area of experience.

3. *Psychosocial needs of the individual*—Acceptance, security, recognition, achievement, affection, self-respect, adaptability. Growing up emotionally and understanding the relationships of emotional behavior to total health is a tremendously important aspect of human growth and development. Health education can contribute to this area of human needs through inclusion of appropriate learning experiences in the health curriculum.

4. *Hazards to life and health*—Hereditary and congenital anomalies, developmental disorders, disease-producing organisms, violence and injury, poisons, certain drugs, alcohol, chemicals, radiation, and other actual or potential causes of disability. The understanding of the many possible hazards, together with preventive measures, is an important and extensive area of health education. Hazards change with changing environmental conditions and with advance in the age of individuals. Teaching people how to avoid hazards and prevent illness is of great importance.

5. *Progress in human health and the scientific bases for health care*—Understanding and appreciation of the scientific advances that have been made in the achievement of a greater measure of health and longevity for more people is a valuable area of learning. Coupled with this is a need to understand what constitutes adequate and scientific health care and to know where to secure needed health supervision and treatment.

6. *Health in the home and family*—Meeting the biological and psychosocial needs of family members through understanding the nature and variations in health needs of husband and wife, infants, children, adolescents, and elderly people. Healthful housing, budgeting for health services, health care of young children, home care of illness and injuries, healthy, happy family life, emotional climate of the home, and interpersonal relationships of family members are areas of experience and instruction that merit attention.

7. *Health protection and promotion provided through community services*—Pure water, safe food, clean air, sewage disposal, control of communicable diseases, healthful housing, fire prevention, accident prevention activities, health and hospital facilities, utilization of health and medical care. The many areas of health protection that depend primarily upon group action give rise to the need to understand various ways of meeting these needs. Public health departments, voluntary health organizations, voluntary hospital and medical care plans, rehabilitation programs, public safety and traffic control, housing regulations, and fire prevention are some of the community programs which should be understood and supported by the informed citizen.

8. *State, national, and international needs, problems, and programs in health.*

The planning of the health curriculum and the basis for selecting curricular experiences for particular groups of children or adolescents are discussed in Chapter Six. From the areas of the health curriculum listed experiences can be organized from kindergarten through high school that meet individual and group health needs.

The health information needed by teachers in order to teach adequately cannot be included in this volume. The references at the end of this chapter will prove helpful in building a background of sound knowledge in the various areas of health education. The application of scientific research to health understanding and behavior is a major task for the teacher of health.

SCIENTIFIC RESEARCH AND HEALTH EDUCATION

Research is constantly adding to and modifying the cumulative knowledge of man's health and survival. This information about internal conditions and external forces that affect the many aspects of growth, development, function, and protection of the human organism continues to increase in amount and complexity. Application of significant scientific information to living becomes necessary before man can profit individually from the results of research.

One of the inherent problems in the utilization of research for improved living is the lag which exists between the discovery of new knowledge and its application in the lives of people. Interpretation of the results of research to the lay public is often difficult, particularly when the information is contrary to accepted beliefs and practices. Even more difficult is the incorporation of new ways of behaving into the actual living pattern.

The accumulation of scientific knowledge poses another problem for health education. New research findings may partially or completely abrogate or discredit beliefs which are founded upon incomplete research and experience of former years. For example, recent research in genetics is altering some concepts relative to genetic determination of human characteristics. It is now generally accepted that the chromosome count in normal human beings is 46 per cell rather than 48. Further, it is strongly suspected that congenital anomalies with chromosomal aberrations are the result of abnormalities in the DNA (deoxyribonucleic acid) found in the chromosomes of all cells. Experiments on altering the DNA component of certain bacteria and viruses indicate that such alteration changes hereditary characteristics in succeeding strains of the organism in question. Congenital disabilities in human beings are being studied in the light of this new research, and health educators as well as biologists are challenged to keep abreast of findings as a basis for teaching.

It becomes necessary to teach people that there are bound to be changes in recommended health practices, based on new findings accumulated from research and experience. The teacher needs to avoid absolutes and finalities in his attempt to transmit health information to boys and girls. One must be able to say, "These are the facts as we know them today," and to point out that research is constantly seeking answers to questions that may result in the necessity of stating, "This was once believed to be true, but later findings have showed we were mistaken."

The importance of helping pupils to become acquainted with authentic sources of health information needs emphasis. The concept that science may change present knowledge as a result of future research in no way discredits the body of proved research findings now available. Being able to discriminate between sources that represent bias, vested interest, or actual quackery and charlatanism, and those that represent scientific research, professional opinion, and proved practice requires a high level of intelligent understanding. Teachers and pupils alike need to strive toward this goal.

Applications of health science to living and the consequent improvement in health and prolongation of life are legion. A significant role of health education in the utilization of health science is illustrated in four pertinent examples. Each shows the fundamental relationship of science to survival and to health improvement, and the need for the health educator to be correctly informed and to be able to teach in accord with new scientific knowledge.

Microorganisms and disease. The discovery that microorganisms cause disease was the first major scientific basis upon which modern health education was founded. The need for health education became obvious when Pasteur and Koch proved that many diseases are caused by bacteria, and when Lister demonstrated the helpfulness of antibacterial chemicals. Subsequently, the direction of health education was more specifically indicated when the methods of transmittal of communicable disease were defined as: (a) by intestinal discharges; (b) by discharges from the respiratory system; (c) by animal vectors; and (d) by direct and indirect contact with persons who have the disease and contact with articles which have been contaminated by the infected individual.

Discovery and definition of such facts inevitably shaped the content of health education. If such knowledge is to be useful, the public must be correctly informed and then motivated to apply its learning. Presumably, the right kind of health education, properly implemented, would result in improved living habits through utilization of such procedures as immunization, isolation of the ill individual, and personal cleanliness and sanitation. It would also marshal public support for such public health measures as those designed to provide safe water and milk supplies, proper waste disposal, and effective insect and rodent control.

While not all of these objectives have been accomplished to date, marked progress has been made toward achieving them. However, even before practices catch up completely with one aspect of a health problem, another phase may cause difficulty. As scientific knowledge increases within a given area, new problems may require new approaches in health education. Lately, for example, improved control of bacterial disease by prophylactic measures and specific drugs has enabled certain viruses and fungi to replace many bacteria as parasites of man. This, in turn, has resulted in a marked increase in the incidence of known viral and fungal diseases as well as the development of new diseases caused by these agents. For many of the latter diseases there are as yet no specific effective treatments, and for the present, defense against them depends on available individual resistance and personal hygiene. Obviously this will require modification and intensified utilization of health education.

The science of nutrition. Nutrition as a science was born in the early years of the twentieth century, but it was preceded by discoveries and deductions based on keen observations and experiments in various parts of the world and during different eras of history. In the eighteenth century it was found that the addition of lime juice to the diet of sailors in the British navy prevented scurvy; this was one of the early discoveries in nutrition. The observation of sick chickens in an East Indian prison yard in 1897 caused Christian Eijkman to experiment with feeding some chickens on unpolished rice and some on the polished rice used in the diet of the prisoners. This eventually led to the identification of thiamine (vitamin B_1) as the essential dietary element which prevents a common disease of the Orient, beriberi. Likewise, the conquest of pellagra and the eventual identification of niacin resulted from deductions and experiments made by Joseph Goldberger of the United States Public Health Service while he was working in the hospitals and orphanages of the Southern states. Out of these exciting episodes came medical and public health progress, and determination to discover more facts about nutrition.

Laboratory research in nutrition, utilizing experimental animals, began in the early 1900's with efforts to identify the nature and sources of all dietary elements and their effects on human nutrition. The nutrition laboratories of the world have continued to add to an impressive body of knowledge about nutrition and to provide the information needed for improved health and longevity.

Many of the findings of nutrition research gradually have found their way into the eating practices of the people. Education can be credited with much of the progress in nutrition, together with the wholesale enrichment of basic foods with essential minerals and vitamins. Research has led to determination of the chemical composition of many nutrition essentials, and it has become possible to produce them in the laboratory and make them available to the public in concentrated form. This poses a new problem in health education—that of helping people to understand that a well-balanced diet is the most preferable and least expensive method of meeting normal nutritional needs.

Nutrition has become one of the prime targets of the quack, the faddist, and of some commercial interests intent on making money by preying on the gullibility and, in some cases, lack of knowledge of people. Health education is vitally concerned with helping people to know the scientific facts about nutrition and to make discriminating judgments on the basis of sound information.

Dental health and fluorides. The interest of science in the relationship between the intake of fluorides and their effect on teeth was first aroused by the problem of dental fluorosis or mottled enamel. Early observations and subsequent extensive studies established the fact that mottled enamel is caused by a disturbance in the calcification of enamel and dentin, and that the condition was endemic in some communities and completely absent in others. In those areas where dental fluorosis was prevalent, the water supply was identified as the source of excessive intake of fluorides.

Studies continued, and some important facts were revealed:

1. Practically all potable waters contain at least trace amounts of fluorides.

2. The amount of fluorides in community water supplies ranges from infinitesimally small quantities to as much as 14 or 15 parts per million.

3. In those communities in which the fluoride level in the drinking water exceeds 1.5 ppm (parts per million), the amount of dental decay among the residents is extremely low, even though their teeth are more or less mottled.

4. No harmful effect, other than mottled enamel, has ever been found in any of the several million people who regularly consume water with 1.5 ppm or more of fluorides.

5. Below a fluoride concentration of 1.5 ppm there is no evidence of mottling or any other harmful effect.

These facts raised a question about whether or not there is an optimum fluoride level for drinking waters—a level which will produce maximum resistance to dental caries (decay) without causing mottling of the teeth. A concentration of 1 ppm appeared to be the right amount, and experiments were established in which the fluoride content of selected community water supplies was adjusted to that level. The findings from these experiments dramatically showed that only one-third the amount of dental decay was present in those persons who consumed water with 1 ppm of fluorides from birth through age fourteen, as compared to those who were drinking fluoride-deficient water. The experimental work also demonstrated that raising the fluoride level to 1 ppm does not affect the taste, color, or odor of the water, and does not impair use of water for industrial purposes.

On the basis of extensive and carefully collected data from research studies and field experiments, it is recommended that communities adjust the fluoride content of their water supplies to 1 ppm as a measure of protection against dental decay. Important professional and scientific groups support this recommendation. These include the American Dental Association, the American Medical Association, the United States Public Health Service, and the World Health Organization. Many communities throughout the country have instituted programs for adjusting the fluoride content of their water supplies to 1 ppm. Today, over 36 million people in the United States are residing in communities with sufficient fluorides in the water supplies to benefit the dental health of the residents.

The implementation of recommendations based upon scientific research and actual field tests have run into a storm of opposition in many communities and among particular groups. The objections to adjusting the fluoride level of the water supply, even though it has been shown to be beneficial rather than harmful, sometimes have resulted in campaigns against the program. In some communities the efforts of groups who oppose this public health measure have been successful in blocking public action.

The need for health education is clear. The participation of the individual citizen in a vote to approve or disapprove fluoride adjustment of the water supply is all too frequently influenced by the emotional rather than the scientific approach to a decision which affects health. Therein lies the challenge.

The antibiotic drugs. The discovery of the antibiotics, as with so many other scientific advances, was something of an accident. While culturing staphylococci, the British scientist, Alexander Fleming, noticed that small areas on the culture plate were free of these germs. Under the microscope he found the culture had been invaded by other microorganisms, a common type of mold that grows in bread and cheese. It is known today that this mold was producing a chemical called penicillin, which can stop the growth of staphylococci and many other bacteria.

After extensive experimentation, commercial production of this first antibiotic was undertaken. From this beginning has come a host of powerful antibiotics, and new ones are continuing to be identified and developed in research laboratories. In the comparatively brief time since their advent, antibiotics have caused a major revolution in the prevention and treatment of infectious diseases. They have vastly cut the mortality and morbidity rates for pneumonia, syphilis, and many other serious diseases. They are also used to control and prevent the recurrence of rheumatic fever, and to reduce the frequency and severity of infections in patients with chronic or other debilitating disease. But in spite of all these benefits to man, antibiotics have their limitations and disadvantages. These can be delineated briefly as follows:

1. They are not helpful in curing major virus diseases, such as measles, influenza, or hepatitis.

2. Some of them cause so-called side effects in susceptible individuals, producing rash, dizziness, deafness, and sometimes severe allergic reactions and even death.

3. The use of an antibiotic over a period of time leads to the emergence of strains of disease-producing bacteria which are resistant to that antibiotic.

4. Administration of antibiotics does not insure that a person will develop lasting resistance to disease.

5. They may encourage pathogenecity (the ability to produce harmful effects) of otherwise inactive fungi in the digestive tract.

6. No one antibiotic is successful against all disease organisms.

What relation does this have to health education? Actually, the implications are obvious and important. A major conclusion to be drawn is that self-medication with the antibiotics is hazardous. In taking antibiotics casually, one may sensitize himself to the drug, so that when it is needed for serious or even lifesaving purposes, it will not be usable for him.

By federal regulation, antibiotic drugs can be prescribed only by a physician. This regulation is circumvented by friends who may offer the unused portion of a prescription they have taken for a condition "just like yours." The patient himself may have a leftover supply from a previous illness which he believes to be the same as the new condition, or perhaps another member of the family may have had a prescription for a condition which seemed to resemble the present trouble. Finding ways to combat such questionable, unscientific, and often dangerous practices challenges the ingenuity and resourcefulness of the health educator. The problem is much larger than merely the misuse of antibiotics. To counteract the practices of self-diagnosis and self-medication the health educator is vitally involved in the task of teaching the intelligent use of health products and services.

These four examples illustrate the scientific bases for health education. They show clearly the relationships that exist between health science and the health education needs of children, youth, and adults. Also, they indicate desirable approaches for health education and in some measure suggest its content. Finally, they point up the importance of the health educator's scientific preparation and his need to keep informed of advances in health science.

SOCIOLOGICAL BASES FOR HEALTH EDUCATION

An understanding of cultures in which people live and the socioeconomic environment which surrounds them constitutes the second great area of concern for the health educator who is planning programs and experiences for his pupils. Behavior of individuals is rooted in the family, the ethnic group, the religious sect, the socioeconomic stratum. Knowledge of scientific fact and principle is in itself insufficient in the process of health education. The motives, feelings, previous experiences, and socioeconomic status of those the educator is trying to teach are of supreme importance. The health educator has need for firm grounding in the principles drawn from economics, sociology, anthropology, social psychology, and other aspects of the social and behavioral sciences if he is to function effectively.

Health problems are so closely intertwined with social problems that the two can hardly be considered or treated separately. Numerous sociological factors are involved in this interdependence. For purposes of illustration some examples will be given: (a) problems created by the socioeconomic status of a population; (b) problems relating to the cultural patterns of certain ethnic groups; and (c) problems evolving from the growing mechanization of present-day society. These illustrations are presented to demonstrate the interaction between sociological and health problems and to show how these relate to programs of health education.

Socioeconomic status. Not only do crime, vice, delinquency, and other social ills thrive in areas of poor housing, low income, overcrowding, and bad sanitation, but disease and disability also run rampant. Under such conditions a disease may manifest itself as an overt symptom of underlying social sickness. Consequently, there is little value in treating the symptoms of the disease without doing something about the basic causes. Tuberculosis is a case in point.

It has been demonstrated that high rates of tuberculosis incidence are found in congested areas, in which poor housing and low income prevail. In one well-known study, the incidence of tuberculosis in a crowded metropolitan district was 665 per 100,000 as compared with a rate of 252 per 100,000 in a nearby residential area.[1] In the same study it was found that the average family income in the congested district was $3073 as compared with a figure of $4121 for the less crowded residential section. Likewise, 18.5 percent of the dwelling units in the crowded city area were run-down and dilapidated in contrast to only 4.7 percent in the outlying residential district. Such statistics for tuberculosis furnish only one example of the greater general incidence of certain kinds of health problems among those in poor socioeconomic circumstances.

What are the implications in these facts and what directions do they set for health education? The facts point rather obviously to the need for the health educator to be concerned about the socioeconomic background of the people with whom he works and with measures to better the situations of those in poor circumstances. Such facts also indicate the need for priorities in health education among particular groups of people and for particular health problems.

What can health education do about poor socioeconomic conditions? Children in schools are the workers, homemakers, parents, voters, and political figures of the future. Even in the immediate present the school exerts a powerful influence on the homes of its children. One educator has labeled school children as "thirty million salesmen,"[2] in writing about ideas they take home with them and the impression such ideas make upon the home.

A study by a high-school class of the costs of supporting slums in terms of disease, welfare, and delinquency offers a practical approach. The fact that one analysis showed the difference between taxes collected and funds spent for these purposes in one city to be nearly $1,750,000 could make a consider-

---

[1] Lowell, Anthony M. "TB and the Environment." *Bulletin of the National Tuberculosis Association* 43: 3-4; January 1957.

[2] Knoph, Edward. "Thirty Million Salesmen." *NEA Journal* 35: 295; September 1946.

able impression.[3] As future voters and officeholders these young people might not permit such a drain on the city to continue. For the present, attitudes of their parents might be influenced by comments and observations of the young people.

The desirability of improving slum areas from a health standpoint is hardly debatable. The *method* of improvement is controversial, but the health educator need not take sides in the controversy. The task of health education is to stress the need and reasons for improvement, not to determine methods of attaining it. For example, the health educator should see that the case for both public and private housing is adequately presented, leaving it to students to draw their own conclusions.

Pupils in schools located in areas with low socioeconomic status often present different (or more obvious) health problems than pupils attending schools located in neighborhoods with a higher socioeconomic level. In such schools health education programs should not only be at their best but also should be geared realistically to the specific needs and problems of the area. This is not to say that health education is any less important in areas of better socioeconomic circumstances. It is merely that problems are different.

While recognizing that social ills in slum areas need correction before solid results can be realized in health progress, there is much that can be done through health education, concurrently with social improvement. In the appraisal of results, however, it must be remembered that the evaluation of health education is a long-term process. Some immediate gains may accrue, but the greatest benefits may not occur until new families are formed from among those now participating in the health education process.

Study of the health education needs of young people coming from homes of low socioeconomic status may reveal, for example, that

1. The food dollar is not being expended wisely.

2. Standards of cleanliness and sanitation of the homes are poor.

3. The daily balance of study, work, rest, and play is faulty.

4. Money is being wasted on proprietary drugs, vitamins, and other products for self-medication.

---

[3] Bolton, Francis P. "In This Corner—Slums." *Congressional Record* 103: A4769-70 (Mo. 104); June 17, 1957.

5. Many families are unfamiliar with the health resources available to them.

6. Budgeting part of income for sickness and for health and accident insurance is neglected.

Such problems are not completely under the control of the child attending school, but the child's learning at school influences to a degree the character and activities of the home. In situations in which counseling with pupils and parents is a part of the health education process, the parent is more actively involved. Care should be taken to prevent the health education efforts of the school from reflecting negatively on the home or creating conflict between children and their parents. Effective health education is vigorous and continuous, but it is also discreet.

Cultural patterns and health behavior.   The patterns of living and the values held by particular families and groups exert a strong influence on health behavior and health status. Health behavior in the child is almost exclusively a product of the culture in which he lives. As persons grow older and begin to gain information and think for themselves, weigh scientific evidence, and modify their cultural backgrounds, they may begin consciously to choose different ways of behaving. However, health behavior grounded in family, cultural, and ethnic patterns tends to persist. This makes the effort to change undesirable health behavior patterns of individuals and groups a difficult and often disappointing process. The educator is faced with the need to become acquainted with varying cultural backgrounds and to recognize the strength of custom and belief.

To illustrate the effect of cultural attitudes and mores, two examples of health-related behavior are described—one relating to attitudes toward first aid and the other concerned with eating patterns. These are only two of the many examples that could be given to show the relationship between custom and tradition and health practices, and to suggest needed emphases in health education.

First aid for minor injuries is considered routine in many elements of our society, but in certain families and groups, doing anything about minor injuries, particularly for the male, is looked upon as "sissy." Manliness requires that he disclaim any pain and minimize or even hide his injury. Most people who subscribe to this belief have some realization of the potential

for infection in the neglect of minor injuries. Probably everyone
has had some instruction in first aid or has seen illustrations of
the results of neglect. However, people holding this belief cannot conceive of serious consequences in terms of their own behavior. They may visualize unhappy results for others from lack
of care, but not for themselves. They may rationalize in terms
of "what is to be will be." They may close their minds and
refuse to think ahead at all.

The cues for health education seem rather clear. The basic
concepts underlying the need for proper care of minor injuries
need re-emphasis. In addition, the climate must be changed so
that one can retain his manliness while reporting and receiving
care for minor injuries. In the first instance the consequences
of neglect in terms of infection and possible disability can be
clearly shown and vividly illustrated. The best approaches are
those calculated to build a healthy respect for this potential
rather than to use scare techniques which may breed unwhole-
some fear. A matter-of-fact presentation of the processes involved, with study and visual illustration, frequently will prove
effective. To develop a climate that encourages the reporting of
minor injuries is a more difficult task. Key persons in the group
can sometimes be persuaded to lead the way. An athletic team
may provide the instrument to demonstrate that it is more heroic
to have minor injuries cared for and stay in play than to be
eliminated by an injury aggravated by neglect.

The problem of first aid for minor injuries furnishes one
example of how tradition and custom influence health behavior
and how the health educator may condition his approaches for
this and similar problems. The matter of eating patterns within
cultural groups offers another interesting illustration of a somewhat different character.

It has been rather clearly demonstrated that proper educational approaches for a sufficient period of time can be effective
in modifying the eating habits of a given group.[4] But this is true
only when attention is given to the cultural patterns and social
concepts of the group. Immigrants to this country brought with
them the patterns of eating which had been traditional in their
native lands. Many of these patterns or certain aspects of them
have persisted, although in some instances these were in need of

----
[4] Cassel, John. "Social and Cultural Implications of Food and Food Habits."
American Journal of Public Health 47: 730-40; June 1957.

modification from a nutritional point of view. In early attempts
in this direction health educators sometimes tried to bring about
wholesale changes in the diets of immigrant groups. Such
"Americanization" of long-standing patterns of eating was
markedly unsuccessful. The groups concerned often rebelled
from the beginning or, if partially converted to the new diet,
soon reverted to habitual eating practices.

The lessons implicit in this experience were heeded in more
mature attempts to improve the eating patterns of such groups.
Eating practices were analyzed in terms of a balanced diet and
shortages were noted. Attempts at modification were then
directed only at those phases of the eating pattern which showed
deficiencies. For example, it was found that the basic diet of
certain Spanish-American population groups, consisting basically
of pinto beans and corn products, with relatively small amounts
of meat and certain bulk vegetables, was fundamentally good.
Supplemented with milk products and certain fruits and vegetables, these foods provide a nutritionally adequate diet within
the means of the families concerned. Health education programs
designed to encourage supplementation were satisfactory in contrast to earlier efforts to change the entire eating pattern. This
emphasizes an important principle for health education, namely,
"to start where the people are." It is a serious mistake to try to
substitute divergent customs merely because these customs and
beliefs are effective in our own cultural background. Too many
programs have failed because this basic tenet of health education has been ignored.

Our growing mechanical civilization. Health problems of still
another kind have arisen because of the increasing mechanization of living. Pertinent examples of the hidden hazards to
health evolving from growing automation are found in problems
of air pollution and in the threat of excessive radioactivity in
the environment. Both examples provide dramatic illustrations
of health hazards resulting from social change.

Air pollution is not new in industrial cities, but the problem is
one of increasing magnitude. Recognition that the exhausts from
motor vehicles are a major contributor to air contamination
means that few localities can escape it. Certain areas are likely
to experience more difficulty than others if they are hemmed in
by mountains and subject to temperature inversions, due to the
fact that fog may combine with smoke and other contaminants
to form "smog."

Obviously, the problem is one of control of the sources of air contaminants, including those emanating from industrial plants, motor vehicle exhausts, commercial and family incinerators, and home heating plants. The greatest strides have been made by industry because of early recognition of the problem and the institution of control measures. Despite these efforts, increasing industrialization, combined with a growing population and the mechanization of its living, has resulted in an advanced stage of air pollution in many communities. Protective ordinances have been enacted in some cities with varying degrees of success. Health education has a double-barreled task with respect to air pollution. First, it must help the individual to see the necessity for control of his own behavior in relation to air pollution practices and, second, it must assist in obtaining public support for adequate control measures.

Excessive radioactivity in the environment poses somewhat similar problems, although the effects of radioactivity are more insidious and less apparent. Public awareness and concern about the hazards of exposure to ionizing radiation have been expanded to the point at which some persons have developed unfounded fears about the medical uses of radiation. While social evolution has produced a radiation problem of great significance for health, at the same time health education has the opportunity to share in its solution. The task of health education is to interpret the problem to the public without arousing undue fear and to help in showing the need for appropriate regulation of atomic industry as it develops. Further, the health educator needs to clarify facts relative to the precautions employed in the medical uses of radiation that have made use of the x-ray and other sources of radioactivity safer over the years.

In a sense, both of these problems have their own built-in motivation. But unless they offer an immediate threat the public may become complacent. We know that neither awareness of a health problem nor knowledge about it alone affords any guarantee of desirable behavior. Health education must go beyond information-giving in order to have better assurance of action. Students need to be involved in serious reading and discussion of problems, in reporting and debating health issues, in interviews with experts, in special programs and projects, and in other experiences that stress personal participation. Such involvement is no panacea for the solution of every health problem, but it offers some hope of influencing desirable attitudes.

SELECTED REFERENCES

BAUER, WILLIAM W. *Your Health Today*. New York: Harper & Brothers, 1955. 514 p.

BYRD, OLIVER E. *Health Instruction Yearbook*. Stanford, Calif.: Stanford University Press. Published and revised yearly.

BYRD, OLIVER E. *Textbook of College Hygiene*. Second edition. Philadelphia: W. B. Saunders Co., 1957. 496 p.

CALLAHAN, DOROTHY, and PAYNE, ALMA SMITH. *The Great Nutrition Puzzle*. New York: Charles Scribner's Sons, 1956. 189 p.

DAVIS, ARTHUR F., and SOUTHWORTH, WARREN H. *Meredith's Hygiene*. Fifth edition. New York: McGraw-Hill Book Co., 1954. 906 p.

DIEHL, HAROLD S. *Textbook of Healthful Living*. Fifth edition. New York: McGraw-Hill Book Co., 1955. 802 p.

HEIN, FRED V.; FARNSWORTH, DANA; and RICE, THURMAN B. *Living*. Third edition. Chicago: Scott, Foresman & Co., 1959. 406 p.

HOLBROOK, STEWART H. *The Golden Age of Quackery*. New York: Macmillan Co., 1959. 302 p.

JOHNS, EDWARD B.; SUTTON, WILFRED C.; and WEBSTER, LLOYD E. *Health for Effective Living*. Second edition. New York: McGraw-Hill Book Co., 1958. 507 p.

KILANDER, HOLGER F. *Health for Modern Living*. Englewood Cliffs, N.J.: Prentice-Hall, 1957. 494 p.

LANGTON, C. V., and ANDERSON, C. L. *Health Principles and Practice*. Revised edition. St. Louis: C. V. Mosby Co., 1957. 491 p.

SCHIFFERES, JUSTUS J. *Essentials of Healthier Living*. New York: John Wiley & Sons, 1960. 335 p.

SCHIFFERES, JUSTUS J. *Healthier Living*. New York: John Wiley & Sons, 1954. 928 p.

SHERMAN, HENRY C., and LANFORD, CAROLINE SHERMAN. *Essentials of Nutrition*. Fourth edition. New York: Macmillan Co., 1957. 505 p.

TURNER, C. E. *Personal and Community Health*. Eleventh edition. St. Louis: C. V. Mosby Co., 1959. 446 p.

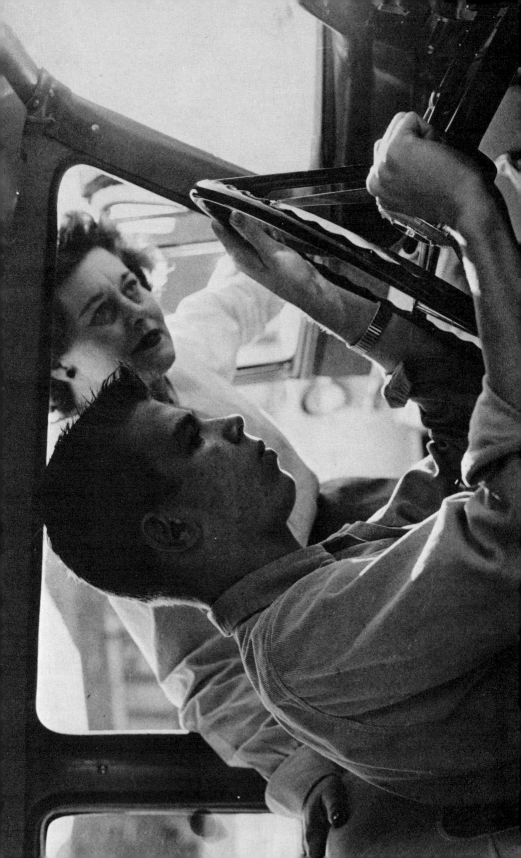

Attitude and Behavioral Change

Teachers face a dual problem in their work; namely, what to teach and how to teach it. Instruction in the area of health education involves acquaintance with a body of information, the application of which is important in the protection and improvement of health and the prolongation of life. More significant is the motivation of behavior in the learner which occurs when people become sufficiently concerned to act. The teacher faces the problem of influencing understandings, attitudes, and beliefs so that pupils will not only know the facts relating to correct health behavior but will also apply such facts in action.

In this chapter some of the attitudes and beliefs that appear to generate health action are reviewed, with some of the factors crucial to changing attitudes. Factors discussed are of importance not only because they affect the acquisition of knowledge, but also because they affect changes in attitudes. How knowledge is translated into a belief or attitude that can affect behavior is not fully understood. However, it is clear that attitudes or beliefs that affect behavior do so because they are intimately related to the motives of the learner. When a health educator tries to create the conditions that will facilitate changes in a person's attitude, he needs to consider his approach in terms of *the motives and beliefs that underlie or support the attitude.* Thus, in this chapter some of the attitudes that appear to be necessary before particular kinds of health action occur are delineated. Some problems that may be peculiar to changing these health attitudes or beliefs are also noted.

At the outset a caution needs to be stated clearly regarding the material to be presented. The scientific and experimental study of behavior is comparatively new. The emancipation from armchair philosophy took place 80 years ago, and the period of greatest activity and growth in knowledge has spanned a little over 25 years. Thus, although all scientific "facts" are provisional hypotheses, those of the behavioral sciences tend to be more provisional than others.

HEALTH BEHAVIOR

Before discussing attitudes and health, it may be helpful to consider the kinds of behavior we are trying to influence. For convenience, health behaviors are grouped in two categories. The first and most obvious is that of *action taken when ill*. The health educator undoubtedly is striving to encourage people to take appropriate steps when ill, such as calling the doctor, seeing the dentist, taking medicines as prescribed, curtailing activities as requested, or having adequate rest.

The second category, perhaps the one with which the health educator is most concerned, is *preventive health action*. This would include regular medical and dental checkups, brushing teeth, following a reasonable diet, having sufficient exercise, securing immunizations, and similar practices. The health educator's job is to convince people to do these things, as often and as carefully as possible, in order to ensure their own well-being.

Many readers will sense an ethical problem in the last statement. Is the health educator acting in an ethical fashion when he convinces people to do things? His job is to educate, not to coerce. Although this issue will not be discussed in detail, an analysis of the causes for behavior may help the reader to decide what entails coercion. At the outset it should be realized that there are *many ways*, including coercion, of convincing a person to take a preventive health step or to be ready and willing to do something when the need arises, such as to rest or call the doctor when ill. This rather obvious point is often overlooked. It must also be remembered that different people may do the same thing for different reasons, that the same person may take the same action for different reasons at different times, and that when a person acts, many motives typically are involved in the cause of the action. By examining some of the more frequent conditions for health actions, clues may be obtained as to what to teach and how to teach in order to facilitate changes in behavior.

Concepts Needed To Understand Behavior

In attempting to account both for consistency of and change in behavior, psychologists have found it useful to use certain concepts. We have been able to understand behavior by determining (a) the motives, drives, or concerns which are being satisfied by the action, and (b) the attitudes and information that the person uses to decide what response he should make in a given situation. One must not identify the action or behavior as equivalent to the motives for it or the knowledge and skills guiding it. A motive can be defined as a person's basic predisposition to reach for or strive toward a general class of goals. Motivated striving may be based upon biological needs and upon needs and desires acquired through an extended period of past experience. [1,2] Attitude, on the other hand, is a more circumscribed concept. It can generally be conceived of as an inner factor predisposing one to react positively or negatively toward particular objects, acts, or institutions. A person's disposition or attitude toward an object is likely to depend upon (a) the basic motives with which the object is associated, and (b) the degree to which the object is perceived as instrumental for satisfying or blocking these motives. [3] Some examples will clarify this, as well as illustrate the role of motives and attitudes in learning.

Behavior when ill. Converting ourselves temporarily into omniscient beings, let us look at 17-year-old Bill Smith. When Bill awakens we see him clear his throat and act as if he does not feel well. This does not surprise us since we know that streptococci have invaded his system. The bacteria produce a disturbance or irritation which stimulates Bill. In fact, the stimulation is so intense that it *motivates* him. His *goal* is to eliminate the pain in this throat. Impelled by this motive, he thinks of all things he might do to reach this goal. Bill recalls the soothing feeling of water, and since his attitude toward water is favorable, he *behaves* by taking a drink. Since several drinks of water do not alleviate the discomfort (motive, or drive), Bill engages in thought once again. Next he tries a throat lozenge. He has not forgotten how to drink water, nor has his attitude toward water as a usually refreshing substance changed. However, he may have *learned* that it would not soothe his throat now, and since it is not instrumental for goal attainment, his favorable attitude toward it as a remedy may change.

[1] Atkinson, J. W., and Reitman, W. R. "Performance as a Function of Motive Strength and Expectancy of Goal-Attainment." *Journal of Abnormal and Social Psychology* 53: 361-66; November 1956.

[2] Rotter, J. B. "The Role of the Psychological Situation in Determining the Direction of Human Behavior." *Nebraska Symposium on Motivation, 1955.* (Edited by M. R. Jones.) Lincoln: University of Nebraska Press, 1955.

[3] Rosenberg, M. J. "Cognitive Structure and Attitudinal Affect." *Journal of Abnormal and Social Psychology* 53: 367-72; November 1956.

If the pain is not too intense, or if sucking on a lozenge is sufficient to reduce it somewhat, Bill will soon be off to his usual activities. Competing and more compelling motives and their goals, such as the ball game or friends, direct his perception so that he is less sensitive to the cues from the less salient motive (illness). With his attention diverted from the health motive, the direction of his behavior is controlled by other factors so that nothing more may be done about his health. Clearly, then, motives and attitudes are factors within the organism that produce behaviors but do so in competition with other such factors.

Fortunately, or unfortunately, for Bill, his mother may have noticed that his appearance is somewhat peaked, and insisted that he stay in bed or call the doctor. Another source of influence has been introduced. The mother establishes in Bill some pressure to behave. Health actions are now taken for different reasons than they would be if Bill did them on his own. The motive is elicited from without, not within. He did not call the doctor because he was intensely motivated to recover or because his attitude toward doctors was favorable. He acted because of external pressure. That the mother can exert this pressure is due to many factors. Bill may obey because he loves her and desires her affection, or perhaps because he is afraid she will punish him. If Bill is fond of his mother, under certain conditions we may expect him to continue to follow her advice. If, however, the only way she can control him is through punishment, we should not be surprised to find that in her absence he does not follow the action she prescribes. In both cases he complied, but only in the former is it likely that he has the same attitudes as his mother.

It is possible, however, that changes in the internal motives or beliefs may occur even if Bill was unwilling initially to take the action. One condition that would facilitate his internalizing or taking on attitudes that are favorable toward the more or less compulsory act would be the outcome of the action. If the doctor were to come, give Bill a "shot" and quickly cure him, then he would be rewarded by relief from the irritation of the illness and also by the opportunity to satisfy, undisturbed, his drive for his usual activities. Of course, one of the problems for Bill in acquiring the "correct" beliefs is that the value of the cure (reward) is seldom instantaneously perceivable and he may not perceive the treatment as being effective in curing him. However, it is immediately perceivable that treatment may require doing things, such as staying in bed and missing a game, which interfere with the satisfaction of other drives. In this case, there is a *conflict* produced and calling the doctor for an illness may well be perceived as having negative as well as positive value. This is the condition for *vacillation*; the stronger the negative incentive value of calling the doctor, the more likely the call will not be made.

The example illustrates, then, that attitudes toward specific actions are a function of more basic motives. Although Bill is favorably disposed toward water, it is irrelevant and unfavorable for curing his pain. This he finds out by trial and error. His attitude toward the doctor is similarly dependent upon what motives are satisfied or blocked by calling the doctor. For water there is a powerful underlying demand that keeps one's attitude positive. For calling the doctor, however, as many or more deprivations may be experienced as satisfactions gained.

Negative qualities can also accrue to the health act for other reasons, such as anxiety about getting vaccinations, or fear that something serious might be discovered. These factors could minimize the likelihood of rational action and maximize defensive acts whose purpose is to alleviate fears by taking one's mind away from thoughts of illness and treatment.

Preventive health behavior. Preventive health action is a complex affair which also deserves our attention because of its great significance for maintaining health and for deterring chronic diseases and ill health. Such action can be classified into three general categories: (a) those preventive behaviors that occur voluntarily; (b) those that occur through group pressure, such as "all the other mothers are vaccinating their children"; and (c) those that occur under requirement or compulsion, such as medical examinations for school entrance, jobs, or insurance policies.*

The health educator's interest is most likely to center in the first category. He is interested in teaching the person, and in his teaching he strives to create conditions that will set in motion processes within the student that will lead to attitudes which will result in interest in and utilization of preventive health measures on a continuing basis throughout his life. There have been a

---

* It should be clear that health behaviors during illness can be similarly classified. In the prior examples we saw each type of force generating action. One difference, of course, is that there is usually an internal stimulus, such as pain or discomfort, during illness.

number of investigations that have revealed the kind of beliefs that underlie taking preventive health action. In a study of reasons for seeking chest x-rays, Hochbaum[4] found that people had to believe that they were vulnerable to tuberculosis before they would voluntarily submit to x-rays. A summary of the findings in the area of polio vaccination[5] also indicates that people did not voluntarily seek vaccination unless they genuinely felt susceptible. Similarly, in studying reactions to the Asian influenza epidemic,[6] among the people who were immunized significantly more of them had believed prior to the immunization that they were susceptible to the disease. Although this may seem to belabor the obvious, it must be made clear that the belief that one is susceptible to an illness is different from knowing it. Thus, practically everyone knows that anyone can contract tuberculosis, polio, or influenza, but when people are asked reasons for their beliefs, one is able to separate those who are just giving information from those who actually feel that what they say applies to them.

While the belief that one can contract an illness has been demonstrated to affect behavior, there is also reason to believe that a person must also perceive the effects of an illness as potentially serious, either for his physical, economic, or social well-being, before he will act preventively. If adults think polio is serious only in children, or that the effects of the illness will be slight, if any, in adults, they are not likely to be motivated to prevent the illness. Believing that one is vulnerable to an illness which may have serious effects provides the motivational background in which a favorable attitude toward vaccination may develop. It is of little value to change a man's attitude so that he is more favorable toward polio vaccination if he doesn't *believe* that polio will seriously harm him.

There are occasions when the entire life outlook of a person will make it unlikely that he will take health action. From interviews with farm families in the Great Plains, Leventhal and

[4] Hochbaum, G. M. *Public Participation in Medical Screening Programs: A Socio-Psychological Study.* Public Health Service Publication No. 572. Washington, D.C.: Superintendent of Documents, Government Printing Office, 1958. 23 p.

[5] Rosenstock, I. M.; Derryberry, C. M.; and Carriger, Barbara K. "Why People Fail to Seek Poliomyelitis Vaccination." *Public Health Reports* 74: 98-103; February 1959.

[6] Leventhal, H.; Rosenstock, I. M.; Hochbaum, G. M.; and Carriger, Barbara K. *The Impact of the 1957 Epidemic of Influenza upon the General Population in Two Cities.* U.S. Department of Health, Education, and Welfare. Washington, D.C.: Superintendent of Documents, Government Printing Office, 1960.

Rosenstock[7] concluded that the self-perceptions of these farm people as being hardy pioneers was incompatible with believing they were susceptible to disease or subject to serious harm from disease. Even in the presence of symptoms of serious heart disease or other internal conditions, these individuals would insist they were well. They often had to be forced to the doctor by relatives and friends who could see otherwise.

Although beliefs in vulnerability to disease and in the seriousness of a disease may determine motivation to act, they do not determine the kind of action to be taken. Other attitudes and beliefs will determine what a person will do. For example, a person may believe he and his children are susceptible to polio, but instead of vaccination, the preventive behavior consists of keeping away from people or keeping the house clean. In several exploratory interviews, Leventhal[8] found individuals who strongly believed polio was caused by dirt. They felt that keeping themselves and their houses clean was the only "reasonable" preventive action to take. A number of people were afraid of the polio vaccine, and some mistrusted the physician. It is clear then that in order to take a specific action such as vaccination, one must have favorable attitudes toward the vaccine, as well as beliefs that generate motivation. Whether or not one's attitude toward the vaccine will or will not be favorable, however, is also a result of the person's beliefs about (a) the cause of a disease; (b) the value and safety of preventive action or a cure; and (c) the trust or acceptance of the *source* recommending the action.

IMPLICATIONS FOR HEALTH EDUCATION

Some of the conditions related to the determination of health behavior have been touched upon briefly. There are a number of other possible causative factors, such as hypochondriacal concern with the body and other mental health problems which are not covered, but for many health problems the concepts are applicable. The implications of the findings for teaching methods and ways of changing people's attitudes are also of importance in health education.

It is always stated that good practices can and should be

[7] Leventhal, H., and Rosenstock, I. M. "Identification of Subjective Health Needs in a Plains Community: A Pretest." Unpublished administrative report. Washington, D.C.: Behavioral Studies Section, U.S. Public Health Service, 1958.

[8] Leventhal, H. "Exploratory Interviews on Reactions to Polio Vaccination." Unpublished material, 1957.

taught. If the teacher is not to become unduly frustrated at lack of success, perhaps he should realize from the outset that *many health practices, per se, cannot be taught in school.* Helping a pupil to develop a habit, a particular action, involves motivating the subject so that he responds and then *rewarding the desired response.* Many health acts, however, are not produced in school and the teacher is not likely to be available at the right time to stimulate the behavior to occur and to reward it. How then do we convince Bill Smith to call the doctor, or stay in bed if he is ill? How do we reward him for doing these things? How do we reward the child for brushing his teeth after meals? How do we reward a good night's sleep or not eating sweets? In most cases the teacher cannot control the situation as in a laboratory study in which the person may be directed to act and then is rewarded for his actions. The pupil, not the teacher, must decide when and how to behave, and often must provide his own reward for acting. The aim must be to provide the information and experiences that can generate personal attitudes and beliefs. These beliefs will then lead him, under his own power, to seek and follow the correct advice when ill, to seek out and respond to requests for preventive health action, and to feel a sense of reward when he does so.

If it seems reasonable that attitudes and beliefs rather than habits should be taught in such a way as to promote transfer to behavior outside the teaching situation, how can the teacher facilitate this?

In order to teach successfully, the teacher must (a) stimulate the students so that they are *interested,* and *want* or *try* to learn; (b) *organize* experiences and *present* materials in a comprehensible fashion; and (c) help the students to *accept* as personal beliefs what they have learned and to act in accord with these beliefs.

Once again, then, the core of the problem is to generate the *motivation* of the student to attend, to practice, and to accept beliefs. Learning cannot take place economically unless the organism is motivated. If a person is unmotivated, he will not pay attention, practice, or struggle to comprehend, and more important, will not be ready to accept the beliefs as his own. The aim of teaching in health education is for the student to acquire knowledge and beliefs co-ordinated with his own motives or drives that are themselves capable of producing *motivation.*

Attention and Interest

Gaining the pupil's attention is the first step in teaching. However, this involves not only initially reaching the student, but also maintaining contact. The advertiser uses many attention-getters, such as the cartoon, colorful pictures, or slogans. These devices often fail since they may not maintain motivation. In fact, they may motivate interest in something other than the ideas being taught. A good example of this occurred at a health fair in a large city. To teach people facts about cancer, a ring toss game was set up where each pole represented a question about cancer. Success in ringing a pole led to receiving the answer to the question. Although this device created considerable motivation to play ring toss, few people who played paid attention to the questions and answers about cancer.

The best kind of attention is that which develops from interest in the task itself and what evolves from it. Activities, subjects, and skills are in themselves challenging. The young child in school is interested in activity, in doing things. He likes to manipulate, to construct, to imitate, to participate. He learns to wash his hands or to brush his teeth correctly by practicing the skill under supervision. He values the approval of his teacher, and endeavors to follow instructions and suggestions relative to health behavior. As he progresses into the intermediate grades, his interests and curiosities relative to himself and to the world around him are legion. He likes to explore these interests and curiosities, to participate in a variety of activities, many of which are directly related to health. Of course the motivation to learn can also be enhanced by making the problems and content relevant to the needs and goals of pupils.

The needs and interests of many teen-agers often center in athletic and social skills, and several health problems are inter-related with these goals. Interest can be promoted in health matters by showing how taking certain steps may result in more satisfying living and enhanced enjoyment as a result of better health. The teacher must be careful, however, to be plausible in relating health to the teen-agers' interests. Losing one's credibility as a health teacher can too easily take place through such ridiculous promises as, "Early to bed, early to rise, guarantees center field on the Yankees."

There are many ways in which honest and convincing relationships can be drawn between health and other life needs. In dental health, for example, attention is often drawn to the cosmetic value of good dental care. While the pupil may be concerned about the appearance of his incisors, this concern may not extend to his molars. If this is so, the pupil needs to learn that destruction of the molars can result in caries and twisting of the incisors and to difficulties in eating his favorite foods. A careful working through of the reasons for an action and how it relates to his own needs is likely to be more successful than preaching to the student to brush his teeth three times every day and to see his dentist every six months. Persuasion of the latter type, such as repetition of "brush your teeth," can too easily be perceived by the student as someone else's attitudes, rather than his own. Beliefs backed by knowledge are more likely to be seen as part of one's own value system, and are better able to support and reward one's behavior.

Perhaps the teacher needs to have greater faith in his pupils, and believe that they may be interested in learning about the human body and its care without any unnecessary inducements. Children and young people are interested in themselves. They have many questions concerning physical development and appearance, how the body functions, the causes of illness and disability, and the progress of science in protecting and prolonging life and health. New interests can be developed through the process of relating them to recognized interests and drives and as a result of the very real enthusiasm which accompanies good teaching.

Problems in Understanding

The first thing a teacher needs to consider is the individual pupil's ability to comprehend. If the pupil does not have a certain amount of *experience* and *ability* in dealing with verbal symbols, teaching, as we conceive of it, will not take place easily. Experience and ability together make up the achievement level, or mental age, of the child.

Consideration is given to the ability and experience of the pupil so that the teacher can adapt health concepts to the pupil's level of understanding. One barrier to communication is using words the pupil is not able to understand. A pupil often can grasp a difficult concept if it can be framed in words intelligible to him. The pupil often may appear to "understand" the terms, however, when he is unable to grasp the concept. For example, telling a younger child that a germ is "alive" may communicate a very different concept to the child than we intend to communicate. To him, "alive" may mean a "wriggling," "breathing," "walking" object. It would not be surprising that he finds it difficult, if not frightening, to conceive of live germs being in him. Such "errors" can set up serious barriers to communicating. Making a thing understandable, then, involves language and concept difficulties.

Another problem is the mode of presentation of material. Typically, this brings to mind use of visual aids and other such techniques. While these are helpful if used intelligently, this is not the only issue in presentation. Perhaps more important is the organization of the material. In what order is it presented? How are the parts related? Have earlier materials set the stage for later ones? For example, in trying to change people's attitudes to be favorable to taking polio vaccinations, one might organize his message keeping in mind the factors of susceptibility, severity, and means of prevention. Perhaps one would concentrate first on the notion that it is not exclusively a disease of infants. Then, an attempt might be made to indicate the cause of the disease and how it often spreads even in clean areas, because people from these areas are less likely to have acquired immunity from frequent casual contact with the virus of polio. These arguments are integrated into a lesson to prepare the student for the recommendation of vaccination. If we give the latter message first we may find that the student immediately makes light of it because he does not believe he is susceptible. This leads to a consideration of the issue of acceptance, which will be discussed later.

One thing the teacher can do to facilitate communication with the student is to find out what the student already knows and believes. He may want to do this privately, or by having each child write down his opinions about a subject, thus preventing members of the group from seeing that they share opinions different from those of the instructor. Regardless of how he proceeds, barriers to understanding and acceptance are most easily resolved if the teacher takes the time to find out what they are. Such devices may also be utilized to assess the impact of teaching upon attitudes and beliefs.

The final topic covered is the use of repetition and recitation in learning. In general, it is found that repetition and recitation by the learner will facilitate recall. Like all generalizations, this is true only if other things are constant. That is, repetition is desirable *if* it means additional *motivated* practice. All too often, however, the repetition of material generates fatigue, boredom, and frustration which, if it does not interfere with learning, may well interfere in the acceptance of the attitude.

Acceptance

The major issue involved in teaching health attitudes and beliefs is obtaining *acceptance* by the pupils. The teacher is not just trying to impart information. He is also attempting to establish certain beliefs, attitudes, or opinions as part of a way of thinking, so that these beliefs will produce desirable actions. Acceptance implies, then, connecting a new attitude with underlying motivational forces. Studies of attitude change illustrate that certain factors in the communicator (teacher), the content of the communication, the prior attitudes and beliefs of the audience, and what the audience does can promote the acceptance of attitudes.

The communicator. If the teacher is viewed as expert and trustworthy; that is, possessing greater information and imparting it for the benefit of his listeners, he is likely to obtain greater acceptance of his messages. One possible pitfall for the teacher is that he will be seen as attempting to manipulate his listeners, and as a biased source of information. The pupil may perceive the health teacher as preaching the same old do's and don'ts pressed on him by his parents. Parents ask children to follow many rules (to drink milk, to take naps, to brush teeth, not to eat candy or smoke) which the parents themselves fail to follow. For many children these issues become points of conflict, the child complying or not complying in order to please or punish his parents. It is all too easy, then, for the teacher to be perceived in a parent role, and to bring upon himself the resistance and antagonism that has developed toward parent figures. For the teacher this is unfortunate, since he lacks the strong, positive relationship of the parent to the child that can overcome these resistances. This perception of the teacher will be more pronounced in certain children. It is likely to be most evident in children from other than the middle-class background to which most teachers are accustomed, and in which the teacher is less able to offer the child any positive identification with him. If the student is an adult or teen-ager, the situation may be more difficult, as he may feel the educator is treating him like a child.

The major point is that these problems interfere with acceptance of the communication because following the communicator's advice may be seen as depriving oneself of satisfactions rather than as being potentially rewarding.

The use of emotion. The communication itself can be varied in certain ways which may promote acceptance or rejection of its message. A frequent device used to obtain acceptance is to use a strong motivational appeal. The educator not only tries to gain the confidence of the pupils so that they will believe and accept his advice, but also attempts to introduce in teaching various *promises* and *threats* which have as their aim providing the motivation and reward for accepting his point of view. A major device for motivating acceptance has been the use of fear appeals. We tell the Bill Smiths that when they feel ill, they should call the doctor *or else!* "Or else" is usually elaborated upon as meaning some grave danger to life and welfare. Likewise, we encourage preventive health checks to avoid another series of *or else* fates. We try to convince the person of the dire consequences of smoking, of chronic fatigue, or of overeating. The use of the fear appeal seems to be guided by the assumption that it makes a "deep" impression on the person. By deep impression is meant that the attitudes being established are attached to action-producing motives. How effective are such techniques?

It will be of value to examine the process more closely. First a threat-arousing message is communicated to the person. We say he is vulnerable to some disease. Once fear or anxiety is aroused, the person will do something to reduce this fear, that is, to make himself comfortable again. If, after arousing his fear, he is presented with a clear and definite way of avoiding the threat, he is likely to take our advice. For example, if we convince him that he is susceptible to influenza, that influenza is a serious illness, and then convince him that there is a vaccine that is a perfect preventive, he is likely to be vaccinated. What happens if the vaccine is not perfect, or if there is some discomfort inherent in its use? His fears have been aroused but a clear-cut way of reducing them has not been given. It is reasonably certain he will do something to reduce his apprehension. It is likely that the student will deny that he really can contract influenza. Like all people, he has learned certain ways of handling his fears, and one method of handling an unknown fear is to deny its reality or its applicability to oneself.

If the health educator tries to convince students to take care of their teeth, and shows them slides of deformities and disease resulting from poor care, they are likely to feel fearful when shown how bad tooth and gum infection can become. However, unless a convincing and definite way of preventing these disorders can be provided, they are likely to reject the communication. The student also will deny the applicability of the message. Rather than change his dental practices, a tacit admission of vulnerability, he may show a change away from good dental practices. He will bolster his own position by accepting other "reasonable-sounding" communications that disagree with those that are based on fear. In experimental studies of communication, it has been shown that acceptance of health messages was greater when fear appeals were not used.[9]

One need only think back to our earlier analysis of preventive health behavior to see the significance of this problem. If feeling susceptible or threatened is a necessary part of acting, and threat elicits denial, motivating health action is indeed a difficult matter. The key to the use of fear appeal is likely to hinge on the adequacy of the preventive measure the health worker offers to eliminate the threat.

There may be occasions when the fear appeal can be successfully applied. If the goal is to have as many people as possible act right at the time the appeal is made, it may be effective. In this case, the various denial mechanisms may not have time to minimize the applicability of the danger to oneself. Fear appeals may also succeed if the *action* suggested by the communication is to avoid something. For example, suggesting vaccination after a fear appeal requires a positive or approach response (to a vaccination station) while the natural response tendency toward fear is denial or avoidance. If the act suggested is to *avoid* contact with a diseased person, a certain food, extra exertion, it will be compatible with the natural response to fear and is more likely to be followed unless there is a strong, competing motive to act.

The use of fear appeals involves other dangers. In many cases the elaboration of a dire outcome by a teacher makes the class

9 Janis, I. L., and Feshbach, S. "Effects of Fear-Arousing Communications." *Journal of Abnormal and Social Psychology* 48: 78-92; January 1953.

suspect that he is merely trying to manipulate them through fear. In this case, they may view him as biased, as untrustworthy, and as slanting facts. It is equally fatal to the pupil's confidence to be dogmatic or to misstate the facts. Rest in bed does not of itself prevent disease; an attack of polio does not always result in paralysis; some alcoholics live to a ripe old age; no immunization is 100 percent effective. The teacher who has the confidence of his pupils is the one who neither promises too much nor frightens too much.

Despite the dangers in the fear appeal, the health educator cannot avoid stating the facts. Although the dramatic fear appeal may often be inadequate, there is also a danger in not relating the possibilities in an objective manner.

Attitudinal barriers to acceptance. Throughout life, people have varying contacts with illness and health measures. Thus, the person whose attitudes we are trying to help change already has acquired many beliefs about health. These beliefs may not always be verbalized, but they will serve as a context for interpreting, and thus accepting or rejecting new communications. It may seem unreasonable for a person to believe he is not susceptible to an illness. Yet, in a typical example, a study in 1957 showed that about 90 percent of the respondents in a random sample did not believe they could contract Asian influenza. When people are ill it is found frequently that they have not called a doctor or taken any reasonable steps to treat themselves. It is an historical fact that most individuals recover from sickness. Thus, it is not surprising that they have learned to picture themselves as invulnerable to harmful events. Moreover, when the student tried various remedial and preventive acts he discovered that they did not always work, or worked slowly if at all. There is a multiplicity of factors in the cause and cure of illness, and there are few definite preventives or cures. It may seem unreasonable, unbelievable, and unacceptable to the student that staying in bed, calling the doctor, brushing his teeth, eating proper food, for example, can do what is claimed.

If students are accustomed to thinking of themselves as healthy and relatively invulnerable to illness, then the audience to be convinced may be resistant to the teacher. The health educator may be wise to organize and include in his communications and discussions both the pros and cons of particular health practices. Presenting pro and con arguments tends to be somewhat less effective for strengthening the attitudes of those already in agreement. However, they are more effective for those whose initial position is in disagreement.[10] The organization of material will affect not only understanding, but also acceptance. Presenting the pros and cons can help in that it may discount initial objections and enhance the credibility of the teacher when he shows that he is willing to recognize arguments negative to his stand. In a vaccination campaign one could merely say, "You can get polio. Take shots." A recipient of the message who thinks that the immunizations might give him polio will see this as a biased argument. If the communicator recognizes this belief, and shows its falsity, then the communication has a greater likelihood of success. Again, however, the educator must be wary of *blanket promises*, since a single mishap will discredit him.

The teacher may find himself facing considerable resistance when teaching members of different ethnic groups or people from different social class backgrounds. The religious beliefs of the student, attitudes toward progress, particular beliefs about the moral nature of disease, or hostility toward middle-class authority figures may make teaching efforts seem doomed to failure. The peer group indicates to its members that certain acts or beliefs label one as a sissy or as surrendering to authority. In some cases, the health educator may be able to enlist the participation of these groups; more often, however, he may find the groups unapproachable. In such cases, the best he can do is present his material in a coherent and objective fashion, showing its potential relevance to the various needs of the people to whom he is talking, and also to show its irrelevance to many of the things to which people object. Thus, being vaccinated may need to be presented not just as something the teacher (authority) wants done but as something the student himself should want to have done.

The use of the group in overcoming attitudinal barriers. Previous materials in this chapter have been concentrated on the presentation of material to the individual. The goal has been the individual acceptance of beliefs, so that beliefs will relate to underlying motives or action producers. Earlier, however, it was pointed out that group pressure, or pressure from another person, may induce action in the student. On many occasions the effectiveness of the group in creating health action has been

---

[10] Hovland, C. I.; Janis, I. L.; and Kelley, H. H. *Communication and Persuasion.* New Haven, Conn.: Yale University Press, 1953. 315 p.

clearly demonstrated. To varying degrees, people of nearly all ages will go along with projects sponsored by groups to which they belong. Highly successful polio vaccination campaigns have been carried out among teen-agers in communities where the students themselves managed the campaign. However, there are several problems and dangers to be faced in the use of the group to promote behavior.

First, groups are able to obtain membership participation on issues relevant to the group. While the members of a women's club may be highly motivated to follow mores that are effective in maintaining group togetherness, the group may fail in an attempt to promote cervical cancer tests among its members. This issue is not relevant to the group's purpose, and promoting pressure for such an action may weaken the forces binding the group members together.

Suppose, however, that a group does succeed in getting its members to take some health measure, such as polio immunizations. On what basis is the participation obtained? Is it merely to continue to be accepted as a member of the group? If so, taking the action may fail to effect any change in the attitudes of the individuals. They will be immunized, but will they develop beliefs that help promote the voluntary taking of other preventive health measures? If not, each time a need for action arises, the educator must activate the entire machinery of group pressure to obtain individual action.

Although there are problems in using group pressure to effect health behavior, there are ways in which such pressures can be effective. For example, group pressure might be used to create the opportunity to teach the individual. There is, however, another way in which the group can be used. After a person commits himself to take, or does take, a definite course of action, he will be ready to accept those attitudes and beliefs which make the action seem reasonable. If a student does not believe that vaccination is really safe or that it can prevent a disease, but is vaccinated because of group pressure, he has violated his beliefs. In this case, he is likely to change his beliefs so that they are favorable. There is considerable evidence to indicate that changing attitudes after an action has occurred can be successful. This seems to be because the individual is at a point at which he needs to rationalize or make consistent his beliefs and actions.[11] Evi-

---

[11] Festinger, L. *A Theory of Cognitive Dissonance.* Evanston, Ill.: Row, Peterson, 1957. 291 p.

dence also indicates that when the action was taken in a situation with considerable freedom of choice, and relatively little in the way of ulterior gain, the person will be most susceptible to change.[12]

There are times, however, when the teacher may find that he is unable to reach an individual. Perhaps the person is so negativistic as to be beyond change. At this point the teacher should re-examine his role in the situation. He should ask himself whether he has tried to understand the motives of the student, whether he has applied his techniques adequately, or whether his own motives and emotions have interfered with his role as a communicator and guide.

People are highly complex psychologically. Even though the principles discussed may be accurate, they are abstract, and do not consider all factors affecting health behavior and attitude change. It is for this reason that teaching requires not only knowledge of subject matter and teaching procedures, but also a sensitivity to the needs, feelings, and ideas of the individual student together with an ability to vary and select different techniques when appropriate.

SELECTED REFERENCES

ATKINSON, J. W., and REITMAN, W. R. "Performance as a Function of Motive Strength and Expectancy of Goal-Attainment." *Journal of Abnormal and Social Psychology* 53: 361-66; November 1956.

COHEN, A. R.; BREHM, J. W.; and FLEMING, W. H. "Attitude Change and Justification for Compliance." *Journal of Abnormal and Social Psychology* 56: 276-77; March 1958.

FESTINGER, L. *A Theory of Cognitive Dissonance*. Evanston, Ill.: Row, Peterson, 1957. 291 p.

HOCHBAUM, G. M. *Public Participation in Medical Screening Programs: A Socio-Psychological Study*. Public Health Service Publication No. 572. Washington, D.C.: Superintendent of Documents, Government Printing Office, 1958. 23 p.

HOVLAND, C. I.; JANIS, I. L.; and KELLEY, H. H. *Communication and Persuasion*. New Haven, Conn.: Yale University Press, 1953. 315 p.

---

[12] Cohen, A. R.; Brehm, J. W.; and Fleming, W. H. "Attitude Change and Justification for Compliance." *Journal of Abnormal and Social Psychology* 56: 276-77; March 1958.

JANIS, I. L., and FESHBACH, S. "Effects of Fear-Arousing Communications." *Journal of Abnormal and Social Psychology* 48: 78-92; January 1953.

LEVENTHAL, H. "Exploratory Interviews on Reactions to Polio Vaccination." Unpublished material, 1957.

LEVENTHAL, H., and ROSENSTOCK, I. M. "Identification of Subjective Health Needs in a Plains Community: A Pretest." Unpublished administrative report. Washington, D. C.: Behavioral Studies Section, U.S. Public Health Service, 1958.

LEVENTHAL, H.; ROSENSTOCK, I. M.; HOCHBAUM, G. M.; and CARRIGER, BARBARA K. *The Impact of the 1957 Epidemic of Influenza upon the General Population in Two Cities.* U.S. Department of Health, Education, and Welfare. Washington, D.C.: Superintendent of Documents, Government Printing Office, 1960.

PAUL, B. D., and MILLER, W. B., editors. *Health, Culture and Community.* New York: Russell Sage Foundation, 1955. 493 p.

ROSENBERG, M. J. "Cognitive Structure and Attitudinal Affect." *Journal of Abnormal and Social Psychology* 53: 367-72; November 1956.

ROTTER, J. B. "The Role of the Psychological Situation in Determining the Direction of Human Behavior." *Nebraska Symposium on Motivation, 1955.* (Edited by M. R. Jones.) Lincoln: University of Nebraska Press, 1955.

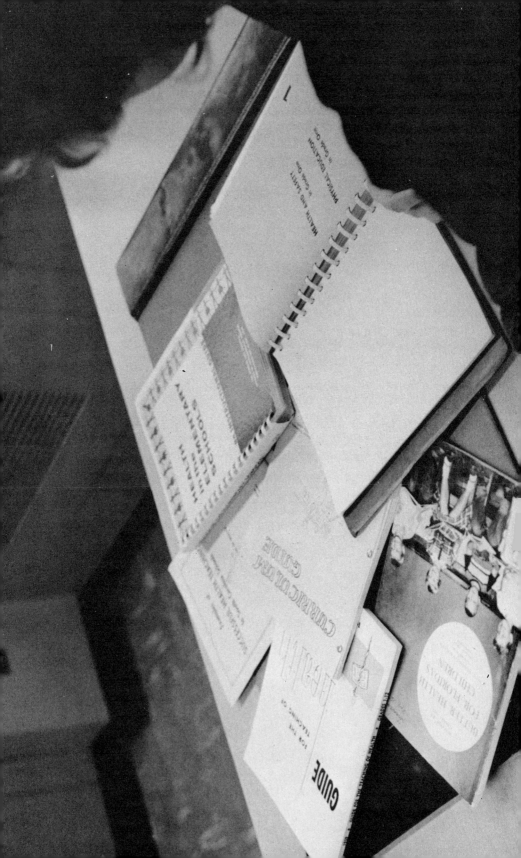

Developing the
Curriculum

There is a growing demand for strengthening the health education curriculum in the schools. Although significant progress has been made during the past half-century, there is considerable evidence to indicate that further changes and improvements are greatly needed. Since educators in the United States are committed to the belief that the improvement and maintenance of health is among the major functions of education, the schools have an obligation, and also an unparalleled opportunity, to promote the health and well-being of children and youth.

The purposes of this chapter are (a) to examine the nature of the curriculum and curriculum change; (b) to explore the place of health education in current curriculum designs at the elementary, junior high, and senior high school levels; and (c) to suggest procedures for developing and improving the health education curriculum.

THE MEANING OF "CURRICULUM"

The curriculum of any school consists of the learning experiences provided under the supervision and direction of the school and is the expression of what those responsible believe education should do for children. Often there is a wide gap between what educators say they believe to be the purposes of education in American democracy and what is actually practiced in schools. Educators are not always in agreement with regard to the objectives of education or the ways in which the curriculum should be organized to attain the stated objectives. These differences in beliefs, and consequently in the organization of the curriculum, often create confusion among educators and the lay public.

The accepted concept of a curriculum suggests ways for its development or improvement. Some think of it as merely a course of study, or as an organized, sequential program of studies, or as the subject matter taught to pupils. The focus of curriculum study for those holding this viewpoint is on the content of the course of study. Mastery of facts, habits, skills, and understandings is the desired outcome.

Others with a more functional view of curriculum consider it as all of the experiences to promote learning which the pupil has under the guidance of the school, including in-class and out-of-class experiences. Here, the various studies, organized activities, and the entire life and atmosphere of the school are part of the curriculum. Each is believed to make its contribution to the attainment of the goals of education. For example, the curriculum thus viewed encompasses, in addition to classroom instruction about eyes and their care, such other experiences as having vision tested, helping to maintain an environment conducive to visual comfort, or taking a field trip to visit a sight-saving class. For those holding this view, curriculum improvement focuses on the kind, breadth, depth, and continuity of experience that will help children and youth grow in desirable ways and function effectively as individuals and citizens in our society. Behavior changes are sought without overlooking the importance of facts, skills, and understandings. The curriculum is developed around the problems and needs of individuals and society and is the means by which pupil behavior is changed.

THE NATURE OF CURRICULUM IMPROVEMENT

Changing the curriculum means changing people. Curriculum change usually occurs to the extent that the people who are responsible for developing the curriculum themselves change. Curriculum improvement occurs only when those responsible for curriculum undergo change in their thinking and subsequently in their educational practice. Such change is more likely to occur as people become involved in co-operative work on curricular problems which are significant to them. Curriculum improvement is promoted by administrative personnel, teachers, parents, and pupils participating in such activities as

1. Clarifying beliefs about what the school should do—including the school's responsibilities for pupil health and safety

2. Gaining insight into the ways children and youth grow and develop

3. Finding out how people learn most effectively

4. Discovering the problems common to the majority of pupils
and the special problems of individuals

5. Analyzing the depth, breadth, and continuity of their experiences in relation to their personal and social needs, interests, and abilities

6. Planning a course of action and carrying it through

7. Evaluating the results

8. Replanning in light of this knowledge.

Preceding chapters of this book have dealt with some of the
problems basic to the development of the health education curriculum. This chapter indicates procedures for applying this knowledge in bringing about curriculum improvement.

Curriculum improvement may be undertaken in various groups
and by differing methods. The individual school with its faculty
and with or without the help of parents and pupils is in a
particularly desirable position to search for the answers to
curriculum problems, try out agreed-upon conclusions, and evaluate results. Consultant help at the local, regional, or state level
may be brought in as needed. Representatives of individual
schools can be brought together to consider curriculum problems
of common concern to a large school system. This requires
leadership with initiative at the local level and a willingness to
devote time and study to these problems.

In the majority of states, the state department of education is
charged by law with a degree of responsibility for determining
what should be taught in the public schools. Curriculum development and improvement are major concerns in the majority of
states, and the participation of local study groups as well as the
organization of state curriculum committees are common practices. Publication of state curriculum manuals often serves as an
impetus to local schools and individual school districts to examine
their practices and to adapt the state materials to local situations.

Within the individual school, the principal can facilitate the
work of planning groups by providing time for teachers, pupils,
and parents to work co-operatively, by seeing that qualified
leadership and material resources are readily available, by helping with the identification of problems, and by encouraging
creative leadership. On the other hand, the faculty must be willing to give time, effort, and leadership to the work to be done and
to carry on experimentation which will lead to improvement in
curriculum. Change occurs when people participate by thinking

through their problems together in a democratic atmosphere and by trying out for themselves different ways of doing things. Change cannot be successfully forced; it evolves.

Various ways of initiating curriculum study have been tried. Greater participation and interest and, therefore, greater change have generally occurred when significant problems of genuine concern to teachers in an individual school and school system have been attacked. Whatever the place of beginning, as a curriculum problem is carefully thought through it inevitably leads to a consideration of those factors that determine curriculum. Choices are made eventually on the basis of individual or group values and should be made in relation to and with full consideration of the total school program.

Science and technology are producing changes in our ways of living at a constantly accelerating rate. Curriculum improvement also must be a continuous process if it is to keep step with changing conditions and needs. Rapid changes in the means of transportation, for example, and the changing distribution of population have created new problems of living. New health problems emerge as old ones are conquered or controlled. Many of these problems are world-wide in scope. An understanding of the health problems of all peoples and of ways of coping with disease that knows no racial or geographical boundaries becomes increasingly important. Such rapidly changing conditions need to be reflected in curriculum experiences designed to help boys and girls improve individual and community living. Therefore, a curriculum for today's schools cannot afford to be static and finished but rather must be dynamic and emerging.

The health education curriculum is a part of the whole and, therefore, is considered in relationship to the whole. Only as the health experiences of pupils in school contribute to the attainment of the general purposes of education can they be justified in the school program. The plan of organization of curriculum experiences in the individual school determines the organization of the health education experiences in the curriculum. The values held and the most urgent needs felt by both the faculty and citizens of the community determine the extent of these experiences within the allotted time of the school day. Awareness of the common health needs of all persons leads to the inclusion of health education experiences within the total curriculum of the school.

DIVERSITY OF CURRICULUM PRACTICES

In contrast with some other countries, great flexibility is allowed in the organization of the curriculum in the American system of education. Thus, schools exhibit marked differences. They range in size from small rural schools with few pupils to metropolitan high schools enrolling several thousand. The program of studies varies from a very limited offering with emphasis on the three R's in some elementary schools and a minimum list of subjects in high schools to an elementary school including 20 to 30 subjects and to a high school offering over 200 subject titles.[1] State requirements for graduation from high school vary widely.

In spite of this great diversity, various factors have combined to result in a fairly common group of curriculum areas and curriculum practices. Some of the factors which have combined to bring about considerable uniformity of practice are:

1. Division of knowledge into subject areas
2. Tradition, with its conventional subject organization
3. The effective role of accrediting agencies
4. The force of college-preparatory requirements
5. The widely accepted purposes of education
6. The influence of national commissions and publications
7. The force of public opinion.

CURRENT CURRICULUM STRUCTURE

Curriculum design refers to the way the curriculum is organized. It is the pattern or framework used in selecting, planning, and carrying forward educational experiences in the school. It relates to the way the component parts are arranged in order to facilitate teaching and learning and to enable schools to develop daily and weekly schedules—the time framework within which the curriculum operates.

The names of the curricular designs are confusing when one attempts to analyze current curriculums in operation. Such terms as subject-centered, experience-centered; correlated, integrated, fused; broad fields, major social functions, persistent life situations, centers of interest; and core, general education, common

---

[1] Saylor, J. Galen, and Alexander, William H. *Curriculum Planning*. New York: Rinehart & Co., 1954. 624 p.

learnings, present a veritable maze which is often bewildering. Distinctions in the designs are not always clear. A brief description of the basic designs is presented here.

There are four basic patterns, according to Stratemeyer and co-workers, by which curricular experiences are organized.[2] First is the organization by *separate subjects,* which is by far the method most widely used today, especially in high schools and colleges. It is also the most traditional design. Logical, systematic bodies of subject matter incorporating the cultural heritage serve as a basis for the organization of learning experiences. It is only necessary then to determine the subjects, such as mathematics or history, to be offered in the curriculum and the body of knowledge to be included in each subject. Scope is determined by the range of subjects included and by the content of the subject; sequence is determined by the internal logic of the various subjects and by the maturity level of the learner. Sound factual information is considered important, but emphasis today is also on application of those facts to problems of living. Health education is taught separately in this type of curriculum.

A second pattern is the organization by *broad fields* or *groups of related subjects.* This is a modification of the traditional subject design by which sharp demarcations that exist in traditional subjects are eliminated to overcome some of the difficulties of the separate-subjects approach. For example, in the broad field of the language arts, reading, writing, spelling, speaking, and listening are "fused" and "integrated" into one area. Likewise, history, geography, and civics become the social studies. Work in general science encompasses content from such separate subjects as physics, physiology, chemistry, bacteriology, zoology, and botany. The content of the curriculum is a broad organization of subject matter of closely related subjects. Emphasis is placed in this design on basic principles and generalizations rather than on information and facts. The scope of the curriculum is still determined by subjects. Designs in which related subjects are grouped are more widespread in the elementary school, although some fused courses are found in high school and college. Health education is likely to become a part of the social studies or of the science curriculum in this pattern of organization.

The designs that approach the curriculum through *broad areas*

---

[2] Stratemeyer, Florence B.; Forkner, Hamden L.; McKim, Margaret C.; and Passow, A. Harry. *Developing a Curriculum for Modern Living.* New York: Bureau of Publications, Teachers College, Columbia University, 1957. p. 86-105.

that cut across subject fields are a third alternative. Those who propose curricular designs which replace subject matter areas as the basis for organization see such centers of curriculum as (a) areas of living, or major social functions; (b) personal and social needs and concerns of learners; and (c) persistent life situations faced by pupils. Scope and sequence are designated from one grade to another. In focusing on the needs of individuals and of the society in which they live, traditional subject organization is replaced by a flexible approach to problems of living. Related learnings are brought together in core programs and problems courses in which emphasis is placed on ways of exploring and solving problems rather than on mastery of subject matter. This type of curricular organization is found in a limited number of schools, but some of the philosophy and recommended practices have spilled over into the more traditional curriculum. The development and maintenance of conditions that promote individual and community health constitute a core activity which leads to an effective type of health education. The physiological, emotional, and social needs of the learner and the need for avoiding and caring for illness and injury are persistent life situations which are recognized within core programs and similarly organized curricular patterns.

Fourth are the designs emerging from the *needs and problems of the group in which neither scope, organization, nor sequence is specifically outlined nor is it preplanned grade by grade.* Each teacher is free to develop experiences in terms of the purposes and needs of his particular class. Facts are used and generalizations developed as children and youth solve problems that are meaningful to them. Emphasis is placed on the problems learners express at the time. This is the type of design one is least likely to find in practice.

Present Trends in Organizing the Curriculum in the Elementary School

Most elementary schools today find it desirable to devote a part of the day to unified experiences organized around broad topics, such as Indian life or community helpers, and the remainder of the day to teaching conventional subjects. The amount of time devoted to each varies. In a few schools half of the day is devoted to each. Others make a distribution in accordance with the maturity of the children. Relatively more time is devoted to unit activities in the primary grades and more time to the teaching of subjects in the intermediate or upper grades. In some schools a division of time for unit teaching is made on the basis of one-fourth of the primary school day and at other levels one-fifth of the school day. In other schools longer periods of time are provided for unit teaching.

A significant trend in the elementary school has been toward scheduling daily blocks of time, double or triple the usual amount of time reserved for lessons in formal subject teaching, for unit activities. This provides flexibility in the program and allows for shifts of emphasis and attention to new problems which may arise; more variability in the program from day to day and week to week; more periods during which individual children work at different projects.[3]

The areas of experience are determined by the basic activities in which human beings engage, the values which society fosters, and the major problems which it faces. The developmental needs of children living in a certain environment are the basis on which sequence is determined. Ragan states, "In many schools social studies have formed the basis for the unified-studies program; in others, science, health and the arts and crafts have been included; still other schools have used significant problems of living which have meaning for children without much concern for keeping experiences within the boundaries of any conventional school subjects."[4] Teachers are constantly developing units of work centering around significant problems of living, utilizing the interests of children in local events and situations, and meeting the growth and developmental needs of children. Most schools in which unit teaching has prevailed for some years tend to plan the year's work around units that have proved successful, while maintaining flexibility and variability. Most of these schools follow a basic pattern for unit teaching in which the scope and sequence have been agreed upon. The details of the units are usually worked out by the teacher and pupils in the classroom. Health learnings fit naturally into this type of curriculum.

Recently there has been a noticeable trend in a different direction which emphasizes the importance of including basic experiences, particularly in the areas of science and mathematics, which will challenge the intellectual abilities of elementary-school children. Unit teaching is not abandoned, but some blocks of

---

[3] Ragan, William B. *Modern Elementary Curriculum*. New York: Dryden Press, 1953. p. 152-53.

[4] *Ibid.*, p. 155. Copyright 1953. Holt, Rinehart and Winston, Inc. By permission.

time are designated as essential for the development of specific understandings and skills.

Trends in Organizing the High-School Curriculum

The curriculum of the vast majority of high schools today is organized on a subject-centered basis. The so-called academic subjects—English, social studies, mathematics, science, and foreign languages—receive major emphasis. Alberty states:

Schools have expanded their offerings to include a wide range of "practical" subjects such as home economics, fine and industrial arts, music, and an impressive list of vocational subjects. The "academic" subjects have also undergone expansion. General language, general science and general mathematics have become quite common. Courses in psychology, conservation and safety are also finding their way into the high school curriculum. It should be pointed out, too, that there is a trend toward unification of subjects. The favorite combination is English and social science, but in some of the more experimental schools, core or fused courses are to be found that utilize subject matter from practically all of the fields. . . .

In spite of the more practical emphases discussed above, schools have not, by and large, given much attention to personal living, or to participation of the students in the socioeconomic life of the community.[5]

High schools have experimented to a limited degree with changes in organization and method that have stressed an experience curriculum based upon needs, interests, and abilities of adolescents in a democratic society rather than a subject-centered curriculum firmly rooted in traditional subjects. Broad comprehensive units of work, planned co-operatively by teachers and students, have found their way into many high-school classes and courses of study.[6]

Since 1957 the high-school curriculum has been undergoing renewed scrutiny, survey, study, and change in the direction of emphasis on academic achievement, particularly for the intellectually gifted student. Science, mathematics, and foreign languages are receiving greater attention, and there has been a resurgence of departmentalization in curricular offerings in grades 8 through 12. Commissions and committees of various national groups, including the National Association of Secondary-School Principals, are defining areas of needed experimentation and research in secondary education to meet the needs of the space age.

[5] Alberty, Harold. *Reorganizing the High School Curriculum.* Second edition. New York: Macmillan Co., 1953. p. 6-8.

[6] *Ibid.,* p. 24.

THE PLACE OF HEALTH EDUCATION IN THE CURRICULUM

The importance of health has been consistently recognized in the stated purposes of education in American democracy and in the "personal and social needs and problems of living" approach to curriculum development. In many schools, however, there is yet a vast difference in practice and professed beliefs regarding the importance of health education in the curriculum, and the school administrator is faced with the practical problem of fitting it into an already overcrowded curriculum.

As the majority of schools are currently organized, there are several ways of including health education experiences in the curriculum. For schools that are organized on a subject-centered basis, definite provision needs to be made for direct health teaching, either as a separate subject or as specified units or topics within other courses which are required of all pupils. Time allotments are important or health education content may be ignored or replaced by other concerns. Recommended time allotments are to be found in *Suggested School Health Policies* [7] and emphasis is placed on the health course as a means of including health education in the secondary-school curriculum. It is recommended that in the elementary school the time allotted to health education should at least equal the time devoted to other major areas in the curriculum. In the junior high school the minimum time allotment for health teaching is set at one period daily for at least two semesters, during the seventh, eighth, or ninth grades. In the senior high schools a similar minimum time allotment of a daily period for at least two semesters is recommended, preferably during the eleventh or twelfth grades.

At a recent national conference, the following recommendation was made concerning time allotment for health education:

We reaffirm and endorse the recommendations in regard to health education which have been made previously by other professional organizations such as the Joint Committee of the National Education Association and the American Medical Association (one unit at the junior high school level and one unit at the senior high school level). We commend those schools or school systems that have attained these goals. Recognizing that many schools have not yet attained these goals, it is recomended that a minimum time allotment of one period per day from grades 7-12 be devoted to the areas of health and safety education and physical education and that time for driver education be alloted in addition to this period. . . . Suggested time

[7] National Conference for Cooperation in Health Education, Committee on School Health Policies. *Suggested School Health Policies.* Third édition. Washington, D.C. and Chicago: National Education Association and American Medical Association, 1956. 40 p.

apportionment of the 12 semesters included in this package plan is not less than two semesters for health and safety education.[8]

There are several subject areas in addition to the health course that offer opportunities for direct health education. Health education units may be included in the content of these areas, such as science courses, social studies, home economics, physical education, and industrial arts. Combinations of health and science courses have been established in some secondary-school programs, which when skillfully planned and taught are an effective curricular pattern for health teaching. The biological sciences particularly lend themselves to the teaching of meaningful concepts relative to human health.

Health content related to other topics in various subjects may also be included. This is known as *correlation*. For example, in studying the organization and functions of local government in social studies, a discussion of the organization and functions of the official agency responsible for the health of the people would normally be included as a necessary part of the unit. Such correlations strengthen and supplement health instruction, but they cannot be substituted for a well-planned, carefully developed health education program. Many boys and girls who do not take some of these courses, such as home economics, fail to receive this instruction. If it were included in required courses, all students would be reached.

In unit teaching in the elementary school or junior high school in which the social studies have largely formed the base, and subject fields are drawn upon as needed for facts and concepts, some health experiences may be provided according to the unit being studied. For example, in studying about the people of other countries, consideration of their food habits, clothing, and disease problems would probably be included and compared with our own. In unit teaching the whole unit may center around a health problem, such as learning to select an adequate diet or understanding growth changes occurring in early adolescence, during which other subject areas would be drawn upon as needed. Subject lines are submerged in such units and information is sought in answer to problems which have been raised. Unless such opportunities are an integral part of a carefully planned,

[8] American Association for Health, Physical Education, and Recreation. "Health Education (including Safety and Driver Education)." *Youth and Fitness. A Program for Secondary Schools.* Report of the National Conference on Fitness of Secondary School Youth. Washington, D.C.: the Association, a department of the National Education Association, 1959. p. 24.

unified, total program of health education, the health experiences of children may be haphazard, incomplete, and lack continuity.

In addition to planned instruction, there are many out-of-class situations in the school program that offer excellent opportunities to educate about health. Discussing a health problem with the physician or nurse at the health examination, learning to use properly and take care of school equipment and facilities, selecting the school lunch, discussing problems of smoking and drinking with the coach, or getting ready for a field trip are examples of such opportunities. Unusual events such as a new discovery like the poliomyelitis vaccine, voting to fluoridate the community's water supply, a civil defense practice, an epidemic, a tornado or hurricane are incentives to enthusiastic study. These may be in the nature of homeroom discussions or regular class activities. An injury on the playground may offer an opportunity both to demonstrate and talk about the proper care of a wound. This is incidental instruction, and such events may provide excellent firsthand learning experiences. However, these "teachable moments," as valuable as they are, can only supplement, never replace, an organized instructional program.

BASES FOR SELECTING CURRICULUM EXPERIENCES

Meaningful health education experiences help children and youth at their respective maturation levels to meet their needs, concerns, and problems in their own environment, both as individuals and as members of a group. Such experiences are developed around the interests and abilities of the learner. Since many boys and girls do not attend college, health problems of adult life need consideration in high school. If carefully planned, these experiences enable youth to maintain and protect their own health and lives as well as the health and lives of those for whom they will be responsible. They contribute to helping young people become increasingly competent to assume their civic responsibilities related to health. The experiences provide for an understanding of and an insight into the health problems of a constantly expanding environment—home, school, and community at the local, state, national, and world-wide levels. Some experiences, of course, are individual and help a child meet his special health problem; some are planned for small groups interested in a particular problem; others are for all boys and girls since certain health needs are common to all.

Consideration of the following bases for determining needs and problems of boys and girls by a curriculum study group will enable them to locate specific needs around which units of work may be developed. Some of these also are suggestive of the maturation level at which they are most appropriately included in the curriculum.

Biological needs. Many of man's activities revolve around meeting his basic life-sustaining and life-continuing needs—taking in food, breathing, exercising, resting and sleeping, eliminating wastes, reproducing. Learning behavior that provides optimum conditions for growth and well-being and protects the body from harm is an essential part of the education of all children and youth.

Characteristics of children of different age levels: their growth and developmental needs. What normal children are like as they grow from childhood to adulthood and the developmental tasks confronting them at each stage of growth give insight into many individual and group health problems associated with growing up. They also indicate the time or age placement at which certain experiences are most beneficial. During adolescence, for example, the body grows very rapidly, puberty is reached, and there is a struggle for independence from parental authority. Many boys and girls develop poor posture and skin disorders at this time. For some it is a period of inner turmoil with frequent family conflict. Providing school experiences which will enable them to understand or overcome their problems at this time aids them in making better adjustment to life, often improves health and also family relationships, and provides for a smoother transition into adulthood.

Health problems as revealed through a study of mortality records by age groups. Death may result from lack of knowledge or failure to apply what one knows. The causes of death by age groups highlight certain problems at different age levels which education may help prevent. County, state, and national mortality records are valuable sources of information.

Health status by age groups as revealed on health records, accident and illness records, special studies, and surveys. A true picture of health problems cannot be shown by a study of mortality alone. There are many conditions which are disabling and impair health but are not necessarily fatal. Acute illnesses and chronic diseases, including heart disease, diabetes, visual and hearing difficulties, and emotional disturbances are such problems. It is more difficult to determine the range and prevalence of these problems than it is to determine causes of death. Data on medical causes of rejection of men for the armed services during war periods; periodic surveys of illness; county, state, and national morbidity records; hospital records; school health and accident records; and records of causes of school absences are some sources of information. Consultation with physicians, health workers, and parents, and observation of children also aids a teacher in determining the health problems of his particular group. Usually problems discovered from local data arouse more interest and concern.

Analysis by age groups of activities related to health in which the majority of boys and girls engage. One of the functions of the school is to teach boys and girls to do better those desirable things that they are likely to do anyway. For example, learning to come to school safely, riding a bicycle or driving a car; or dating, selecting a mate, getting married, having a baby, rearing children, and caring for illness in the home are common activities which, if carried on successfully, require attitudes, understandings, practices, skills, and appreciations which the school has a responsibility to help develop. Failure to do so often results in tragedy, great suffering, and cost, both to the individual and society.

Analysis of environmental health hazards at school and in the home and community. People live in groups and the health and safety of all are affected by the health practices of individuals. Likewise, co-operative health measures are necessary to protect the health of the individual. A consideration of environmental factors, such as fire and water hazards, problems arising from nuclear developments, polluted air, insects and rodents, sanitation of public eating places and trailer courts, gives us important clues in regard to problems requiring attention.

Analysis of citizenship responsibilities relating to health. As a member of a democractic society, each person needs to be an informed, active participant in the affairs of that society. Group decisions usually are based on facts and represent the will of the majority. For example, understanding health and safety laws and the purposes, program, and cost of official and voluntary health agencies which protect life and promote health is needed if one is to support or reject them intelligently. Boys and girls in school today will vote tomorrow on many problems related to health; some will serve on city or county commissions and in

legislative bodies; some may be involved with international
health problems.

Analysis of major social trends relating to health. Such problems as the mobility of the population, greater participation in
voluntary health insurance, the increasing tax-supported care of
the medically indigent and other groups, and the increasing age
of the population have important implications for the health
education curriculum. These problems require critical and creative thinking.

Analysis of vocational opportunities in health education.
High school is a time when adolescents are considering vocational possibilities. There are natural opportunities in some
health education units to indicate possible careers related to
health such as medicine, nursing, and public health at a time
when student interest is high.

WAYS OF IDENTIFYING HEALTH PROBLEMS

Significant problems can be identified by careful observation of
health practices and activities of the particular age group in
school and out of school, listening to pupils talk and talking with
them, class discussion, and use of checklists, questionnaires, and
skill tests. Surveys of home and community environmental conditions, conferences with parents and those responsible for the
health and safety of the population—physicians, nurses, sanitarians, and safety officers—also bring to light other problems.
As mentioned previously, local, state, and national health and
accident records; related information in the cumulative school
records; and reliable research, surveys, and studies reveal pertinent problems.

As a curriculum group studies interests, needs, and problems
of children and youth through these various avenues, it will find
the same need indicated in data from differing sources. For example, the need for learning to drive a car safely will be revealed
in a study of mortality and accident records, in an analysis of
activities common to the majority of adolescent boys and girls,
and in a consideration of citizenship responsibilities related to
safety. This only emphasizes the need. Other needs may not be
identified until all avenues have been explored.

Many of these problems involve several subject areas. A school
faculty is responsible for providing ways of meeting the needs
discovered in the time allotted within the school day, either in a

subject-centered curriculum or in other designs. Careful analysis is needed to determine the most significant problems with which the school can deal and to avoid duplication in related areas if the curriculum is subject-centered. In considering the problem of duplication, it is important to find out whether all boys and girls are being provided with the necessary health education experiences, and also the content of the experiences and the methods of teaching being used. A conscientious faculty is concerned with the depth with which a problem is studied and with the results obtained in improved individual and community living.

DETERMINING PRIORITY OF PROBLEMS FOR STUDY

There will be far more health needs revealed than the school can deal with in the time allotted to health education in the curriculum. It therefore becomes necessary to make a choice of problems. The following criteria may prove helpful to a teacher or group in selecting problems that are significant to both teachers and pupils:

1. Can education make a contribution to the solution of this problem?

2. What is the frequency and relative importance of the problem?

3. Is the problem suitable to the maturation level of this group?

4. Is this a problem about which pupils are concerned? How urgent is the problem at this age level?

5. Is the subject matter related to the study of the problem appropriate for study in health education?

6. Will this problem provide a new experience and assure growth in learning?

7. Does the problem have possibilities for attaining immediate and long-range goals?

8. Does a study of this problem contribute to individual and social goals?

9. How much time is available?

10. What instructional materials and resources are available or can be secured?

ORGANIZING A FACULTY PROGRAM

In the elementary school.   At the elementary-school level some
faculties have successfully developed or improved the health education program by having horizontal committees composed of
teachers of the same grade level or groups of grades work
together in identifying the most significant health and safety
problems of the children they are teaching. This is done in co-operation with parents, pupils, members of community agencies,
and others as needed. Health problems are identified as physical,
mental, emotional, and social to determine whether growth is
being provided for in all these aspects of a child's life. Experiences are selected from the different categories according to need
to provide balance in the curriculum. The problems which eventually are selected determine both the scope and balance of the
curriculum.

The continuity or sequence of experiences is determined by a
vertical committee composed of teachers of different grade levels.
This committee is concerned with preventing unnecessary duplication and omissions in the child's experience, and the placement
of the experiences at the time when the need is greatest or most
appropriate to his interests and maturity level. It likewise attempts to provide for continuous growth, experiences with
increasing depth, and for expanding the child's horizon and
breadth of interests.

These committees then decide in what ways they can provide
for meeting the health needs of these children within the curriculum in which they are operating. Special health education units
may be developed around some of the needs. Others may be met
in the units which cut across subject matter lines, or in out-of-
class activities. The important point is that the teacher has an
over-all, planned, co-ordinated program with defined scope and
progressive sequence toward which he is working.

Although a faculty develops the broad outlines of the curriculum in this way, enough flexibility can be allowed for the
individual teacher to meet the special needs of his group and of
individual children. If time is a limiting factor, it is better to
select a few problems and deal with them in such a way that
behavior is really changed than to spread one's efforts over too
many problems with little or no influence on behavior.

Planning is continuous within the year and from one year to
the next. There are many ways by which planning is done during

the school year, such as by committees working throughout the school year, preschool and postschool planning conferences, and special planning days. Planning may also be done at workshops during the summer through special courses, or in other ways. Many groups find it advantageous to utilize the best qualified consultant help available at the local and state levels.

In the junior and senior high school. Organization for curriculum improvement at the junior and senior high school level is usually different because the organization of the school is different. Some schools have appointed a health education committee to work in conjunction with the over-all school curriculum committee or with the total faculty, according to the size of the faculty. In either case, the final report is made to the total faculty and accepted, modified, or rejected by them.

In many schools, health committees or councils exist on a continuing basis to consider the problems arising from health and safety needs of pupils and school staff in the total school situation. Such committees or councils frequently operate in the area of health curriculum as a part of their responsibility. In some situations one teacher in the high-school faculty is designated as a health co-ordinator; his responsibility is to assume leadership in organizing and implementing the health program of the school. He works with the health council or committee in accomplishing this purpose.

A health committee operating in the area of curriculum planning and improvement is often composed of the health education teacher, or the person best qualified in health education, and teachers of such closely related subjects as science, home economics, social studies, and physical education. Others with special health responsibilities, such as the nurse, physician, school lunch director, and building engineer, are invited in to work with the curriculum committee as needed. Parents, pupils, and community health workers are also utilized in this process. This committee, just as in the elementary school, seeks to locate needs, concerns, and problems of this age group and determine the extent to which they are being met. It investigates duplications and omissions in the curriculum, searches for ways of providing for needs, and makes recommendations for improvement. The quality of such planning is determined by many factors. Among these are the interest and concern of the principal and curriculum director (if there is one) for the health education program and the general school atmosphere toward curriculum problems. The background and preparation in health education of the chairman of the committee or of the health co-ordinator are of great importance. His ability to work with other people and to interest others in working with him, the earnestness of purpose and interest of the committee, and the time available for planning are added factors which determine success or failure. The most fruitful results usually occur when leadership and consultant help qualified in health education and with special interest and experience in this field are provided.*

Many school systems today have a curriculum director who works on a system-wide basis in improving educational programs. He stimulates and launches curriculum study and co-ordinates the curriculum work of the system. Usually the director works through a co-ordinating council consisting of representatives from various schools, administrative and supervisory staff, and frequently lay citizens. System-wide area committees such as the health education committee are usually represented on the council by the chairman of the committee. A co-ordinating council may engage in such activities as formulating over-all policies for curriculum planning, evaluating the curriculum program, recommending areas in which intensive curriculum studies are to be made, or approving curriculum guides for recommendation to the superintendent.

ORGANIZING CURRICULUM EXPERIENCES AROUND A CENTRAL PROBLEM

Planned instruction is organized around a center that gives unity to the learning experiences. These centers may be pupil needs and interests, persistent or social problems of living, or particular aspects of subjects. The organization of learning experiences around such a center is a unit of work, a major division of instruction.

Plans are made well in advance of teaching, although they may be modified in the actual process of teaching. An organized written plan of suggestions for teaching centered around a certain problem is called a resource unit or teacher's guide. It represents the preplanning done by those who develop the resource unit or guide and is a source of information and ideas helpful to the teacher in developing his own unit of instruction. Since

* For a more complete discussion of the health committee in the secondary school and its role in planning the health curriculum, see Chapter Ten.

many teachers in different situations may use the resource unit, *it contains far more suggestions than one teacher can actually use.* The teacher can then select that which he believes is suitable for his class in his school situation. Of course, he will also use his own ingenuity to develop and try out experiences to fit the special needs of his own pupils. The teaching unit is the unit as actually carried out by the teacher and pupils planning and working together.

Resource units may be prepared locally by individual teachers or groups of teachers or in system-wide workshops, in university workshops or courses, or by professional organizations. Participation in the development of a unit contributes to its effective use. Many school systems now have a file of resource units to supplement textbooks and courses of study.

Preparing Resource Units

Many forms for preparing resource units have been suggested. Although the forms vary, they contain essentially the same kinds of information and differ only in minor details. In general, such a unit states the problem and defines its scope. It suggests desired objectives or outcomes, and possible learning experiences related to the problem. It includes ways for evaluating progress and for determining outcomes in terms of changed behavior in pupils. It lists materials of instruction, including books and other printed materials, audio-visual aids, and any other needed materials. Any form that suits the writer's purposes may be selected if it contains the essential elements in planning unified experiences. The following form is one that has proved useful:

Overview or statement of the problem. The overview gives a brief statement of the purpose and scope of the unit. It explains the significance of the problem, offers evidence to show its relation to pupil need, and defines the grade or age levels for which it is planned. It may include suggestions for use of the unit.

Objectives. The objectives represent the outcomes desired. They are specific and focus on the pupil and the kinds of behaviors expected as a result of the learning experiences. They are expressed as desired understandings, attitudes, practices, appreciations, and skills (when appropriate) which boys and girls should develop.

Approaches. These are the ways of getting started and stimulating the interest of the pupils. A unit may develop in a variety of ways which can be listed. These may include an event of unusual occurrence or community interest, previous work which provides stimulus for consideration of related matters, creation of interest by such sources as a story, a film, or a newspaper clipping. In any event, the teacher builds a readiness and desire on the part of the class to pursue the problem.

Problems. These are the possible questions or subproblems arising out of consideration of the larger problem which determine the scope of the unit. When the pupils and teacher are planning together as the unit is developing in the classroom, the pupils may suggest worthwhile subproblems which need to be pursued other than those contained in the resource unit. *The answers to the questions raised provide the content or subject matter of the unit.*

Experiences. These are the activities engaged in by the pupils to find the answers to the problems raised. In a well-planned unit activities are selected on the basis of their contribution to the attainment of the outcomes desired. The resource unit lists a variety of suggested or possible experiences from which teachers can gain ideas. The choice of experiences is made within the individual class. Listed in the unit are such ways of finding answers to problems as reading, discussing, experimenting, seeing films, listening to a record, going on a field trip.

Some experiences suggested in the resource unit are individual to provide for individual differences; others are group activities to give experience in working together and to learn democratic procedures. Varied experiences are planned to create interest and to help children gain impressions and information in many different ways. Thus they learn. Some experiences are creative, encouraging and developing the creative abilities of the children and providing satisfying outlets for them. Other experiences are planned which will enable children to state a problem or hypothesis, gather data to find the answer, record the data carefully, weigh the facts discovered, draw accurate conclusions on the basis of the data, test the conclusions, and make decisions. This process helps the pupil to develop ability to think critically. A culminating experience at the end of the unit is valuable because it helps the pupil review and draw together what he has learned during the course of the unit into a meaningful, unified whole.

Evaluation. To determine whether the desired outcomes have been achieved and to point up future needs, both the pupils and teacher need to evaluate the progress made toward the objectives. This is done periodically during the unit of work as well as at its completion. Methods of appraisal by the teacher and ways of self-appraisal by the pupils are planned. The kinds of evidence which can be accumulated to show growth in understanding and changes in behavior are included in the unit.

Materials of instruction. These include a bibliography of books and other printed materials for the teacher and the pupils, audio-visual aids, and other equipment necessary to conduct the experiences listed in the unit.

The resource unit clearly indicates the subproblems to be solved within the given problem area, the importance of the problem area, the objectives or outcomes which can be attained, ways to begin, the experiences which will help pupils find answers to the questions raised and result in the desired outcomes, the ways both teacher and pupils can check the results, and the materials of instruction which are needed to execute the unit. *The teaching unit is planned by the individual teacher, adapting the suggestions of the resource unit to the individual situation.* Choices must be made, and materials selected which meet the needs of the individual group, and problems considered which grow out of the needs and interests of a particular group of pupils.

SUMMARY

Curriculum development is a co-operative, continuous process. The greatest improvement appears to occur when time and qualified leadership are provided for involving school and community personnel in working on problems that are significant to them in their situation. The effective health education curriculum is developed in relation to the total curriculum and the curriculum design in the individual school. These designs vary considerably in American schools, although the majority, especially at the junior high and senior high school levels, remain subject-centered. There is a definite trend toward block organization and structured unit teaching cutting across subject matter lines, especially at the elementary-school level and to a lesser extent at the junior high school level. At the senior high school level, this is still largely on an experimental basis. An attempt is being made to make education more functional through the problem-centered curriculum.

The health education curriculum is developed around the needs of the individual and his group as he grows from childhood to maturity and around the problems of living created by his interaction with his environment. Many of these needs and problems are common to the majority of boys and girls, in that they evolve from the basic needs of a living organism in the American culture. Some, however, are peculiar to the individual in his special environment. Curriculum development is concerned with both types of needs.

As in other areas of instruction, the organization for curriculum study in health is a part of the organization for constant school-wide and system-wide planning. The outcomes sought are attitude and behavior changes resulting in improved living for the individual and the improvement of society. Unit teaching has been found to be one method of improving instruction. Therefore, developing and using resource units, which are being used increasingly as a basis for planning with children, is one way of bringing about curriculum improvement. There can be no substitute for a planned, organized curriculum in health education providing for depth, breadth, and continuity of experiences if the school is to fulfill its purposes in attaining self-realization, improved human relationships, economic efficiency, and civic competence.

SELECTED REFERENCES

ALBERTY, HAROLD. *Reorganizing the High-School Curriculum.* Second edition. New York: Macmillan Co., 1953. 560 p.

ALEXANDER, WILLIAM H., and HALVERSON, PAUL. *Effective Teaching in Secondary Schools.* New York: Rinehart & Co., 1956. 564 p.

AMERICAN ASSOCIATION FOR HEALTH, PHYSICAL EDUCATION, AND RECREATION. "Health Education (including Safety and Driver Education)." *Youth and Fitness. A Program for Secondary Schools.* Report of the National Conference on Fitness of Secondary School Youth. Washington, D.C.: the Association, a department of the National Education Association, 1959. 74 p.

AMERICAN ASSOCIATION FOR HEALTH, PHYSICAL EDUCATION, AND RECREATION. *Report of the National Conference on Children and Fitness.* Washington, D.C.: the Association, a department of the National Education Association, 1959.

AMERICAN ASSOCIATION OF SCHOOL ADMINISTRATORS. *American School Curriculum.* Thirty-First Yearbook. Washington, D.C.:

the Association, a department of the National Education Association, 1953. 358 p.

AMERICAN ASSOCIATION OF TEACHERS COLLEGES and NATIONAL COMMISSION ON SAFETY EDUCATION. *Safety Education for Teachers. Part Two. A Guide for College Instructors of Safety Education.* Washington, D.C.: National Education Association, 1947. 123 p.

ASSOCIATION FOR SUPERVISION AND CURRICULUM DEVELOPMENT. *Toward Better Teaching.* 1949 Yearbook. Washington, D.C.: the Association, a department of the National Education Association, 1949. 282 p.

ASSOCIATION FOR SUPERVISION AND CURRICULUM DEVELOPMENT. *What Shall the High Schools Teach?* 1956 Yearbook. Washington, D.C.: the Association, a department of the National Education Association, 1956. 230 p.

BUCHER, CHARLES A. *Administration of School Health and Physical Education Programs.* St. Louis: C. V. Mosby Co., 1958. 470 p.

FRENCH, WILL, and OTHERS. *Behavioral Goals of General Education in High School.* New York: Russell Sage Foundation, 1957. 247 p.

GROUT, RUTH E. *Health Teaching in Schools.* Third edition. Philadelphia: W. B. Saunders Co., 1958. 359 p.

KEARNEY, NOLAN C. *Elementary School Objectives.* New York: Russell Sage Foundation, 1953. 189 p.

NATIONAL CONFERENCE FOR COOPERATION IN HEALTH EDUCATION, COMMITTEE ON SCHOOL HEALTH POLICIES. *Suggested School Health Policies.* Third edition. Washington, D.C. and Chicago: National Education Association and American Medical Association, 1956. 40 p.

NATIONAL EDUCATION ASSOCIATION, AMERICAN EDUCATIONAL RESEARCH ASSOCIATION. "Curriculum Planning and Development." *Review of Educational Research* 27: 237-304; June 1957.

NATIONAL SOCIETY FOR THE STUDY OF EDUCATION. *Adapting the Secondary School Program to the Needs of Youth.* Part I, Fifty-Second Yearbook. Chicago: University of Chicago Press, 1953. 316 p.

OBERTEUFFER, DELBERT. *School Health Education.* Third edition. New York: Harper & Brothers, 1960. 547 p.

OTTO, HENRY J. *Elementary School Organization and Administration.* New York: Appleton-Century-Crofts, 1954. 719 p.

RAGAN, WILLIAM B. *Modern Elementary Curriculum.* New York: Dryden Press, 1953. 570 p.

SCHNEIDER, ELSA, and MCNEELY, SIMON A. *Teachers Contribute to Child Health.* U.S. Department of Health, Education, and Welfare, Office of Education, Bulletin 1951, No. 8. Washington, D.C.: Superintendent of Documents, Government Printing Office, 1951. 44 p.

SCHNEIDER, ROBERT E. *Methods and Materials in Health Education.* Philadelphia: W. B. Saunders Co., 1958. 382 p.

SHANE, HAROLD B., editor. *The American Elementary School.* Thirteenth Yearbook, The John Dewey Society. New York: Harper & Brothers, 1953. 434 p.

STRATEMEYER, FLORENCE B.; FORKNER, HAMDEN L.; MCKIM, MARGARET G.; and PASSOW, A. HARRY. *Developing a Curriculum for Modern Living.* Second edition. New York: Bureau of Publications, Teachers College, Columbia University, 1957. 740 p.

TURNER, C. E.; SELLERY, C. MORLEY; and SMITH, SARA LOUISE. *School Health and Health Education.* Fourth edition. St. Louis: C. V. Mosby Co., 1961.

WRIGHT, GRACE S. *Block-Time Classes in the Core Program in the Junior High School.* U.S. Department of Health, Education, and Welfare, Office of Education, Bulletin 1958, No. 6. Washington, D.C.: Superintendent of Documents, Government Printing Office, 1958. 70 p.

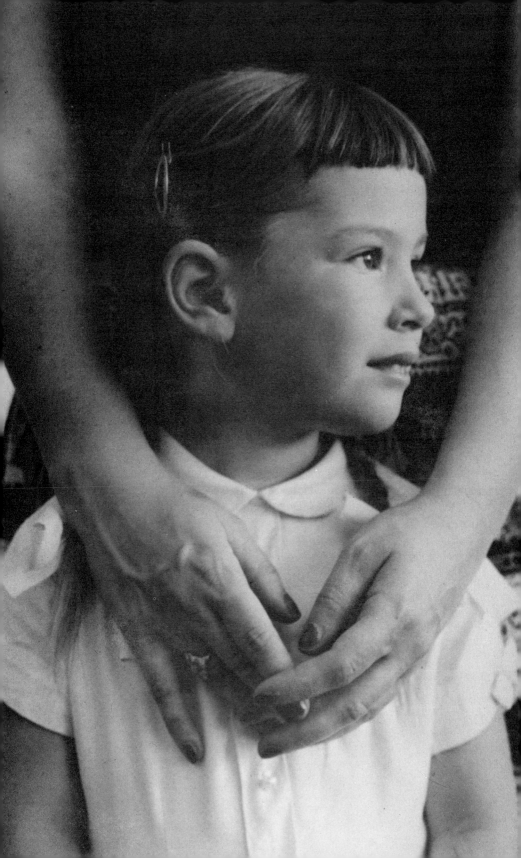

Kindergarten and the Primary Grades

Children are products of their heredity and of a complexity of environments. Their families, playmates, and neighborhoods have had a great impact upon their lives long before they start school. A multitude of experiences in these settings have established patterns of behavior, including health behavior, from infancy. In most cases, when a child is five years of age, the school joins the home and the community as a new environment. This new experience in the life of a young child will play a major role in helping him grow physically, mentally, socially, and emotionally as he progresses toward maturity. Teachers of kindergarten and the primary grades face no task more important than that of helping each child acquire correct information and develop those understandings which will help him make wise decisions and assume increasing responsibilities for his personal life. From the first day of kindergarten, plans must be made for continuous healthful experiences and concomitant learnings to assure growth in positive health behavior. The teacher must cause each child to understand, to feel, and to react so that he will develop to his optimum health potentialities.

There are six basic questions for teachers to consider when planning health education experiences for young children.

1. How are behavior patterns developed?
2. What do the studies in growth and development tell us about the predicted health needs and interests of this particular age group?
3. What techniques can be used to find individual or group needs which cannot be predicted?
4. What are the best methods of teaching in health education?
5. What health education experiences are needed to meet health needs?
6. How can the results of health teaching and experiences be evaluated?

HEALTH BEHAVIOR IS A PERSONAL MATTER

Health practices of young children are the result of their experiences at home and in their neighborhood. When the child enters school, guidance in the development of behavior patterns and attitudes necessary for healthful living becomes a shared responsibility of home and school. Modern psychology has helped us understand that the child's personal qualities and his previous experiences make him what he is. His behavior in the classroom reveals his unique qualities and his acceptance and interpretation of the school world, both of which are influenced by what has already happened to him.

A successful teacher recognizes differences among children. In every group one can find the enthusiastic, the eager, the friendly. Also present will be the aggressive, the shy, the timid. Some children will be quiet; some will be active. Some children learn quickly; others are slow to respond. The teacher's role is that of helping each child interact with his physical and social environment in a way that will be both accepted and satisfying. This is an individual problem for each child because of the uniqueness of personality and the effects of outside forces upon his growth and learning.

Teachers cannot change past experiences of children, but these experiences can be understood and new situations created which will be meaningful. By observations of the child, from conferences with parents, nurse, and physician, by studying the community, and by referring to all available cumulative and health records, the teacher learns about each child. What aspirations do the parents have for the child? What are their hopes, their interests? Will they be partners with the school in helping to define purposes? How has the community affected the child? What is its future role? Do the school and the community work together to solve the many problems of modern living in a rapidly changing world, or will the environment of community living be a detriment to the child's health and development? At what level is the child in his growth pattern? Is there a reason for his ability or inability to succeed in a particular task? What special environment will stimulate the child at his own maturity level? What experiences will make best use of his abilities?

The health teacher faces the problem of providing classroom learning situations that will meet both individual and group health needs. Appropriate activities are based upon past experiences and directed toward a wider scope of learning, but because behavior is a personal matter, each child will interpret his experiences differently with resultant individual health behavior.

UNDERSTANDING GROWTH AND DEVELOPMENT AS A BASIS FOR HEALTH EXPERIENCES

For the teachers of kindergarten or the primary grades, child growth and development serve as a constant guide in planning the sequence of learning experiences in health education. Children are changing, growing, and maturing as they enter school. They are energetic, spontaneous, and active. They express themselves through movement and noise, and learn best through active participation. They are eager to do, to play, and to construct, although their interest span is short and they become restless if a variety of activities is not planned which allows for freedom of movement in the classroom. The daily schedule needs to be planned with allowance for short periods of various kinds of activities, both active and passive.

Developmental Characteristics*

By reviewing the characteristics of children of this age, teachers can find many common health needs. The first permanent teeth appear as the children enter the first grade. Children are interested in discussing baby teeth and in locating the six-year molars. Proper care of the teeth can be stressed and the dentist viewed as a friend who will help them care for their teeth.

During this period of growth certain childhood diseases and infections are prevalent. This calls for health experiences which will help the children develop practices for protecting themselves and others from illness. Health learnings also include ways to improve habits of cleanliness relating to proper use of toilets and drinking fountains, disposable tissues or handkerchiefs, washing hands before meals and after using the toilet, and keeping hands and foreign objects from mouth, nose, ears, and eyes. Children can be taught the importance of wearing suitable clothing for protection against various weather conditions. They need help in understanding the role of immunization as a guardian of their health and of the ways in which physicians and nurses assist in the control of disease and treatment of illness.

---

* See Chapter Three.

Children in the kindergarten and primary grades must play, not only because of their demand for activity, but also because of the growth which takes place as a child learns to play with larger and changing groups of children. The desire for activity and play is present, and teachers have an opportunity for much health teaching through this medium of expression. The fitness of the adult may be traced in part to early habits and attitudes toward activity. The appreciation for a balance between activity, rest, and work can be established early in life. Desirable attitudes can be developed by group play and the opportunities for big muscle activity. Acceptance of the need for adequate sleep at night under desirable conditions, as well as for rest and relaxation during the day is important. Children need to gain an early understanding of the need for a well-balanced program, including both activity and rest or sleep.

Children of this age are interested in their growth and in changes in their height and weight. Good habits of sitting, standing, and walking can be encouraged and practiced. They are also interested in how the body functions; such concepts and understandings should be simple and free of technical details. The wonders of the sense organs are of particular interest to them. Proper care of these organs and encouragement of sight and hearing conservation are important learning experiences.

Teachers sometimes must assist children in getting acquainted with and being willing to try new foods or to enjoy familiar foods. Many opportunities will arise for the teacher to show the relationships between proper eating habits and growth. Probably the greatest learnings about nutrition at this age will center around the acquisition of good eating habits. The need for regular meals and the knowledge of what foods aid growth are important items for discussion.

The intellectual development of this age group is directed toward exploration and experimentation. Basic drives are those of creation, construction, and manipulation. The children are curious about everything in their environment and much learning takes place. The "here and now" is important to these children. Because they cannot deal in the abstract, health experiences for children in the kindergarten and primary grades must be direct. The immediate environment of the home, the school, and the local community will provide the settings for their learning experiences and their appreciation of the members of society who work for their health and welfare.

Play is the emotional medium of expression and learning. Dramatic play is the reproduction of children's perceptual experiences. Needs arise and new concepts are gained as children identify themselves with persons and things. In the primary grades, dramatic play is one method of guiding children's health learnings. Because play is so natural, many learning situations can be integrated into dramatic play situations which could not otherwise be comprehended or be of interest to the young child. In learning about foods by playing store, children find more and more need to expand their play. Out of a series of play activities in which children plan, collect, and construct, they extend their interests and their learnings.

Children in this age group are typically self-centered rather than group-centered in feeling and action. Contact with members of the group is maintained so long as it is satisfying, although by the age of seven a desire to belong to a group and achieve group status is usually evidenced. Group activities are more likely to interest the young child when the number involved is small. Group membership tends to vary and shift. These characteristics imply a need for a good deal of incidental, individual health guidance as well as for opportunities for children to work together in both small and large groups in the solution of health problems.

Children at this stage of emotional development evidence a strong desire for affection and help. They are easily upset. Judgments are influenced by strong likes and dislikes. At this time it is important to build positive mental health attitudes by helping children learn how better to understand themselves and others. Classroom experiences can provide opportunities for every child to become acquainted with the new school environment in a happy, relaxed way so that each can acquire a sense of belonging and acceptance.

It is important that children learn how to work and play successfully with each other and that they discover how to evaluate outcomes of their activities and identify problems. Positive attitudes toward others will grow as thoughtful and courteous practices become a part of classroom procedure. Teachers can find countless opportunities to help young children appreciate each other. Sharing in the classroom and on the playground is of importance. Helping each other and those less fortunate is one of the first steps toward good rapport in the group and is an element in sound mental health.

Self-direction is an important aim in the growth of the young child. To further this objective the teacher can create situations in which children can achieve satisfaction in being independent and self-motivating in a variety of activities.

FINDING CHILDREN'S HEALTH NEEDS

Studying children to find individual or group health needs is one of the first steps in sound health teaching. Desirable health education experiences can be planned only when the teacher understands the physical, social, and emotional requirements of each child. As we have seen, certain of these needs fall into a rather well-defined pattern based upon our knowledge of growth and development. Other individual or group needs may emerge as the teacher studies his class.

Teachers can identify children's health needs in numerous ways. A teacher can observe a child's behavior in various situations, note ways in which he may deviate from the behavior of other children in the same situations, and study the reasons for the deviations. Questions asked by the children and discussions in the group also help to reveal health needs. Other procedures which may be employed to determine the child's health requirements include conferences with the child's parents regarding his problems, habits, interests, and out-of-school activities; talking with the child about his problems; analyzing the child's attendance, scholastic, and health records; talking with a nurse or physician with reference to individual health problems; making and maintaining growth charts; analyzing the results of vision and hearing tests; using tests and checklists to find the child's interests and attitudes; and analyzing the child's assigned and creative work in school.

Observation

Observation may be employed to identify the health needs of each pupil.* The teacher notes any behavior or appearance that appears to deviate from normal. To be more certain that the deviations are significant, the results of continuous observations are systematically recorded, and if possible the reasons for the deviations are determined by consultation with medical and guidance personnel. Some schools provide observation record

---

* A helpful pamphlet to assist teachers in making observations is *What Teachers See*, published by the Metropolitan Life Insurance Company of New York. A filmstrip on this subject is also available from the company.

forms on which a teacher can note a child's study habits, general appearance, food, rest and activity practices, common behavior patterns, and similar items. These records may be analyzed to give clues to the types of activities that are needed in the program of health instruction.

Conferences and Interviews

In conferences with parents, valuable information can be obtained concerning the social structure, emotional climate, and health attitudes and habits of the family. Parents and teachers often differ in fundamental health beliefs, or because of habits or circumstances have patterns of health behavior which may be diametrically opposed. Conflicts can develop in children when such double standards for health behavior exist. Teachers must be aware of this possibility and must teach in such a way that conflict can be minimized without sacrificing scientific truths.

Talking with the child is an especially fruitful way of determining how the child lives at home, his eating and sleeping habits, the extent to which he is disturbed by sibling rivalry, and the degree of love and affection he enjoys. Through such pupil conferences, the teacher can often become aware of existing health problems in the community. Class and small-group discussions likewise reveal many health attitudes and add to the teacher's information concerning the health needs of his pupils.

In talking individually with a child it is most important that the teacher begin by encouraging him to discuss his interests, hobbies, satisfactions, and difficulties. Throughout the talk the teacher tries to sense the child's way of thinking. Following the talks the teacher helps the child interpret his problems and plan ways of solving them. Conferences with a physician or nurse likewise may be helpful in discovering health needs of children which may be met through effective health education.

Needs Revealed by Children's Activities

Many times a child will express his feelings or reveal his needs through art, drawing, or creative writing. A child's reaction to pictures may be used to discover his attitudes about certain health practices. Pictures of health activities may be presented for the child to talk about. While he is talking, the child may name the kinds of foods he likes or dislikes, tell when he usually goes to bed, or reveal his attitude toward the physician and dentist or even toward his parents and brothers and sisters.

Children will often express ideas and attitudes by creating their own stories or by finishing a story started by the teacher. In the kindergarten a story about an area of health learning may be started by the teacher and the children can be encouraged to complete the story. The way the story is completed will reveal past experiences and beliefs.

Records

Cumulative records of school progress provide a logical place to begin a study of a child's needs. In many instances such a study will reveal that a child who is having difficulty in his schoolwork or in relationships with other children has certain health needs. This record, however, is useful only if each teacher has taken time to correlate the pertinent data and record them in a clear, objective way.

The health record is an important aid in determining health needs. Anecdotal records frequently provide a number of clues regarding a child's health. The attendance record may reveal that some of the children have health problems which prevent them from attending school regularly.

Inventories, Tests, Questionnaires, and Surveys

Many types of inventories, self-evaluation tests, surveys, and questionnaires may be used to find the health needs of children. A health practice inventory can be used to advantage to find out about children's usual mode of health behavior. An inventory of this type for the lower grades may comprise a few simple and specific questions pertaining to health, or the practice inventory may be pictorial for the nonreader.

Meeting Child Health Needs

When the health requirements of children have been identified, the steps necessary to meet such needs should be taken. Individual guidance, specific activities, or a change of environment may be needed to help certain children solve their health problems. Other needs may be met through group activities. In most instances children can be guided to acquire those attitudes and practices that will contribute to their sound, wholesome, healthy development.

It is to be expected that most of the health needs of young children will center around their daily activities. The following is a listing of expected areas of health teaching and a statement of how this area is related to helping children to do better or more healthfully what they ordinarily do.

1. *Food and nutrition*—Children should learn to like healthful foods, know how to select an adequate diet, and learn how to behave while eating.

2. *Exercise, rest, and sleep*—Children need to be encouraged to alternate activity with rest, relaxation, and sleep. They need regular and adequate hours of sleep.

3. *Eyes, ears, and teeth*—Children need instruction in oral cleanliness. They need regular dental supervision. Many need care for defects of vision and hearing. They need to know and respect physicians and dentists who help keep them well.

4. *Clothing*—Children should be guided to wear clothing appropriate for weather conditions and for indoor and outdoor comfort and protection.

5. *Cleanliness and grooming*—Children should become increasingly responsible for personal care. They need to become self-reliant in keeping themselves acceptably clean and well groomed and should learn the health and social reasons for such practices.

6. *Mental and emotional health*—Children must learn to adapt to their environment and to other children with whom they associate at school. They need to grow toward emotional maturity, to learn to face reality, and to cope with a wide variety of personal-social experiences.

7. *Communicable disease control*—Some diseases which attack children can be prevented. Children should learn how they can help protect themselves and others from disease. The importance of prompt and appropriate care for illness can also be taught.

8. *Safety*—Children should know that they are subject to accident hazards, and must know how to avoid them and what to do when an accident occurs.

9. *Homes, schools, and neighborhoods*—Children spend their time in schools, homes, playgrounds, neighborhoods. They need to learn how to contribute to safe, healthful living in each environment and to understand and appreciate the contributions of others to their health and safety.

METHODS OF TEACHING

The teacher who is acquainted with the health needs and interests of children is able to formulate health objectives and to decide upon the best method of providing experiences at the child's level of comprehension. Behavior changes only as children *do* or *react* in terms of how they feel from within; thus, intelligent self-direction becomes the major goal of health education.

The fundamental facts of health suitable for children in the lower grades are relatively simple. Most children learn very early *how* to live healthfully, and need to have situations provided in which they can practice healthful living. Meaningful health experiences must be planned to meet the many individual and group needs which may differ greatly according to the variety of past experiences in homes and in play opportunities with other boys and girls. Wise and constant guidance is needed if individual needs are to be met. This continuous guidance is often individualized to meet the ability of each child to assume self-direction and responsibility. Other aspects of healthful living may be taught in the group as the children become ready for group learning.

The alert teacher identifies health problems and provides potential situations that will challenge the pupils. It cannot be stated definitely what the specific learning experiences should be in a particular class or what direction these experiences should take, since all learning situations are conditioned by many factors.

Keeping the past experiences and the present needs of the children in focus, the teacher uses a method which will most satisfactorily ensure involvement of each child in a series of stimulating situations within his range of experience and ability. In the learning process every child proceeds from the known to the unknown. The teacher's role is one of guidance toward a desired goal. This may be done in a variety of ways. The choice of the method depends upon the objectives of a particular teaching situation and its adaptability to the group to be taught. In the lower grades this method, of necessity, is simple, natural, and direct.

Health Within the Total Curriculum

In the kindergarten and primary grades, emphasis is placed upon the integration of health experiences within the total educational experience rather than upon direct instruction in health as such. However, when a health problem of immediate concern presents itself, direct teaching should be done at that time. In the flexible curriculum of the lower grades, health teaching can be readily adapted to the needs of the group and can likewise contribute much to broader areas of interest.

When children begin school they are interested in their immediate environment with relation to activities in the home, school, and neighborhood. Teachers plan their work around these centers of interest and need to be aware of the health experiences which can be integrated into a common core of learning. The teacher who is alert to the needs and opportunities for health teaching will incorporate health education experiences within a wide variety of units. The following activities and experiences are cited as *examples* of the incorporation of health learnings into the kindergarten and first-grade program for children who are experiencing their first acquaintance with school. They should not be construed as a complete program for the lower grades. The objectives are set in roman type; the experiences which help to achieve the objectives are set under them in italic type.

I. The classroom should be a happy place.

A. The teacher accepts each child's feelings and contributions.

The teacher sees that each child has an opportunity to display work showing his best efforts and to share ideas, work, and possessions.

B. The teacher uses the problem solving method to help each child work out his personal-social relationship problems.

During problem solving situations, the teacher encourages the children to talk over their feelings and consider the rights of others, uses literature and the reaction story technique to help solve problems, uses individual conferences with the child to discuss his in- and out-of-school problems, and helps children to set their own standards of behavior.

C. The teacher helps each child to develop democratic behavior patterns which promote personal and social-emotional growth.

By using simple democratic processes the teacher helps the children decide procedures, standards, and rules, encourages children to learn to work in a group and to work independently, and helps each child to make friends.

II. The classroom should be a healthful place.

A. The teacher recognizes that a healthful classroom is conducive to the learning situation and therefore maintains

proper classroom heating, ventilation, and lighting; attempts
to meet each child's postural needs; alternates active and rest-
ful activities; observes signs of illness; and attempts to provide an environment that is educationally stimulating and
aesthetically appealing.

*The teacher attempts to meet the health needs of the environ-
ment by maintaining proper temperature (68-70° F.); by seeing that lights are in proper working order, and that each
child's eyes are protected from glare; by adjusting chairs and
tables to each child's height; by being alert to signs and symptoms of illness; by paying attention to "little things" such as
children having handkerchiefs, washing hands before eating,
and washing hands after using the toilet; by providing an
orderly environment with a place for everything; by helping
each child assume responsibility for various duties which contribute to an orderly and attractive room.*

III. Children are oriented to the classroom and to classroom and
school routines.

A. The teacher arranges for each child to explore the classroom environment, to discuss where wraps and lunches are
stored, and to locate the lavatories.

*The teacher and the children explore the classroom and the
corridor; discuss where lunches and wraps are stored and how
to keep wraps in order; label boys and girls closets with a
picture or provide individual hooks with each child's name;
walk to the boys and girls lavatories; discuss behavior in the
lavatory, use of equipment and materials, use of drinking
fountain, and behavior in the halls.*

B. The teacher orients the children to classroom routines by
explaining how the daily program is scheduled and what these
experiences mean; by explaining what the various bells mean;
by explaining how to participate in and clean up during the
mid-morning and mid-afternoon snack period; by helping the
children to understand how to keep the room in order, how
to eat lunch in the lunchrooms, and how the lunchroom workers function; and by explaining facilities provided for eating
home-prepared lunch.

*The teacher and the children discuss the daily program; the
teacher makes a chart of the daily program using pictures
from reading readiness books to help give clues to the children
as to the meaning of the words; as a reminder, the program*

is periodically read and discussed; the bell signals are explained; the teacher and children discuss and list on a picture chart the proper foods for mid-morning snack periods; helpers are chosen and listed; such procedures as securing milk from the cafeteria, setting the table, table manners, and cleaning up are discussed; the teacher and parents work together on nutrition problems through parent conferences and meetings; a helpers book is prepared by the teacher so that children may choose jobs to care for milk, closets, library, balls, easel, and health corner; children's name cards are inserted in the chart opposite task chosen; the teacher and children discuss various things about the lunch such as the menus, buying a lunch ticket, the cost of food, how to behave in the lunchroom, and handwashing before eating; the children are introduced to the lunchroom workers who show them where the line begins, how to proceed through the line, how to pay for lunch, where to sit, and how to carry trays; and the teacher takes the children who bring lunches to the lunch table and explains where to sit, rules for this area, and where to buy milk.

IV. Safety practices are stressed enroute to and from school.

A. The teacher anticipates problems which may arise enroute to and from school and helps children learn how to ride the school bus, how to walk safely, and how to get into a car safely.

The teacher provides experiences which help children learn and apply desirable safety practices on the school bus; the teacher and the children discuss safe conduct while waiting for the bus, how to get on and get off the bus, and safe behavior on the bus; they discuss the importance of wearing the bus pass tag, courtesy and obedience to the driver, and courtesy to other riders; dramatizations are used to help children work out safe and courteous school bus conduct; the children dictate chart stories to the teacher describing bus experiences, waiting behavior, and what they observed to and from school; children illustrate stories or react to experiences using such art media as easel paint, finger paint, crayola, chalk, clay, and art paper; the children learn how to walk to school safely; children discuss such things as the safe side of the street for walking and safe distances from vehicular traffic; the danger of darting into the street, crossing streets at signals, crosswalks, and corners; looking both ways before crossing the street and obeying the crossing guard; the teacher and chil-dren discuss the dangers of accepting rides from strangers and the importance of going directly home from school, the need of parental permission to visit friends; discuss the impor-tance of being especially cautious on rainy or snowy days; and discuss the importance of respecting private property; the teacher and the children take walks to a traffic light or a cross-walk; become acquainted with the crossing guard; use drama-tizations with the crossing guard; use dramatizations to show safe practices enroute to and from school; discuss how to get into a car safely, the dangers of crossing the street to enter a car, and the dangers of boarding a moving car.

B. The teacher helps parents understand the safety practices which children are learning to secure their co-operation.

Teachers and parents work together through parent meetings and conferences to understand school safety practices.

V. Children are oriented to the school buildings and grounds.

A. The teacher acquaints the children with the school en-vironment including classrooms, offices, and playground areas.

The teacher and the children survey the building and grounds by taking a walking tour to visit the principal's office, nurse's office, custodian's room, classroom corridors, and play areas.

B. The children become acquainted with the principal and learn about his responsibilities.

The teacher and children discuss how messages are carried to and from the office; they learn how the principal helps children and how they can help him; what to do when tardy or absent; who the school secretary is and how she helps children.

C. The children become acquainted with the nurse and learn about her responsibilities.

The teacher and the children discuss the duties of the nurse; they learn how she helps children and how they can help her. They invite the nurse to their classroom and discuss ways of keeping well and strong.

D. The children become acquainted with the custodians and learn about their responsibilities.

The teacher and children discuss the work of the custodians and how they can help keep the school safe and clean.

The teacher and children invite their custodians to explain how they clean the rooms and lavatories and to explain how the children can help them.

E. The children learn safe practices on the playground.

The children and teacher invite the physical education supervisor to visit the playground with them and to discuss such things as activities for the first grade, where activities are played, correct and safe use of apparatus, kinds of equipment used, care of playground equipment, playground rules, and where to get a drink.

Children help develop their own rules for acceptable playground behavior; the teacher records these rules on a chart.

Encouraging and Guiding Health Practices

Helping children to live more healthfully each day, both in and out of school, is one of the important goals of health teaching in the kindergarten and primary grades. Provision of a healthful environment and a balanced routine of activity, rest, eating, work, and play gives children an opportunity to experience desirable health practices.* Children should not be asked to follow patterns of health behavior that are impossible because of environmental limitations. For example, although washing hands before meals is desirable, if there are no facilities for handwashing at school, it is fruitless to try to develop this practice prior to the lunch period unless makeshift arrangements can be provided.

Demonstration of a skill such as handwashing or toothbrushing, followed by practice under observation, teaches children how to perform such skills correctly. Providing standards of cleanliness or grooming *within the reach of possible attainment by each child* and encouraging the child to evaluate his own progress toward the achievement of these goals may help to improve practices. Commending pupils quietly and unobtrusively for evidence of improvement in various types of health behavior brings satisfaction and encouragement. The emphases on competition in health performance, the status-seeking engendered by extrinsic rewards, and the employment of punishment, force, or disapproval as means of trying to motivate health behaviors in children are no longer used.

---

* See Chapter Thirteen.

Young children in school are particularly susceptible to the suggestions, advice, and teaching of a teacher who is loved and respected. They strive to please and consider him to be an infallible source of information. Parents are well aware of the expression which starts, "My teacher says . . ." and the fact that the teacher is therefore viewed as an authority. Teachers need to use this relationship judiciously in encouraging child behavior in health. They must be aware of the limitations of some home environments and should not set standards for behavior which are impossible for the child to achieve. They need to recognize that health needs vary; that not all children should be urged to follow a pattern which may be desirable for the majority; that flexibility and understanding are important in helping children establish desirable health practices.

Incidental Teaching

Many times the most meaningful teaching can result from the use of immediate situations which arise in day-by-day activities. The real impact of the "teachable moment" or of incidental learning depends upon the teacher's ability to recognize the opportunity for health teaching inherent in a situation, to analyze problems as they arise, and to plan the best approach for the solution of the problem or of handling the situation. Many experiences which children have in the early grades provide opportunities for extension of the child's understandings and attitudes in relation to health and for guidance in health behavior.

The alert teacher will capitalize on these opportunities, dealing with some on an individual basis and with others in a group situation. Thus, incidental teaching may vary from a quiet word with an individual pupil relative to some evidence of a health need to the development of a comprehensive unit of instruction as a result of the interest created by the incident. The amount of emphasis placed on the incident is a decision to be made by the teacher as he manages his total educational program and assesses the relationship of this problem to his educational goals.

Some of the commonly occurring incidents or experiences which may be utilized for health teaching are:

1. Home-to-school safety problems, including learning about traffic signals and other safety hazards
2. School safety and what to do in case of an accident

3. Use of such tools as scissors, hammers, nails, and pins

4. Eating problems, especially breakfast and the school lunch

5. Personal appearance and care of clothing at school

6. Habits of personal cleanliness, including care of the teeth

7. Toilet habits

8. Absences from school due to colds and other communicable diseases

9. Getting acquainted with the nurse and school physician

10. Housekeeping problems in the classroom

11. Work habits in the classroom and problems of establishing independence

12. Classroom co-operation and relationships with the opposite sex

13. Rest and play periods

14. The weighing and measuring programs

15. The health examinations, dental appraisals, vision and audiometer testing, and immunization programs

16. Care of pets or of the aquarium in the classroom

17. Sharing of experiences, such as birth of a new baby in a family

18. Current community events.

Each of these, and others as well, possesses inherent opportunities for effective health teaching.

Problem Solving

There is a place for the well-organized health unit based upon problem solving when there is a common health problem which can be explored by teacher and pupils working together. Many of the experiences just mentioned are common experiences and are of interest to an entire group. The teacher must be alert to discovering the problems which are real to the children and to building meaningful experiences around them.

In order to be successful, this technique requires advance preparation. Before the problem is introduced, the teacher needs accurate knowledge as a basis for planning classroom activities. A possible sequence of experiences must then be outlined and a classroom environment created which will challenge the pupils' interests. As work progresses and the children *plan, check, search, select,* and *evaluate,* real health learnings will take place.

The following are examples of problem solving experiences which might be applicable to the primary grades. The problems for which answers are needed are set in roman type; the experiences which help to solve the problems are set under them in italic type.

I. What foods do we need to help us to be healthy?

Talk about foods eaten at the school lunch; discuss the foods which make a good breakfast; display pictures or models of foods making a good breakfast, a good lunch, a good dinner; visit a neighborhood market to see the variety of fruits and vegetables and see how many the children can identify; plan a simple tasting party to try different foods; decide what the group should do to improve food practices.

II. How can we tell we are growing?

Weigh children and measure heights and provide a simple form on which the child can record his height and weight (this is a good activity for the third grade); discuss things which help children to grow (food, rest, activity, avoiding disease); weigh again at end of one month, two months, three months, and add each to record, then have children make comparisons to see changes.

III. How do we protect our bodies in changing seasons?

Plan use of proper clothing appropriate to weather and season; check to see if coats, boots, caps, and other outerwear are in places provided for them during school hours; talk about ways homes and schoolrooms are kept comfortable in cold weather and in warm weather; invite the custodian to tell how he keeps the school at an even temperature.

IV. How can we see that we get enough sleep?

Discuss how boys and girls feel and behave when they have not had enough sleep; ask the nurse how many hours of sleep she thinks children need each night; show number of hours needed for sleep on a cardboard clock face; talk about things which keep children from getting enough sleep (television programs, visitors, playing late, etc.); decide at what time children should go to bed on school nights; select ways to remind children of bed time.

V. How do we help to keep our teeth strong?

Find out why children get a second set of teeth; discuss the importance of keeping teeth clean; using a model, show how teeth should be brushed—if practical, have children supplied with toothbrushes and have them practice correct method of brushing teeth; find out why candy is bad for teeth; find out what the dentist does to keep teeth strong (film, slides, visit from dentist or dental hygienist, charts, pictures); visit a dentist's office to see what he does (if feasible); decide what children should do to keep their teeth strong.

As children enter the second and third grades their environment extends increasingly to include not only personal living practices but also the wider relationships of community living. The following health experiences are based upon the child's interest in community workers and community-wide functions and activities. Children in the second and third grades can experience many health learnings revolving around the bakery, dairy, fireman, policeman, physician, dentist, nurse, sanitarian, and custodian. As before, the problems for which answers are needed are set in roman type; the experiences which help to solve the problems are set under them in italic type.

I. How is milk produced, transported, and delivered to our homes and grocery stores?

Discuss importance of clean, sweet milk as a food for everyone; find out where cows are kept that produce the milk for our city or town; if possible, visit a dairy farm and see how cows are kept clean, how they are milked, how milk is cooled and placed in containers ready for collection; if milk is pasteurized and placed in individual containers at the same location, observe this operation; discuss importance of various steps in the production and marketing of milk; find out the conditions under which milk can spread disease.

II. Similar problems relating to bread making, meat processing, and food refrigeration and storage may be undertaken.

Similar experiences appropriate to the problem may be developed.

III. How are we protected from fire?

Discuss the proper use and storage of matches; find out how the school's fire alarm works; take a trip around the school to observe fire safety equipment; participate in a fire drill; discuss what happens when a fire gets out of control; find out where the nearest fire station is located.

IV. How do policemen keep us safe?

Invite a policeman to tell how he helps keep everyone safe (use policeman who controls traffic at school crossings if one is available); find out where the nearest police station is located; discuss why policemen are friends and protectors of boys and girls.

V. Who are some of the people who help us to stay healthy?

Talk about ways that the physician helps us to be healthy; if feasible, invite a physician to school to talk to the class (a father of a class member or a school physician would most probably be available); discuss ways the dentist helps children; invite a nurse to tell children how she helps to keep them well; ask the sanitarian or the custodian to tell about his work in the school.

VI. How do we help to prevent diseases and infections?

Find out why it is important to take care of cuts, scratches, and other injuries properly; demonstrate first aid for a small cut or a skinned knee; ask the nurse to show how to wash hands properly and why it is important; talk about the reasons why children should be immunized (if immunizations are done at school, plan for questions and answers both prior to and following the experience); find out why it is important to use garbage containers and sanitary facilities when on a picnic, hike, or trip away from home.

The methods used in health teaching are similar to those utilized in other aspects of the primary-grade curriculum. Seeing, hearing, talking, reading, touching, tasting, smelling, manipulating, constructing, dramatizing, planning, executing, and evaluating are the ways in which children learn. The materials of instruction are legion and their careful selection is important in facilitating learning. Chapter Twelve provides additional information on methods, materials, and resources.

EVALUATION

Evaluation is an integral part of teaching and should be a continuous process if effective learning is to take place. In the early grades it is important that teachers and children continually evaluate learning experiences to discover whether established goals have been attained.

The goals of health education are varied. Objectives are formulated not only around desired knowledge or health concepts but also around *doing* and *feeling*. The values and purposes are concerned with the way each child understands, what he does, and how he feels. Therefore, in evaluating the health education program, the teacher considers the progress of each child and is sensitive in appraising, planning, and teaching so that health experiences will have a real impact upon the child and will influence his behavior in a positive way.

The essential aspects of evaluation in health education are the same as those necessary for good program planning:

1. The teacher formulates purposes or objectives based upon the health needs of the group.

2. The teacher selects possible experiences which will meet these needs most effectively.

3. The teacher creates an environment of learning, so that the children and teacher can plan together for possible sequence and direction of experiences.

4. The teacher selects those methods of evaluation which will determine most satisfactorily the progress toward objectives and help in planning for a more effective program and greater learnings.

Evaluation takes place at opportune times. The children are given every opportunity to evaluate experiences as the needs arise. Future plans depend upon what has already been done. In the kindergarten and primary grades much time is spent in identifying new needs of individuals and of the group. All questions, ideas, and statements are considered. Through these experiences children learn to identify goals and plan for action.

Not all evaluation takes place in the classroom. Opportunities are provided for parents and teachers to work together to evaluate health teaching programs, identify problems, and plan for new experiences. Through parent-teacher conferences and other methods of reporting pupil progress, parents and teachers can work together constantly in trying to determine needs and to clarify objectives for future experiences.

This continuous process of evaluation by pupils, teachers, parents, and other persons interested in the behavior of children is fundamental in education. The accumulated results of the various aspects of evaluation provide the teacher with the information needed for the planning of a more effective program for changing health behavior. Chapter Thirteen discusses the evaluation of health education in greater detail.

SELECTED REFERENCES

ALHAMBRA CITY SCHOOL, ELEMENTARY CURRICULUM OFFICE. *Orienting the Child to the School Community. First Grade.* Alhambra, Calif.: the School, June 1958. 26 p. (Mimeo.)

ASSOCIATION FOR SUPERVISION AND CURRICULUM DEVELOPMENT. *Creating a Good Environment for Learning.* 1954 Yearbook. Washington, D.C.: the Association, a department of the National Education Association, 1954. 303 p.

BAXTER, BERNICE; LEWIS, GERTRUDE; and CROSS, GERTRUDE. *Elementary Education.* Boston: D. C. Heath & Co., 1952. 371 p.

BEAUCHAMP, GEORGE A. *Planning the Elementary School Curriculum.* Boston: Allyn & Bacon, 1956. 295 p.

CALIFORNIA STATE DEPARTMENT OF EDUCATION. *Education in Early Childhood.* Sacramento: the Department, 1956. 752 p.

COMMISSION ON TEACHER EDUCATION. *Helping Teachers Understand Children.* Washington, D.C.: American Council on Education, 1945. 468 p.

FLORIDA STATE DEPARTMENT OF EDUCATION. *Better Health for Florida's Children.* State Department Bulletin 4E. Tallahassee: the Department, February 1957. 101 p.

GANS, ROMA, and OTHERS. *Teaching Young Children.* Yonkers, N.Y.: World Book Co., 1952. 454 p.

GREAT NECK PUBLIC SCHOOLS. *Science Experiences Related to Social Studies. Kindergarten—Three.* Great Neck, N.Y.: the Schools, August 1957. 18 p. (Mimeo.)

GROUT, RUTH E. *Health Teaching in Schools.* Third edition. Philadelphia: W. B. Saunders Co., 1958. 359 p.

HYMES, JAMES L., JR. *Child Development Point of View.* Englewood Cliffs, N.J.: Prentice-Hall, 1955. 145 p.

HYMES, JAMES L., JR. *Effective Home-School Relations.* Englewood Cliffs, N.J.: Prentice-Hall, 1958. 264 p.

KUHLEN, RAYMOND G., and THOMPSON, GEORGE. *Psychological Studies of Human Development.* New York: Appleton-Century-Crofts, 1952. 399 p.

LOS ANGELES CITY SCHOOLS. *Guidance in Elementary Schools. A Handbook for Teachers.* Publication No. 439, revised. Los Angeles: the Schools, 1957. 157 p.

NATIONAL EDUCATION ASSOCIATION, DEPARTMENT OF ELEMENTARY SCHOOL PRINCIPALS. *Health in the Elementary School.* Twenty-Ninth Yearbook. Washington, D.C.: the Department, 1950. 383 p.

ROGERS, DOROTHY. *Mental Hygiene in Elementary Education.* Boston: Houghton Mifflin Co., 1957. 458 p.

SCHNEIDER, ELSA, and MCNEELY, SIMON A. *Teachers Contribute to Child Health.* Department of Health, Education, and Welfare, Office of Education, Bulletin 1951, No. 8. Washington, D.C.: Superintendent of Documents, Government Printing Office, 1951. 44 p.

SMITH, HELEN NORMAN, and WOLVERTON, MARY E. *Health Education in the Elementary School.* New York: Ronald Press Co., 1959. 359 p.

STRANG, RUTH. *Helping Children Solve Problems.* Chicago: Science Research Associates, 1953. 48 p.

WILLGOOSE, CARL E. *Health Education in the Elementary School.* Philadelphia: W. B. Saunders Co., 1959. 450 p.

the Intermediate Grades

Because the needs of pupils in the intermediate grades are many and varied, health teaching for this age group can be interesting and challenging. Interests of these pupils are expanding from their own narrow world, centered in themselves and their immediate environments, to the wider world that circles the globe, and to the worlds about them in outer space. These students are ready for simple problem solving. They come to school with some knowledge of educational procedures, with the basic skills necessary to the pursuit of learning, and with the first elementary techniques for group work. They are at a new level of maturity. They are eager and curious, and they have unbounded zest for activities that capture their imagination and enthusiasm. They will explore many avenues in search of the exact answers to their questions. These pupils like to experiment. They can learn to work in groups and committees, thereby utilizing their penchant for "gang" and group activity.

The ingenious teacher, eager to vitalize teaching beyond texts and outlines, need only center planning around his group of 9- to 12-year-olds to find important needs to be met, real life situations to be faced, and challenging problems to be solved. With teacher and pupils together setting goals, deciding on ways to achieve them, executing their plans, and evaluating their success, a more dynamic health education program for the middle grades will take shape. It can be one that will provide significant learning experiences.

In the modern school, in which the teacher is regarded as a professional person who helps to set goals and purposes, in which courses of study and textbooks are considered as tools and teaching aids rather than as immutable requirements, and in which *how* the child learns is of equal importance with *what* he learns, much is demanded of the teacher. Responsibility in health education as well as in other areas of teaching has shifted from merely covering prescribed subject matter to organizing a variety of curricular experiences for a particular grade. As Lee and Lee point out:

> The teacher is no longer regimented to the teaching of a prescribed course of study and a given text-book. She has become the guide to the learning-experiences of children; she has become the "director of curriculum" in her classroom. The traditional program required of the teacher primarily a knowledge of the subject matter she was to teach. The newer program requires much more. It requires a much broader knowledge of children, the way they grow, their interests, their emotions, and the way they learn. It requires an understanding of profitable learning experiences and the way to organize and present them. It requires that the teacher utilize all these factors and forces in providing an educational program.[1]

It is no small task to guide the health learning experiences for a specific grade. The teacher who becomes involved in the process finds rich rewards in the heightened interest such experiences engender in the health teaching. When the core of the health curriculum is made up of purposeful activities and meaningful problems which the pupils have helped to plan, they find freshness and vitality in the teaching material and show enthusiasm toward it.

For the classroom curriculum builder the preceding chapters of this book are a source of information regarding today's health problems on which to base content. They supply needed information relating to the characteristics of preadolescents, and to recent findings and theories on how learning takes place. Against the backdrop of theory, this chapter will outline the practical steps to be taken in setting up meaningful health learning experiences for preadolescents. To do this it will consider such problems as:

What can be accomplished through health teaching in the intermediate grades? What are the purposes? The goals? How are these determined?

How may the health needs and interests of pupils be discovered? Their personal needs? Their social needs? How may these findings be used?

What are procedures for selecting and organizing health learning experiences?

What learning activities have been found most useful for this age group?

[1] Lee, J. Murray, and Lee, Dorris M. *The Child and His Curriculum.* Second edition. New York: Appleton-Century-Crofts, 1950. 710 p.

These are some of the questions frequently asked by teachers of the intermediate grades. This chapter will center its consideration of the broader topics of health content, teaching procedures, materials, and resources around these questions.

SETTING GOALS

Emphases

It is generally agreed that emphasis in the primary grades should be given to the establishment of *sound health practices* and that many of these should be a part of daily living routines by the time the pupil reaches the intermediate grades. With its emphasis on motivation, modern psychology reminds us that *attitudes* are prebehavioral, and that attention must be given to pupils' feelings, interests, and purposes due to their effect on readiness for practice. At the primary level today, attitude building as a basis for practice is accorded priority over other goals. Specific *factual information* is acquired as a concomitant of the broad health program carried out in today's primary school, but the emphasis is not on subject matter as such.

When pupils enter the fourth grade, they manifest various stages of achievement in the aspects of health education previously cited—practices, attitudes, and knowledge—depending not only on what the school has attempted to do, but also on family standards, attitudes, discipline, and other manifestations of family culture. Since health practices and health attitudes are personal in nature and often cause conflicting drives and motives, they cannot be counted on to be either automatic or fully established when pupils complete their primary education. Both health attitudes and health practices continue to be the concern of teachers and pupils of the intermediate grades. New emphasis will be given to the health understandings on which practice rests. The "why" and the "how" are added to the "what" of everyday health behavior.

The emphasis on health understandings with related content material in the intermediate grades is consistent with the curiosities and interests of children in understanding themselves and the world around them. These curiosities and interests are basic to the entire science program, of which health science often becomes a part. The nature of body organs and processes and an elementary understanding of the progress which has been made in medical and allied sciences hold absorbing interest for boys and girls in this age group, as their capacity to reason unfolds and develops. This is the period when elementary anatomy and physiology are of interest to children; when questions about the stomach, heart, lungs, and liver are frequent and fascinating; when understanding and respect for the human body can be nourished. The heightened interest in all aspects of the environment, the curiosity about why things happen and what makes them so, and the avidity for "research" in satisfying their interests provide natural motivation for children to learn such essential health information as is meaningful at this stage of growth and development.

Briefly, then, preadolescent pupils can be guided in developing attitudes of appreciation and responsibility for their own health and the health of others. They can be helped to live healthfully, and they can be provided with health learning experiences that will broaden their understanding of the factors underlying personal and community health practices.

Finding the Health Needs of Preadolescent Pupils

In keeping with the best educational practice, health learning experiences at any level are based on the needs and interests of the learners. The classroom teacher outlining a year's health teaching plan should remember that these needs must be specific for his pupils, if the activities and experiences based on them are to be meaningful. This involves preliminary fact-finding as a basis for determining the year's objectives.

Some questions the teacher may ask are these:

What are the pupils' present habits and practices?

What kinds of accidents do these pupils have? Where and under what circumstances do they occur?

What health problems necessitate absence from classes?

What are the past health education experiences of the pupils?

What health understandings do they have now?

What present misconceptions militate against the establishment of needed health practices?

What maturation needs are of concern within the group?

What health problems are demanding the attention of the local community?

Which of these would be meaningful to 9- to 12-year-olds?

Are there significant family health problems?

What recurring health situations do these boys and girls face?

Which will they have to meet in the foreseeable future?

If the classroom teacher can answer questions such as these, he is in a position to begin outlining the scope of his health education activities.

There are many acceptable methods for securing the basic health data for a specific class. One of the best is the teacher's *continuous observation* of his pupils. A primary purpose of observation is to note deviations from normal health and well-being. A second purpose is to utilize observation as a basis for curriculum planning. Habits of cleanliness practiced by pupils, their usual good posture or lack of it, the suitability of their clothing for changing weather conditions, the use of glasses by those who require them, the kinds and types of lunches carried to or purchased at school, the safety practices of pupils, and other persistent behaviors may need to be changed in the interest of well-being. *Conferences* with the nurse who serves the school, with the physician, and with parents may add to the teacher's understanding of the health of his group.

Surveys of present health practices are used in many school systems to establish a baseline for teaching activities and measurement of progress. The three-day diet survey in which each pupil records all food eaten during a specific time period is one of the most commonly used. Records of health practices taken at random periods may also produce useful information, especially concerning habits practiced at home.

In modern school systems there are *records* that can provide a ready source of help in answering the teacher's question, "What are the specific health problems of my pupils?" Cumulative records, including records of health examinations, screening tests, health histories, reports from the school psychologist or guidance staff, and reports from previous teachers or from the nurse may be available and are sources of health information. Teachers can use various sociometric tests or employ *The Friendship Test*,[2] the results of which help to give new insights into group adjustment problems and to bring into focus pupils who are isolated from the class social structure. Records of school absences and accidents may uncover specific health problems for

---

[2] Published by and available from Scott, Foresman & Co., Chicago, Illinois.

class use. The local police department can supply needed information about highway and traffic accidents in the area.

The criticism that health education courses are repetitive and lack the sequence desired in a good educational program has often been made by general educators. Pupils call it "the same old stuff." Planning within the school and an awareness of content and experiences for health teaching suggested for different grades will help to eliminate excessive repetition and fill gaps in the health teaching program. Teachers intent on developing a sequential health program will want to become familiar with the recommended continuity of experiences and explore both the experiential and educational backgrounds of the class. *Paper-and-pencil tests of health information and health attitudes* have been used for this purpose, although most of the published tests in this category have been designed for secondary-school use.* Tests of health superstitions and false beliefs may be used with sixth-graders to find specific needs for correct, scientific information.

Second only to the personal needs of the class are the needs of the community of which the school is a part. Those needs which can be understood by pupils in the middle grades naturally will receive priority, as will those which can be integrated with, or aligned to, the personal health problems being studied. Community health needs often are unique because of their regional or geographical origin. Others will be found to be of importance in any community all of the time, or some of the time. Normally, farming accidents are not a worthwhile problem for consideration in a mining community or in a metropolitan area. On the other hand, dental health problems and the concomitant need for fluoridation of drinking water are important throughout the country. Community tasks such as the provision of clean water, sanitary sewage disposal, clean eating places, safe beaches in lake and coastal regions; the control of insect vectors of disease; pasteurization of milk; food protection against filth or chemical contamination; and measures for the control of communicable diseases are continuing programs in all localities. They are not beyond the understanding of intermediate grade pupils when taught at the appropriate level.

The teacher who has studied the personal needs of his pupils thoroughly will also want to survey health problems and needs

---

* See Chapter Twelve.

of the local community. Information secured from the local health officer or agent of the board of health and from members of the area health council and officials of various health agencies will acquaint the teacher with those health problems in the area which are considered important. The daily or weekly newspaper, the minutes of the town meeting or of the city council, and various health reports are also good sources of information. Not all problems found will be suitable for consideration by children in the intermediate grades, but the teacher's survey of the situation will give him a broader understanding of the community and invaluable health information to supplement his background. Boys and girls can help to select the community health problems which they understand and which are of interest to them.

This firsthand study of needs and problems will always be the teacher's best source of pertinent data for development of significant learning experiences. However, the classic sources of information, such as research studies, published reports of the United States Public Health Service, the National Education Association Research Division, the Metropolitan Life Insurance Company, the National Safety Council, state and local health departments, the American Medical Association, and the American Dental Association, as well as expert opinion expressed in yearbooks, textbooks, and other similar works, will furnish extremely useful leads for determining the health problems of school-age children on a national basis. It should be recognized that the teacher need not always "start from scratch" in determining health needs of boys and girls. The considerable amount of literature on child development, together with the body of health knowledge and principles established as the result of research and experience, provides a common basis for planning health teaching programs for preadolescent children, regardless of where they live. Coupled with analysis of the health needs of a specific group of children, these provide the teacher with the information he needs to plan a truly significant program in health education.

This method of studying the health needs and problems of a particular class may be used to uncover the total range of pupil health problems or it may be used to uncover those in a specialized area. The following outline indicates the application of this method to the area of safety.

*Aids in Setting Objectives and Preparing
a Teaching Program in Safety Education*[3]

A. Survey of present program
  1. Analysis of legal requirements
  2. Analysis of types and extent of previous education in safety.
B. Determination of the safety problems of the age group
  1. Analysis of accident records of age group
     a. Frequency and types of accidents
     b. Time of accidents
     c. Accident trends
  2. Analysis of environmental hazards to discover exposure to accidents
     a. Analysis of school hazards
        (1) Buildings
        (2) Grounds
        (3) Equipment
        (4) Transportation
     b. Analysis of home hazards
        (1) Socioeconomic status
        (2) Types of homes
        (3) Location of homes
     c. Analysis of community hazards
        (1) Population (size of community)
        (2) Type—rural, urban, industrial, agricultural
        (3) Transportation
        (4) Recreational facilities
        (5) Street hazards
        (6) Industries
        (7) Accident frequency at certain danger spots
  3. Analysis of activities of children by season to determine probable exposure to accidents
     a. In school
        (1) Types of activities
        (2) Frequency of accidents
     b. Out of school
        (1) Types of recreational activities
        (2) Frequency and types of accidents

---

[3] Adapted from: American Association of Teachers Colleges and National Commission on Safety Education. *Safety Education for Teachers. Part Two. A Guide for College Instructors of Safety Education.* Washington, D.C.: National Education Association, 1947. p. 66-69.

4. Analysis of safety responsibilities in the home, school, and community

5. Techniques for determining safety problems

  a. Study of available accident records

    (1) School accident reports

    (2) Reports from local and state safety organizations

    (3) Police, motor vehicle, and fire department reports

    (4) Health department reports

    (5) Reports of supervisors of recreational departments

    (6) Reports of insurance companies

  b. Systematic surveys

    (1) Checklists

    (2) Home inspection blanks

    (3) Bicycle counts

  c. Questionnaires

    (1) Children

    (2) Parents

  d. Inquiry or personal interviews with

    (1) Recreational supervisors

    (2) Teachers

    (3) Police

    (4) Fire chiefs

    (5) Physicians

    (6) Nurses

    (7) Parents

  e. Observations

  f. Diary records.

C. Comparison of findings with experience of similar groups: analysis of courses of study and textbooks.

D. Analysis of characteristics and interests of age group.

E. Survey of community agencies interested in promoting safety, their programs, and aids for schools.

Determining the Health Interests of Pupils

It has often been said that "health" per se is of primary interest only to the sick in search of well-being. Nevertheless, since self-interest and self-preservation are of paramount importance to all human beings, much of the content material of health can be linked to the natural curiosities of growing boys and girls. Many of the questions they ask indicate at least an acquired interest in health subject matter as this ties in with their everyday experiences:

Do we have to eat cereal every day for breakfast?

Is there any special food that must be eaten every day?

How do Japanese, Chinese, Mexicans, and others have good health, since they don't eat the same foods we eat?

Can you see a vitamin?

Where does the air you breathe go to?

Why do we have to have inoculations?

Why did Pat get measles when I didn't?

My mother's sick with "the virus." What's that?

Why did some of the people get ill at the church supper when others didn't?

Our textbook says we should have adequate light for reading. What is adequate light?

Do we have adequate light in our schoolroom?

How is milk pasteurized?

Why can't we drink from a clean-looking stream when we're on our camping trip?

My father had malaria when he was overseas. Will I catch it?

Why do people say you shouldn't swim after eating a full meal?

These and similar questions asked by children in the intermediate grades indicate pupil interests that have a definite potential for health teaching. They likewise indicate that the teacher who will be able to help children find answers to their questions must keep abreast of scientific, accurate health information. If a number of these questions cluster around a particular problem or topic, this may indicate more than temporary interest and perhaps point to a recognized need for understanding on the part of pupils.

Surveys of Health Interests

Paper-and-pencil tests of health interests are often used as a basis for planning the health curriculum in a school system as well as in charting the health education activities in a classroom. Most health interests are acquired rather than innate and therefore are dependent on environmental factors and past experiences. For these reasons, surveys of health interests will vary from one group to another, although some interests seem to be almost universal among children in the middle grades. These are the interests rooted in the nature of the child and in the expectations of the culture.

The pioneer Denver study of health interests of children, first published in 1947 and reissued in 1954,[4] indicated that the most frequently checked interest among boys in the fourth, fifth, and sixth grades was "to learn how to build muscles" and among girls it was "to wear clean clothes." Without doubt, both of these are an outgrowth of the expectations of family and peer culture, and when the Denver test has been used in other cities and situations, similar expressions of interest in these items have been encountered. Other items of great interest to children in Denver when the test was first given are not repeated in new situations because some of the experiences which produced the interest in Denver have not been a part of the lives of children in other communities. The survey proved valuable in pointing out not only the content areas of interest to Denver children but also the methods preferred in learning. Content areas of major interest included safety and first aid, how the body works, cleanliness and grooming (girls), social adjustment and popularity (girls), muscle building and sports participation (boys). Methods preferred revolved around "doing" rather than listening or memorizing.

Systematic methods of uncovering and recording health interests of pupils can be fruitful in planning teaching emphases and activities. Tests for this purpose are more likely to be helpful when locally developed and administered. Such tests are valuable because they reveal the nature and extent of health interests beyond the evidence of interest shown by an oral question from an individual pupil. The wise teacher will utilize both the spontaneous question and the planned survey as guides for health teaching.

What the Intermediate-Grade Pupil Needs To Know

A survey of the needs and problems of a particular class will identify specific needs for that specific group. Results from many such surveys indicate that in general pupils of this age group need to know some of the following:

[4] Denver Public Schools. *Health Interests of Children; a Report of a Research Study.* Revised edition. Denver: Colorado Board of Education, 1954. 121 p.

How to avoid accidents

How to avoid disease and infections

How to accept themselves and make the best adjustment possible to defects or limitations

That all people have fears, anxieties, conflicts, and frustrations which must be faced and resolved in an acceptable manner

How to establish themselves with their peers

How to improve their interpersonal relationships

How to care for their teeth and maintain good dental health

How to select an adequate diet, even on a limited budget. The relationship between food, rest, exercise, sleep, fresh air, good emotional health, and nutrition

How bodies function—as much information as called for by their interests, the problem under consideration, and their maturity

How the community protects the health of the people

Why simple everyday health practices are important; the scientific reasons underlying health behavior

How to begin to take responsibility for their own health

The relationship between health and health behavior.

Problem Areas for Health Instruction

A study of the health needs and interests of pupils will show that the problems can be grouped into categories. An examination of various state and city courses of study or teachers guides in health education reveals that the categories or areas of health instruction recommended for the intermediate grades generally include most of the following:

1. Nutrition and growth

2. Activity, body dynamics (posture and body control), rest, relaxation, recreation

3. Cleanliness, grooming

4. Care of eyes, ears, and teeth

5. Mental and emotional health and social adjustment

6. Structure and function of the human body (including reproduction)

7. Protection against infection and disease

8. Accident prevention (safety) and first aid

9. Environmental health in home, school, and community

10. Evaluating health services and health products.

This grouping of problems into related areas does not mean that teaching of health subject matter as such is necessary. The starting point is the problem or situation to be met which will require subject matter from various areas of health science for its solution. The question, problem, responsibility, or situation serves as the focal point for integrating pertinent subject matter. Such groupings as those indicated facilitate planning the scope of the program by a teacher or group of teachers and the evaluation of the continuity and orderly progression of health learning experiences from one grade to the next. In the modern elementary school some of this health content material will be integrated into units under "Social Studies" or "Science," since health is considered an aspect of all living. Some will be taught through incidental instruction and some in specific health units. Whether the unit which is the vehicle for health instruction is labeled "Agriculture in the Twentieth Century," "Man's Conquest of Disease," or "Our Community," the health content requires definite planning in order to make its optimum contribution to health understandings.

Objectives and Goals

The task, then, of the teacher in the intermediate grades is:

To continue to build the attitude that health is important—important for those things which are meaningful for this age group—for growth, sports, fun, achievement, appearance, and important in some times and places, even for survival

To continue to build the attitude that through their everyday behavior pupils are increasingly responsible for their own health and for the health of others in their environment

To develop in pupils basic understandings in areas in which their recurring health problems and responsibilities lie: nutrition, emotional health, safety, prevention of infection, and promotion of health

To guide pupils in establishing such daily health practices as are essential for healthful living in the areas of emotional, social, and physical health

To teach pupils the first techniques of how to solve their health problems through the use of professional assistance available locally, through group planning and group activity, through understanding of sources of help and information, and through a knowledge of how action can be achieved.

ATTAINING THE OBJECTIVES

As soon as a classroom teacher has set the objectives for the year's health program, the structure of the program takes shape, since objectives indicate the direction in which growth in this area of learning will occur. The objectives set the limits within which teaching-learning experiences will be organized. They determine the content, procedures, and activities to be used in guiding the learning process. They state specifically the standards by which concurrent progress should be measured and the final evaluation made. For these reasons, the teacher in the intermediate grades will want to select his own objectives, using those suggested here or those found in various health texts and teachers guides as references only.

Motivation of the Learner

Although leads to the motivation of the learner have been discussed earlier in this chapter, as well as in other chapters of this book, the principles of motivation as they apply to the intermediate grades deserve reiteration here, since motivation is central to all effective health education. Earlier methods of motivation through the use of extrinsic rewards for health achievements have fallen into disrepute. Emphasis today is placed on intrinsic motivation, on the forces within the learner which move him to want to change his health behavior. Three of the procedures for motivating learners in this age group are inherent in modern teaching procedures. They are: (a) the use of fundamental drives within the learner to satisfy his basic needs for self-esteem, security, affection, acceptance, and recognition for achievement; (b) the utilization of group influences, since these youngsters usually do not change their attitudes and behavior for ones which run counter to the standards of their group (they may do this at a later age when maturity brings independence in thought and action); and (c) the building of group attitudes leading to the use of class or group decision to do something specific in relation to a health practice. These procedures require an opportunity for pupils to participate in decision making.[5]

The acceptance of the aforementioned data from studies of individual and social psychology necessitates the use of methods in which pupils are involved from the beginning of the learning process by taking an active part in planning their health units and selecting their health activities. Good teaching has always employed the principle of involving the learner not only through reading, recitation, and discussion, but also more recently through allowing pupils to set their goals, to plan how to achieve them, to carry out their plans, and, lastly, to evaluate the results of their experiences. These, carried out under the careful guidance of the teachers, are the first steps in good teaching.

Teacher-Pupil Planning

How is this method applied in the intermediate grades? A sixth-grade class, studying the importance of careful food handling in a community, had read the material in the textbook as a starting point for class discussion. In the discussion period questions were raised which the text did not answer. Several questions were concerned with local practices, rules, and regulations regarding food care. "Glib" answers could have been given by the teacher, but such answers would have been forgotten easily. Instead, he chose to make the follow-through on the pupils' curiosity a meaningful health learning experience for them.

Under the teacher's guidance many questions were correlated into several topical questions which would serve as the goals toward which basic understandings would be developed. They were:

How is the food which comes into our homes protected in local markets, shops, and stores?

How can we be sure that our food is safe for home use?

As the unit grew and developed, an interest was manifested in local eating places, such as restaurants, cafeterias, and drugstore counters, and the original goal was enlarged to include the added factor of "eating out." The question then became: How can we be certain that all the food we eat is safe and nutritious?

After the goal was clarified, planning proceeded to determine needed content and the methods of acquiring it. Questions raised

---

[5] Spencer, Mary E. "An Educator Talks About Motivating People." *Journal of the American Dietetic Association* 25: 209-12; March 1949.

by class members were listed on the board for later grouping under related headings. Examples of questions posed are:

Is the food in a small local market as safe as that in the larger supermarket?

How are meats cared for in any market?

How are meats refrigerated before they arrive at local markets?

What do the stamp marks on the meats mean? Are these required by law and, if so, why?

Could deteriorated meat be frozen and sold as good meat?

What are the local, state, and federal laws that apply to food sold locally?

Is homogenized milk better than Grade A milk?

How can we be sure that glasses and dishes used in restaurants are clean?

Why don't all public places use paper cups?

Are there any rules about salesclerks who handle bakery products?

Should we ask the salesclerks to use a tissue in handling muffins and other baked goods?

Should people with colds serve or handle food in the restaurant or hotel?

These and dozens of other equally worthwhile problems were posed by interested 11- and 12-year-olds during the exploratory period. After grouping the questions into categories, such as the care of food in transportation, the care of food in the market, the health of food handlers, local food regulations, and others, questions relating to ways of obtaining information were discussed as follows:

Would visits (field trips) to local establishments be worthwhile?

Should information be sought from the local health officer or from the state board of health?

Should various local persons be invited to talk to the group?

What material is available in pamphlets, regulations, articles, reference books?

Should the class as a whole plan a visit to a local market?

How could arrangements for such activities be made?

Discussion on methods of procedure finally led to a division of labor. Committees were selected, since they provided the best method of interviewing, visiting, and reporting back to the group as a whole.

As the last step in the planning process, decisions were made concerning the form in which both progress reports and the final report would be made to the entire class. Naturally, much interest was engendered because every pupil was an active member of a committee or group which had a job to do and on which the class as a whole depended. Best of all, the tasks were self-assigned.

HEALTH LEARNING EXPERIENCES

Selection

The learning experiences selected for pupils in the intermediate grades can be devoid of interest because they are largely verbalizations—reading and reciting; or they can be exciting and full of interest because they are meaningful to students at this age level. Health experiences which are meaningful for 9-, 10-, and 11-year-olds are those closely related to the satisfaction of children's needs as outlined earlier. These needs center around problems which occur in everyday life. They are experiences which bring pupil satisfactions—experiences which bring recognition, approval, and acceptance by their group, as well as other goals near to the desires of the preadolescent child. Meaningful experiences provide for a variety of activities, and these are life-centered rather than book-centered. Such experiences as learning how to brush teeth, fundamental in the primary grades, become trite and boring when presented again, even in a different guise, when children are older and should have mastered their ABC's in health as well as in the language arts. Real learning experiences are sufficiently challenging to stimulate the child's best efforts as well as his passing curiosity. They result in changed perceptions, new meanings, broader understandings, useful attitudes, and improved behavior.

Organization

There are many ways of organizing learning experiences. The most commonly used, although frequently a combination of methods, is found in what is called the subject matter unit.

The experience unit, commonly called the unit, begins with the needs and purposes of the learner. A problem, purpose, or life situation, such as one or more of the following, is the starting point of the experience unit.

Do the kinds of food I eat make a difference?

How can I overcome my fear of dogs?

How can we make our homes safe?

What can we do to reduce the number of colds in our class this year?

How can tooth decay be reduced?

The use of this kind of unit calls for teacher-pupil planning, a wide variety of experiences, the use of many resources, and some method of determining whether or not pupils have achieved their goal. In searching for answers and solutions it is necessary to cut across subject matter lines as these become integrated through the activities carried on.

The subject matter unit is usually planned in advance, but the initiation of the unit may follow an expression of interest or concern by the learner. The teacher may employ a number of ways of stimulating questions and arousing interest, for example, by showing a film, posting interesting pictures on the bulletin board, or reading a news story. Teacher-pupil planning, variety of experiences, and use of many resources occur in the well-organized and skillfully taught subject matter unit whether the unit is concerned with "The Conquest of Communicable Diseases," "The Heart and How It Works," "The Discovery of Vitamins," or with some other subject vital to the total learning experience. In the hands of an effective teacher it is often difficult to distinguish between the organization of the experience unit and a series of activities organized around a subject matter unit.

In some school systems subject matter lines have disappeared and the majority of class activities are grouped around such "centers of interest" as "Home and Family Living," "Home and School Life," "The Neighborhood," or "The City." Health instruction, in the curriculum of such schools, is integrated throughout the various units in which man's food, clothing, shelter, and other needs are considered. In this type of organization health instruction is principally an aspect of social studies.

An examination of courses of study used in health education throughout the country shows that all three of these forms of organization are in current use. Perhaps the unit method is regarded more favorably in educational circles because it comes closer to what is known about how children learn. The intermediate grades usually mark the point at which definite units in health instruction begin to appear. Their number is many and their content varied. One such course of study lists the following units for intermediate grades:

Our health examination

How are we growing?

The making of an athlete

Choosing meals that work for you

Does food make a difference?

Gateways to the mind

Our hobby show

Getting ready for junior high school—our inventory time

The fluoridation story.[6]

The development of a unit on dental health is illustrated in the following account.

A Sixth-Grade Class Studies Dental Health

A community was holding a series of citizens' meetings to discuss the pros and cons of adding fluoride to its water supply as a partial preventive of tooth decay. To find out if there really was a tooth decay problem, the local dentists conducted a survey of the teeth of all elementary-school children.

The sixth-grade classroom teacher discussed the survey with her pupils, and together they decided they would like to know about the findings relating to the children in their class. A committee of pupils was appointed to obtain information on the survey. The classroom committee found that the results of the study were available from the chairman of the survey committee. Since the findings of the survey were tabulated by age of pupils, the children decided that they wanted the information on 11- and 12-year-olds.

The chairman of the survey told the class committee that the average 11-year-old had 2 decayed teeth, 0.4 missing teeth, and 3 filled teeth. The average 12-year-old had 2.9 decayed teeth, 0.7

---

[6] Malden School Committee. *Teachers Guide to the School Health Curriculum.* Malden, Mass.: the Committee, 1960. p. 370-74.

missing teeth, and 4 filled teeth. These figures applied only to the permanent teeth. The survey had also revealed that the teeth of the children in the community were probably neither better nor worse than those of children in other communities in which the water had not been fluoridated.

The committee's report led to a more detailed study of dental health by the class. The children, with the teacher's guidance, listed the following things about which they wanted to learn more:

What causes tooth decay?

Can tooth decay be prevented? If so, how?

Why does a tooth have to be removed?

What happens when a tooth is lost?

What causes "crooked" teeth?

How can "crooked" teeth be corrected?

Can "crooked" teeth be prevented?

Is toothbrushing really helpful?

Does use of toothpaste prevent tooth decay?

Does fluoridation of water supplies prevent tooth decay?

How does food affect the teeth?

Are the "baby" or first teeth important?

The children decided upon these activities to obtain the needed information:

Search health and science textbooks.

Write to organizations for pamphlets, charts, and other material.

Contact local or state health department.

Talk with personal dentist.

Draw cross sectional pictures of a tooth. Show how tooth decay progresses.

Borrow models of teeth and extracted teeth from dentist.

Survey class to find out how many have been to the dentist in the last year. Do this in a way to embarrass no one.

Make a study of modern dental care as compared with that of 50 years ago.

Find out what nearby towns have fluorine added to their water supply and how dental health of other children compares with own.

When study is almost completed, invite a dentist to help solve unanswered problems.

The class was formed into committees, with each assigned specific problems and questions. Reports were made; discussions were held. The important new information included in the reports can be summarized as follows:

Tooth decay is caused by bacteria acting on sugar to produce an acid; this acid dissolves the tooth enamel. Thus begins decay.

It is important not to eat too many sweets, especially between meals. Eating sweets gives cavities a chance to start.

Decay does not heal itself like a cut. Only a dentist can repair the damage.

Acid is formed from sugar minutes after you eat it. This is why it is important to brush the teeth right after you eat. If you cannot brush your teeth, rinse your mouth vigorously with water.

A cavity that is not filled by a dentist will get deeper; finally an abscess will be formed, and the tooth must be removed.

Regular visits to the dentist at least once a year, and preferably every six months, will save money and, what is more important, will help prevent the loss of teeth. Teeth, properly cared for, can last a lifetime.

Teeth can often be prevented from becoming irregular or "crooked" by regular dental care. A special dentist called an orthodontist can correct irregular teeth.

Irregular teeth may make a child self-conscious and can affect his whole personal appearance.

The primary teeth should be retained until they are ready to come out because they save space for the permanent teeth. This helps prevent malocclusion ("crooked" teeth).

Cavities can be filled without much discomfort, especially if they are small. A dentist uses x-ray pictures to help find cavities when they are small.

Use of toothpaste cannot prevent tooth decay. It is brushing that is important, because it helps remove food particles from around the teeth and gums.

Fluoride, a chemical, added to water supplies can prevent much decay.

Fluoride solutions can also be painted on teeth to help prevent decay where water is not fluoridated.

How can this knowledge be put into action?

Substitute such things as fresh fruits, milk, nuts, and meat sandwiches for sweets, particularly between meals.

Brush the teeth right after eating instead of before breakfast and before going to bed.

When it is impossible to brush the teeth after a meal, rinse the mouth with water.

Obtain dental care regularly.

As a culminating activity, mothers were invited to visit the class. A report of the dental health project was given. This was followed by a lunch prepared in accord with what was learned about the cause of tooth decay.

To evaluate the dental health lesson, the usual paper-and-pencil test was given. In addition, the class members agreed to report on their dental health practices at the end of the following month. This report was to cover food habits, toothbrushing habits, and visits to the dentist. The pupils were also asked to write an evaluation of what they thought they had gained from the study. The most obvious result was the interest and enthusiasm for what had previously been to them a dull, uninteresting subject.

METHODS AND TOOLS FOR TEACHING

Irrespective of the kind of organization of learning experience which exists in a classroom, today's outstanding health instruction programs in the intermediate grades are marked by three characteristics: (a) They are experiential programs in which the learner is involved in listening, reading, finding information, solving problems, answering questions, or sharing his findings with others. Judicious use of reading and listening are important in the learning process, but the passive listening class, or the mere reading of pages in the health text, have little to recommend them. (b) Audio-visual methods of teaching are used more extensively to provide, if not firsthand experience, at least a reasonable facsimile of it. (c) There is wider use of community resources. School and community have come closer together as the school goes out into the community to seek the life situation, and the community comes to the school with its resource personnel and materials to enrich the quality of the learning experience.

Activities

Some of the health instruction activities in which pupils in the intermediate grades engage include:

Conducting animal feeding experiments and experiments to test for food nutrients

Taking field trips to local dairies, markets, restaurants, bakeries, water supply and sewage treatment plants, and to housing projects

Visiting museums

Preparing charts and graphs for visualizing class statistics, such as absence due to colds or school accidents

Making pin maps of sources of mosquitoes, rubbish depositories, and slum areas

Making health posters

Setting up room and corridor health exhibits

Preparing health bulletin boards and displays

Making murals and dioramas

Maintaining class temperature charts

Arranging a library corner of health materials on the subject being studied

Using sources of printed material—reference books, texts, bulletins, newspapers, and magazines—for the study of a particular topic

Giving reports in various ways—chalkboard talks, dramatizations, role-playing, panels

Serving on the safety patrol

Joining the bicycle safety club

Participating in a home or school clean-up campaign

Planning menus

Preparing meals for class mothers or other guests

Sharing health programs with primary grades

Securing a health examination

Having all dental corrections made

Taking inoculations

Keeping records of growth through charts or graphs

Keeping diaries of health practices

Studying text or references to find answers to problems

Thinking through solutions to problems

Applying in daily practices health principles learned.

Audio-Visual Methods

To bring reality closer to the learner, audio-visual methods of teaching are being used with increased frequency at this age level. The health filmstrip, film, or slide is a part of and not a substitute for teaching. For most effective use the class must be prepared for the viewing as they are for the field trip by having an objective and certain things to look for, or questions to answer. Following the showing, class discussion clarifies moot points, extends information, and summarizes the understanding to be taught by the use of this method. There should always be a reason for the use of a film or a filmstrip, and its use should be determined after previewing by the teacher to decide on its suitability for the purpose and the age group in question. For a complete discussion of audio-visual methods and materials the reader is referred to Chapter Twelve.

Wider Use of the Community

Health instruction today shares with other areas of instruction the exploration and use of the local community as a rich resource for teaching. The field trip, the interview, and the conference find a place among the techniques of learning used in grades 4, 5, and 6 as well as in the junior and senior high schools. Again, these are methods which should be decided on in the teacher-pupil planning period in answer to the questions: Is this the best method of obtaining the information? Will the use of these techniques provide deeper and richer experiences for boys and girls than reading or class discussion? Through its governmental and voluntary health agencies, and through its professional people, every community provides many resources which should be increasingly tapped as pupils grow into a maturity sufficient to profit from their use.

Using a Health Textbook

A good health text can render much service for the finest of teachers if it is acknowledged as the teaching tool that it is. In the hands of the neophyte, however, the use of the text can degenerate into the hearing of a passive reading lesson. Health instruction is not instruction in reading, and reading aloud from a health text is not even good reading instruction. Unfortunately, too many teachers utilize today's modern health texts without benefit of the accompanying teachers manuals which are replete with worthwhile suggestions. As a result, the health period becomes a dull, perfunctory reading period.

Health textbooks organize teaching material with varying degrees of satisfaction. Some provide breadth of problems, are well graded, and insure some continuity from one grade to the next. They also help and bolster the security of the teacher whose preprofessional training may be inadequate. No matter how well done, there is no health text which is a substitute for the teacher's own planning to insure meaningful health experiences for his specific group of pupils.

Textbooks can be valuable aids to teaching if pupils are taught to go to the book in search of an answer, to get an overview of an area, or for the purpose of raising questions that are in need of further explanation. The text is a starting point from which development, expansion, and enrichment of concepts and experiences are provided. The questions that introduce the chapter, the topic headings, the concluding summary, and the review questions with suggestions for further activities are all valuable teaching aids that are essential parts of the text and deserve to be put to use. In addition, the text is *one* and perhaps *the* basic resource for the pupil and helps to provide continuity of and direction in health learning experiences. Although the ingenious teacher can get along without a textbook, he finds many aids to learning in a properly used text. Also, even the most experienced teacher usually finds the text and the teachers manual an aid to better performance. A well-planned health experience program, supplemented by a textbook, visual aids, and community resources, gives the teacher and his class the proper perspective in this area of instruction.

SELECTED REFERENCES

BLOUGH, GLENN O., and BLACKWOOD, PAUL E. *Teaching Elementary Science. Suggestions for Classroom Teachers.* U.S. Department of Health, Education, and Welfare, Office of Education, Bulletin 1948, No. 8. Washington, D.C.: Superintendent of Documents, Government Printing Office, 1948. 40 p.

BURROWS, ALVINA T. *Teaching Children in the Middle Grades.* New York: D. C. Heath & Co., 1952. 280 p.

CUNNINGHAM, RUTH, and ASSOCIATES. *Understanding Group Behavior of Boys and Girls.* New York: Bureau of Publications, Teachers College, Columbia University, 1951. 446 p.

DENVER PUBLIC SCHOOLS. *Health Interests of Children; a Report of a Research Study.* Revised edition. Denver: Colorado Board of Education, 1954. 121 p.

FLORIO, A. E., and STAFFORD, G. T. *Safety Education.* New York: McGraw-Hill Book Co., 1956. 327 p.

GROUT, RUTH E. *Health Teaching in Schools.* Third edition. Philadelphia: W. B. Saunders Co., 1958. 359 p.

KYTE, GEORGE C. *The Elementary School Teacher at Work.* New York: Dryden Press, 1957. 530 p.

LEE, J. MURRAY, and LEE, DORRIS M. *The Child and His Curriculum.* Second edition. New York: Appleton-Century-Crofts, 1950. 710 p.

NATIONAL EDUCATION ASSOCIATION, DEPARTMENT OF ELEMENTARY SCHOOL PRINCIPALS. "The Elementary School Health Program." *National Elementary Principal* 39: 1-48; February 1960.

NEW YORK ACADEMY OF MEDICINE. *Psychological Dynamics of Health Education.* Proceedings of the Eastern States Health Education Conference, April 13-14, 1950. New York: Columbia University Press, 1951. 134 p.

PATTISON, MATTIE; BARBOUR, HELEN; and EPPRIGHT, ERCEL. *Teaching Nutrition.* Ames: Iowa State College Press, 1957. 212 p.

SCHNEIDER, ELSA, and MCNEELY, SIMON A. *Teachers Contribute to Child Health.* U.S. Department of Health, Education, and Welfare, Office of Education, Bulletin 1951, No. 8. Washington, D.C.: Superintendent of Documents, Government Printing Office, 1951. 44 p.

SCHNEIDER, ROBERT E. *Methods and Materials of Health Education.* Philadelphia: W. B. Saunders Co., 1958. 382 p.

SMITH, HELEN NORMAN, and WOLVERTON, MARY E. *Health Education in the Elementary School.* New York: Ronald Press Co., 1959. 315 p.

SPENCER, MARY E. "An Educator Talks About Motivating People." *Journal of the American Dietetic Association* 25: 209-12; March 1949.

SPENCER, MARY E. "Health Texts . . . Contemporary Style." *Grade Teacher* 78: 81-90; April 1960.

WILLGOOSE, CARL E. *Health Education in the Elementary School.* Philadelphia: W. B. Saunders Co., 1959. 450 p.

the Junior High School

The modern junior high school, consisting of seventh, eighth, and ninth grades, brings together almost all of the youth in a community who are, or soon will be, in the early adolescent years. At no other educational level does one find a more diverse population of boys and girls, or a group with greater problems of adjustment. For most of these youth these years are a focal point in their development. New qualities of personality and character emerge. The problems of physical maturation can become increasingly difficult as they are complicated by social demands and pressures. The nature and direction of such development may be greatly influenced by the kind of learning experiences in health education selected to aid each individual through these transitional years. Accordingly, those responsible for health education in the junior high school play an important role in providing an effective program of education suited to the needs, interests, and abilities of early adolescents.

The junior high school is not merely an extension of the elementary grades, nor a junior version of the senior high school; rather, it is a transitional stage in the continuum of education with its own particular purposes and characteristics. In its purposes it recognizes the values of broad, general education while providing opportunities for exploration in new areas of specialized interest and activity. By so doing it strives to assist pupils to move toward making intelligent decisions and wise choices in self-direction as they learn about participation in today's social order. Yet, being the newest division of the system of public education, there is much confusion concerning the purpose, organization, and program of the junior high school in the United States.

Effectively planned health education will reflect the nature and purposes of the junior high school, and ultimately contribute to their fulfillment. Methods, materials, and guidance will be adapted within this framework, and welded into a unified sequence of interesting and challenging experiences. Through this process, health education becomes more than a "subject to be taught." The best contribution is made as health teaching influences the development of well-integrated personalities capable of making wise choices for optimum health.

Development is a key concept in the health education of young adolescents. During these years, the pattern of physical growth has considerable bearing upon emotional development. New relationships are developed with members of the opposite sex. Social values and standards of childhood are replaced by those which conform to a peer-centered code as adult-imposed restrictions are challenged. New interests and understandings broaden the sphere of activity. As social and psychological factors assume new significance and demand recognition in the maturation process, it is quite natural that many health problems arise. It is the task of health education to aid each pupil to identify and resolve these problems so that he may understand more fully his health status and behavior, and continue to progress toward optimum health as he matures into adulthood.

CURRICULUM ORGANIZATION

The scope of the health education curriculum in the junior high school is broad. It may be considered as including all of the situations, experiences, and activities in the controlled environment of the junior high school. This concept implies the importance of an environment conducive to safe and healthful living and of health services which are educational in nature. Obviously, the three components of the school health program, health services, healthful school living, and health education, are all mutually supportive and essential to providing opportunities for desirable learning experiences in health. It is imperative that health experiences be co-ordinated in a co-operatively planned, sequential curriculum adapted to junior high school pupils who ordinarily are making the difficult transition from the self-contained classrooms of the elementary school to departmentalized instruction at the secondary-school level. Understanding of the interrelationships among the major areas of the school health program is requisite to intelligent planning of experiences in health instruction.

In planning specific instruction for health, recognition must be given to curricular plans built around broad subject fields and core programs in the junior high school curriculum as well as to the more traditional organization by subject matter fields. Health education can be so organized that it fits into the general curriculum pattern of any junior high school.* How this is accomplished remains a task for local consideration, but it needs to be done with a full awareness of the need to synthesize the knowledge, understandings, attitudes, and skills related to health into personal behavior patterns.

In the departmentalized junior high school the various subject matter areas offer many opportunities for health teaching, and there is great temptation to rely heavily upon widely separated experiences for achieving desirable health outcomes. In such situations there is need for the regularly scheduled health education class to draw together the contributions of related areas into a meaningful whole and to fill gaps not otherwise covered. A frequent recommendation of national committees is that a daily health education class for one year be included in the junior high school program.[1] It is to be expected that in core programs synthesis is a major objective, not only with respect to a dynamic concept of health which is reflected in behavior but also to the meaningful relationship of health to many life activities. Whatever approaches are utilized, the systematic organization of learning experiences in the health education curriculum as an integral part of the total curriculum must be carried out with full awareness of the functions of the junior high school.

Considerable flexibility in the health education curriculum is essential at this educational level. Junior high school pupils usually come from several neighborhoods and have varying backgrounds in home and school experiences. Thus they bring with them a broad range of health problems and interests which reflect the traditions, mores, and beliefs of a variety of cultural backgrounds. Effective health teaching recognizes the wide diversity within the group by organizing learning experiences in terms of the learner's maturity and his interests, needs, and capacities. Curriculum designs which provide opportunity to discover and explore specialized interests and problems encourage learning and utilize the early adolescent's desire for experimenta-

---

* See Chapter Six.

[1] See: National Conference for Cooperation in Health Education, Committee on School Health Policies. Suggested School Health Policies. Third edition. Washington, D.C. and Chicago: National Education Association and American Medical Association, 1956. 40 p.

tion and adventure. Exploration of the wonders of medical science and progress in human health or of the intricacy and durability of man's biological endowment capture the interest and enthusiasm of many boys and girls at this age.

While emphasis is directed toward individual adaptation of learning experiences, the curriculum structure should also provide for sound methodology adapted to the needs of early adolescents as they live and learn together. Teacher-pupil planning of experience-centered units permits a variety of learning activities which lead to more effective group relationships. Numerous small-group activities may grow out of broadly organized units of instruction as individuals and small groups are guided in the development of subtopics of the health unit. As the pupil participates in planning, in the functioning of small groups, and contributes to the success of the larger group, he undergoes a practical experience in human relationships.

Guidance is one of the recognized purposes of the modern junior high school. That the health education curriculum can contribute to the guidance function is indicated by the fact that many problems which have been ameliorated through group guidance stem from and have a direct bearing upon health. The organization of a balanced health education curriculum takes into account the complementary function of health guidance concerned with helping early adolescents to solve immediate health problems common to members of the group. Junior high school pupils have a continuing need for group guidance in matters regarding their physical health, growth and development, boy-girl relationships, and mental health practices. Group guidance emphasizing health maintenance and desirable health practices merits recognition in the activities of homerooms, clubs, and assemblies. Specialized health personnel can meet a major responsibility for health guidance through contributions to the testing program and the records basic to guidance, as well as by working with individual pupils as need and opportunity arise.

PLANNING FOR HEALTH INSTRUCTION

The health instructor in the junior high school is responsible for providing learning experiences which will not only help young adolescents to acquire suitable health information, but which also will influence their health attitudes and health practices favorably. Health learning experiences are effective to the extent that they are consistent with (a) the nature of early adolescence; (b) individual differences operating in a cultural setting; and (c) the level of the learner's maturity.

Understanding the Pupil

Today, the junior high school teacher of health utilizes a full understanding of the developmental needs and characteristics common to the boys and girls with whom he is working. These have been discussed in Chapter Three. However, this knowledge functions most effectively when the teacher realizes that every pupil is what he *is* not only because he is one of a class of young adolescents, but also because he is an individual person.

In many instances, health education has placed too much emphasis on the physiological aspects of growth and development in explanation of the health problems of early adolescence, and too little stress on the social and psychological factors in the environment which affect the developing personality. Problems encountered by youth stem from both physical and cultural factors, for growth and development is a biosocial process. Consequently, the implementation of learning experiences which are centered around total development of the young adolescent demands a shift in emphasis from the traditional physiology-centered subject matter to the needs, interests, and abilities of individuals seeking solutions to health problems.

As pointed out previously, adolescents are interested in themselves and in the changes they are undergoing. Whether or not this period is particularly stressful is determined not so much by the traits of physical development and inherent disposition as by the environmental stimuli which impose restrictions on the person in his or her particular developmental state. Early adolescence should not be considered primarily as a period of storm, physical turmoil, and stress, nor as being uniquely different from other phases of the total development of the individual. Although different aspects of personality development—physical, social, emotional, intellectual—proceed at varying rates, growth is continuous and the total development of the personality has continuity.

The types of problems faced in adolescence are related to childhood experiences. How the individual adjusts to these problems depends upon the results of his interaction with the environment—whether it is pleasing and satisfying to his needs and interests, or whether it is a frustrating experience that blocks his attempts to be accepted for his own worth. The self-concept of the pupil in relation to his environment is capable of change. Recognition and acceptance of each pupil as an individual is a first step toward providing the kinds of experiences which will favorably modify this concept of self.

Health Needs and Interests

The needs of young adolescents are not necessarily consistent with interests, nor are needs always "felt." Needs denote the lack of something requisite or useful to an individual, and which, if present, tend to give satisfaction. On the other hand, through expression of interests, motives for further identification with an object, idea, or situation are either directly or indirectly indicated. Although closely associated, and often interdependent, the presence of the one does not guarantee the presence of the other. Consequently, it may be necessary to help the young adolescent become aware of his real health needs through the identification of his health problems, and to stimulate interest beyond a point of curiosity so that the pupil will be carried toward need satisfaction. In this process it is important not to confuse mere whims or superficial curiosity with fundamental interests or needs.

The health needs of the early adolescent may be categorized as being related to the organic growth pattern and also to the social structure of the environment. Rapid physical growth and maturation, or the lack of it, may cause the junior high school pupil to develop temporary health problems that can become permanent. Attention and concern for status become self-centered as comparisons are made with age mates in the peer group. Social pressures which attach undue importance to temporary body disproportions and deviations frequently cause worry about being normal. Temporary growth anxieties may appear and become a source of deep-seated emotional conflict. Ignorance and misunderstanding may lead to serious misconceptions about growth changes. As individuals vary, so will needs vary among a given group, but all will need scientifically accurate information about the many factors affecting growth and development.*

Faulty eating practices and dietary excesses associated with the greatly increased caloric requirements of the adolescent growth spurt may be complicated by irregular routine, emotional stress, and increased activity. Postural difficulties, awkwardness,

---

* See Chapter Three.

and apparent laziness may reflect overfatigue, or may simply indicate that the individual has not yet developed the confidence necessary to co-ordinate a rapidly growing body. Dental caries continue to be a problem, with orthodontic braces becoming either a "badge of honor," or the center of concern for personal appearance. Minor illnesses and eye and ear defects occur frequently, although the young adolescent is relatively free from communicable disease. Accident frequency reaches a peak at this age, with accidents being the leading cause of deaths among the early teen-agers.

Each pupil should have knowledge of human growth patterns; the effects of diet, exercise, rest, and sleep; the importance of the proper care and use of the special sense organs; posture; illness; and accidents. He has need for interpretation of these facts and for a growing understanding of their significance.

The developing youth needs to belong, yet he needs freedom to learn to accept successfully a proper share of the responsibility for self-direction. There is security for him which comes from belonging to a peer-centered culture as he gropes his way toward new relationships within his environment. He needs help in understanding his newly arrived status in regard to parents and siblings, school authority, and activities with age mates both in and out of school. In short, he needs to be accepted for what he is—an adolescent, no longer consistently a child but not yet an adult.

The health interests of junior high school pupils characteristically evolve in accordance with the developmental changes which occur with puberty and during early adolescence. Since this age group is relatively free from physical illness and disease, it is quite natural that interests center on self-adjustment. The Denver Health Interests Study suggests a variety of special health interests which emerge at this level, in addition to those which persist throughout the years, closely associated with maturation.[2] While seventh-grade boys are reported to be most interested in maintaining body efficiency and developing skills involving large muscles, seventh-grade girls, most of whom are in early adolescence, are primarily interested in personal attractiveness. Eighth-grade pupils are chiefly interested in developing skills and knowledge which give them a feeling of security in meeting the "disturbances and uncertainties" of early adolescence. The in-

---

[2] Denver Public Schools. *Health Interests of Children; a Report of a Research Study.* Revised edition. Denver: Colorado Board of Education, 1954. p. 69-72.

terests of ninth-grade pupils center chiefly on improving personality and personal adjustments.

This statement of health interests is not necessarily representative of the health interests of all junior high school youth. It is indicative of the types of interests to be found within specific groups, and those associated with developmental changes of early adolescence. The interest pattern of a group reflects the breadth of previous experience, socioeconomic factors, physical and mental capacity, and the degree of skill and understanding achieved through previous experience. Interests are affected by the expanding level of intellectual maturity and the greater ease of dealing with abstract matters which permits serious challenge of ideas previously accepted at face value.

With this background for the continuous study of pupils, the teacher grows in ability to discover health needs and interests, to determine those topics that are significant in health instruction and those that are unimportant. Also, he learns to know when and where to turn to authorities for interpretation of observations and findings which are beyond him. Through gaining understanding of his pupils, and understanding of himself in relation to those pupils, the teacher is better equipped to foster friendly relations with his classes and among the members of different groups. This is a crucial factor in promoting an informal cooperative situation both in the classroom and in conference with the individual pupil. This easy, but not too familiar, informality is the key to effective health teaching. Such a relationship increases the chances of obtaining uninhibited expression of pupils' health problems and of reconstructing long-established health attitudes and practices on the basis of new understandings and appreciations.

Motives and Learning

Early adolescence is a transitional period complicated by developmental problems which give rise to new needs and new interests. It is characterized by intense friendships, a strong desire to get along with others, and desire for popularity which seems to demand conformity to group standards. Childish, self-centered behavior gives way before the impact of the value systems of the peer group. The individual challenges adult authority in his efforts to gain a measure of independence through peer acceptance. The desire for group acceptance promotes the alignment of personal values, beliefs, and ideals with those of the group;

these become powerful driving forces in the determination of behavior.

Each pupil is constantly perceiving and learning, but perhaps not always what we wish him to perceive and to learn. Although he may apparently progress quite satisfactorily through a logical sequence of subject matter, his doing so is no guarantee of improved health practices. The problem, then, becomes one of directing his learning into channels favorable to the development of desirable health behavior. The adult cannot command the development of desirable attitudes or improved health behavior, for the very nature of the early adolescent personality makes it less amenable to external authority, or even to direct suggestion. However, it may be necessary for the adult to impose certain controls and practices to protect the health and lives of young adolescents and of others. It is to be hoped that these necessary controls will become self-directed and that pupils can be helped to set their own rules, but situations exist in which protection comes first. Examples are to be found particularly in the areas of safety and disease control. If the ultimate goal of health education is intelligent self-direction and personal action in health matters, the factors which motivate pupils of this age must be duly considered. The achievement of such self-direction requires the teacher to exploit those motives which determine adolescent behavior.

The key to motivation for healthful living is the understanding of individual health problems so that potential drives in each pupil can be directed into purposeful channels of learning activity. The factor of individual differences suggests that motivation is an individual, personalized matter. There are no group norms for motives—they are many and represent a wide variety of likes and dislikes as reflected by interests, needs, and values. What the young adolescent does is determined not only by his needs and interests, but also by how he perceives what is happening around him, and how he interprets and evaluates these happenings according to what he feels and what he has learned from past experiences.

The developmental tasks which characterize the early adolescent's efforts to achieve the goals which will bring him satisfactions have deep implications for health behavior:

1. Establishing a growing independence of adults in various areas of behavior

2. Accepting one's self as a worthwhile person, really worthy of love

3. Behaving according to a shifting peer code

4. Strong identification with one's own sex mates

5. Learning one's role in heterosexual relationships

6. Recognizing one's thoughts and feelings about one's self in the face of significant bodily changes and their concomitants

7. Accepting the reality of one's appearance

8. Controlling and using a developing body

9. Using language to express and to clarify more complex concepts

10. Moving from the concrete to the abstract and applying general principles to the particular.[3]

Health for its own sake is not an effective motivating factor for improving adolescent health practices. However, health does begin to assume a greater significance to youth when seen as a means to an end—as a tool or quality which will enable him to gain desired goals. This situation requires that educators find ways of stimulating and guiding the motivation process if health practices are to be favorably influenced.

There is no simple formula which will guarantee the individual's motivation, but there is a great deal the teacher can do to facilitate the process. First, he can help young people to establish clearly defined goals, not the teacher's goals, but those which are purposeful and satisfying to the pupil, goals that are attainable and foreseeable. Second, he can *assist* the pupil to arrive at his own set of worthwhile values. Havighurst[4] suggests three ways in which values are formed which seem to have special import for motivation in the junior high school student:

1. *Through satisfactory emotional experiences.* The young adolescent encounters innumerable conflicting forces as he attempts to adjust to a new status. He tends to place high value on those factors in his experiences which reduce conflict and

---

[3] Association for Supervision and Curriculum Development. *Fostering Mental Health in Our Schools.* 1950 Yearbook. Washington, D.C.: the Association, a department of the National Education Association, 1950. p. 84-87.

[4] Havighurst, Robert J. *Developmental Tasks and Education.* New York: Longmans, Green & Co., 1950. p. 57.

bring about feelings of security and adequacy in his search for adult acceptance. Successful experiences in accomplishing tasks and objectives tend to be emotionally satisfying.

2. *Through association of something with the love or approval of persons whose love and approval is desired.* The adolescent identifies strongly with his peer group. This fact suggests the effect on personal values of group opinion and practice because of the need "to belong."

3. *Through reasoning or reflective thinking.* As the early adolescent develops the ability to move from the concrete to the abstract, he learns to formulate some values. He may analyze his own health behavior, consider its effect on his own well-being, and arrive at a judgment concerning the relative values of various health practices.

Finally, the teacher can help each youth to develop a favorable concept of self that is consistent with reality. Each developing personality needs help in this task. Its accomplishment is basic to attitude formation as each young person attempts to "feel" and to find proper perspective in the social scheme of things, and ultimately, the reason for learning the "why" (knowledge) as a basis for intelligent health behavior.

Selection of Content

Selection of content for health instruction in the junior high school is not a simple matter. It requires expert leadership and co-operative planning, for there is no single body of subject matter in health education that can be arbitrarily assigned to specific grades and then be expected to fit all situations. The determination of content through which youth learns is primarily a matter to be decided in each school according to (a) the needs, interests, and abilities of the pupils in that school; (b) the content of the total school program; (c) the curriculum pattern for health education; and (d) available resources.

Constructive teamwork among those who guide the health experiences of the pupils is essential in the allocation of content to be emphasized in each grade. The contributions of related areas of study need to be fully evaluated. The final decision concerning the placement of content is conditioned by the provisions made for specific health courses, and the potential for health teaching in such subjects as general science, home economics, physical education, and social studies.

It is the consensus of experienced health educators that the emphasis in health education in the junior high school be "placed on each student's personal health problems, and on helping him secure an increased understanding of the scientific basis of health behavior in the home, school, and community."[5] This concept implies that content not be limited to "book-learning," but be broad enough to allow its functional application in daily living experiences according to the health needs of the particular group concerned. However, certain health topics deal with the health needs and interests of practically all junior high school pupils. The mobility of our present-day population indicates that the content of health instruction in any given school cannot be restricted to local interests and problems.

The following outline is suggested only as a *tentative guide* for the selection and allocation of content in a particular junior high school curriculum. It is recognized that emphasis may be modified by such factors as (a) the quality and extent of previous instruction; (b) the range of individual differences in the group; (c) availability of resources; and (d) community attitudes, problems, and beliefs. The following broad areas are concerned with the physical, mental, emotional, and social aspects of health in the growth pattern of early adolescence, and are appropriate for the health education curriculum of the junior high school.

SUGGESTED AREAS OF CONTENT

1. *Physical growth and development*—Normal structure and function of the human organism; physiological development associated with adolescence and its relationship to personal and family health; patterns of growth in height and weight; individual differences

2. *Living practices*—The need for a balanced program of work, rest, and recreation and the use of leisure-time activities; exercise; control and use of the body; values and precautions in physical activity; rest, sleep, and relaxation; resistance to disease

3. *Health maintenance and improvement*—Professional health services and health products; importance of health examinations; correction of remediable defects; dangers of self-medication; healthful daily routine; effects of alcohol, tobacco,

---

[5] National Conference for Cooperation in Health Education, Committee on School Health Policies, *op. cit.*, p. 13.

narcotics; dental health and orthodontia; care of the special senses

4. *Food and nutrition*—Food values and an adequate diet for growth; individual responsibility for food selection; care and handling of foods; psychological factors related to personal eating habits

5. *Mental health*—Adjusting to changing emotions; getting along with others at home and in school; appreciation and understanding of one's own personality and of the personalities of others; management of personal problems; accepting reality; appreciation of mental health in individual and group living; relationship of mental and physical functions and health

6. *Personality development*—The influence of physical, social, and emotional factors on personality development; relationship of the individual to environment in school, home, and community; personal appearance related to personality; clothing, grooming, and posture

7. *Family life*—Appreciation and understanding of the family and one's place in it; relationships with parents and the development of independent self-control; health in the home; care of children; home care of the sick

8. *Sex adjustment*—Adjustment to a maturing body; sex problems related to growth; boy-girl relationships and social customs; making adjustments to the family

9. *Safety and first aid*—Responsibility for safety; school safety; home safety; safety in recreation, work, and travel; safety with bicycles, motorbikes, and other light motor vehicles; causes and prevention of accidents and injuries; first aid procedures and skills

10. *Community health*—Community problems in health, safety, and recreation; school and community health activities; services of public health agencies; individual responsibilities in the public health program; control of communicable diseases; science and disease; possible careers in health.

In the selection and allocation of the content of health education, questions such as the following are important.

Is the content directed toward satisfying the interests and meeting the health needs of the pupils?

Is emphasis placed on the functional value of health content to pupils in meeting their problems of day-by-day living as well as looking forward to the future?

Is the content appropriate to the maturity of pupils in the grade in which it is to be used?

Does the placement of content promote the articulation of experiences at various grade levels?

Is the content co-ordinately placed in related subject areas so that it will reach *all* pupils?

What content is most effectively presented in specific health courses?

Is content consistent with available resources?

Does the content allow flexibility for recognizing developing health problems and needs in the community?

Does the content contribute to the larger goals of education?

TEACHING METHODS

Despite the importance of content, teachers cannot assume that the possession of health information will motivate desirable health behavior. The extent to which the pupil applies what he knows about health to his own behavior in the home, school, and community is a major criterion for successful health teaching. The answer to how this may be accomplished lies not only in what is taught, but even more important, in *how* health concepts are developed.

The inherent characteristics of the adjustive process in early adolescence point out the importance of attitude development. What a young person does is largely dependent upon his feelings about a particular type of behavior. He is most apt to apply to daily living those concepts which he values and judges to be important. If the individual has a satisfying experience in checking the safety features of a motorbike, he values it, feels good about it, and wants to use the understanding and skill thus gained. Since intelligent action requires reliable information, and since the adolescent seeks to be self-dependent, he needs to be provided with sufficient authentic sources of information and taught to use these sources so that he can seek out and acquire understandings that he recognizes as both authoritative and significant to his problem.

Appropriate teaching methods provide opportunities for pupils to put their knowledge into action in school, home, and community. The effectiveness of even the most modern teaching techniques is largely lost when synthetic experiences and health facts are taught in an isolated classroom situation. Nearly every junior high school boy and girl is exposed to such health experiences as physical and dental examinations, screening devices, measuring height and weight, and food selection. When classroom teaching is tied in with these pupil activities, pupils gain the advantage of associating knowledge with practices through experience. Methodology that utilizes the adolescent's spirit of adventure, urge for experimentation, and desire for activity will extend learning experiences beyond textbook content and the classroom to greater opportunities throughout the school and community. Obviously, this kind of health instruction involves the co-operation of many people. Parents, pupils, school administrators, supervisors, health service personnel, and community health agencies share with teachers the responsibility for making real-life learning experience possible.

Textbooks can provide much valuable health information and many suggestions for significant activities; but, as commonly used, they may limit educational outcomes. Methods tend to become stereotyped when the textbook is allowed to determine the content of the course and when outcomes are measured in terms of pages covered and facts learned.

The application of modern educational psychology to the selection and implementation of teaching methods indicates a dynamic approach which recognizes the characteristics of early adolescents and the nature of their education for healthful living. These facts suggest the use of methods which emphasize co-operative planning, sharing of experiences, the integration of what is learned into the behavior pattern.

The Problem Solving Approach

There is considerable evidence to indicate that problem solving lends itself particularly well as an *approach* to the health instruction of early adolescents. Junior high school pupils are primarily concerned with fundamental questions and problems; they are not concerned with detailed data except as these data are seen in relation to specific issues. Problem solving facilitates pupil activity with the emphasis on learning by doing. It enables each pupil to work toward the solution of *his* problems under the leadership and guidance of a teacher who seeks excellent opportunities to help pupils discover projects which they can undertake successfully. Inherent motives function as the learner becomes involved in the solution of problems of personal living, group relations, and home and community experiences. As the pupil practices the democratic procedure of co-operating with his peers, he learns both as an individual and as a member of the group.

The problem solving approach helps to establish firmly a scientific attitude toward decisions concerning health behavior. Pupils learn to organize, to apply principles to new situations, and to interpret new data. It has been demonstrated that pupils gain as much knowledge of content through the problem solving approach as in other approaches, but have the added advantage of greatly improved attitudinal tendencies and ability to think critically.[6] Pupils can learn to distinguish between facts and opinion, truth and superstition, and to recognize the importance of properly relating such facts to the problems. They are stimulated to acquire and utilize information and thus become better equipped to evaluate both sides of an issue in making wise choices of behavior.

The problem solving approach is a complex of many functions. It involves the use of a wide variety of methods and pupil activities in attempting to find solutions to the problems of individuals, problems common to small groups, and problems of interest to the entire class. Pupils require close guidance in identifying and facing their problems; in gathering, analyzing, and applying the data necessary to solve them; in developing and testing hypotheses; in generalizing the findings, drawing conclusions, making decisions, and evaluating the results. As the investigation of problems proceeds, there is a shifting from one method to another in a continuum of pupil activity and shared experiences under the guidance of the teacher. Teaching methods are selected as they lend themselves to the activities and functions of each phase of the problem solving process. This is illustrated by the following brief account of a *unit on grooming* as taught to the boys and girls in an eighth-grade class in a small midwestern city.

---

[6] Gross, Richard E., and McDonald, Frederick J. "Classroom Methods: The Problem Solving Approach." *Phi Delta Kappan* 39: 259-65; March 1958.

"How Can We Make the Most of Our Appearance?"

A recognition of the frequent use of questionable grooming practices and extremes in faddish dress led to teacher preplanning of the unit long before it was introduced to the class. Outcomes to be sought were written down in terms of understandings, attitudes, and behavior. The methods and activities which might best provide the learning experiences for effecting the desired outcomes were included in the planning. Appropriate resource materials were selected and gathered.

Early in the unit, a lively class discussion developed as pupils stated their views concerning appropriate clothing and grooming practices. Comments and questions from the pupils led to identification of the problem as one common to the group, and to the realization that more information was needed for its solution. The class was divided into groups of six to discuss a possible course of action. Each group was directed to select one student in the group who would record and summarize the group's ideas and suggestions for later reporting to the total class. In the ensuing discussion, the pupils decided upon several small-group projects through which they hoped to answer the question, "How can we make the most of our appearance?"

Records of progress and results were carefully maintained as projects were developed and culminated. One group, acting as an interview team, developed and used an interview form to gain the viewpoints of parents, teachers, the school nurse, and fellow pupils. An all-pupil panel was presented on "Personality and Personal Appearance." A pupil moderator directed the discussion with two pupils presenting the teen-age point of view while two other pupils spoke from the adult viewpoint. A home economist was consulted in planning a demonstration to illustrate the fundamentals of good grooming and attractive dress. Interest was greatly increased by the use of three-dimensional posters, live models selected from the class, and a doll collection used for exhibiting major points of the demonstration.

Other groups conducted similar investigations of products used in grooming, clothing costs and styles, and the relationship of personality to good grooming. Upon completion of the projects, the findings were summarized by group consensus. A code for good grooming was worked out and used for self-evaluation. At the suggestion of the class, and with the principal's approval, the code was circulated as a health bulletin to all homerooms.

Methods Used in Solving Problems

The actual methods used are largely determined by pupil-teacher planning in a specific class. Excellent descriptions of the many specific methods which have evolved from practice are available in several sources. Many of these methods can be used in various ways and combinations in the learning situation for which they are selected. Some of the methods applicable to problem solving at the junior high school level may be roughly grouped as follows:

1. *Oral expression.* The importance of the expression of thoughts, ideas, and information at each stage of problem solving is evident in the understanding that it brings and the action it engenders. Buzz sessions, narrated illustrations, and panel discussions lead to critical listening and group analysis. These activities provide structure and purpose to class discussion resulting in the development of concepts and plans which can be achieved in no other way. As pupils participate, they gain a deeper appreciation of each other's feelings, needs, and viewpoints; they learn to respect individuality, and at the same time to identify with the values, standards, and goals of the group.

2. *Laboratory.* Demonstrations, experimentation, field trips, surveys, and project development provide direct learning experiences with people and things, procedures and processes, and conditions in the environment. For example, pupils in eighth-grade science classes prepared and presented projects as part of a learning unit on health and the structure of the body. In each project, a specific aspect of science was related to the pupil's own health needs and interests. Parental interest in working with the students was encouraged; individual conferences were held between instructors and individual pupils; pupils exchanged information and shared ideas about their projects through class discussion.[7] As reliable information is established through cooperative fact collecting, laboratory experiences expose the individual to the lack of validity of his own beliefs and attitudes, and provide opportunity to practice desired behavior.

3. *Dramatization.* Sociodrama is best employed where natural situations arise in which certain points need clarification. Pupils develop insights to procedures, processes, and reactions which affect the attitudes and behavior of people through the spontaneous acting out of the real-life roles played by others

---

[7] Daly, Ruth P. "Health Projects in Eighth Grade Science." *Health Education Journal* (Los Angeles City Schools) 21: 10-11; November 1957.

in the course of experimentation, research, and school and community health activities. The use of information gathered for problem solving takes on new meaning as an awareness is developed of how people feel in a given situation and the results which their actions are apt to evoke.

4. *Evaluation.* Testing, observation, interviews, inventories, and other appraisal techniques add variety and interest to the learning situation, and for best results such evaluation is continuous throughout the problem solving experience. Measurements of knowledge and attitudes, and self-evaluation by pupils reveal progress and give redirection to the planning of learning experiences. (See Chapters Twelve and Fourteen.)

Pupil Activities

Numerous opportunities for "learning by doing" are present in every junior high school. The school and the community are excellent laboratories for diversified and integrated learning experiences. The teacher is concerned with helping pupils discover those activities which they can successfully carry through toward problem solution. Junior high school pupils can

Conduct safety surveys of danger areas in school and community

Develop effective visual aids based on environmental conditions

Prepare health bulletins

Organize and participate in health clubs

Visit public health departments and agencies

Demonstrate the effect of diet through animal experimentation

Study community recreation opportunities and prepare suggestions for their improvement

Gather and evaluate popular literature concerning health problems.

To this list may be added countless other activities which help pupils translate knowing into doing.

The diversity of activities for meeting individual needs and interests requires many and varied teaching aids. Even the most competent teacher needs appropriate instructional materials to give pupils the help and direction they need in the successful solution of their health problems. The availability of wisely selected texts and reference materials provides a wealth of information, increases pupil interest, and helps to make meanings clearer as boys and girls seek significant information in the learning process.

Teaching Through Health Counseling

Not all health problems can be solved through group guidance and health instruction. In any given junior high school group there is apt to be a wide range of individual variations in the physical, emotional, and social development of the pupils, accompanied by a great diversity of problems related to varying stages of the pubertal growth cycle. Because of his insecurities and the desire for social approval and acceptance, the young adolescent is frequently afraid to be different. Anxieties which may evolve from the individual pupil's lack of understanding of his own developmental characteristics in relation to those of his age mates indicate the important function of health counseling as an integral part of health education.

Although basically a health service function, the responsibility for certain aspects of health counseling is shared by various personnel. Counseling is effective as a method of teaching, and the teacher has an important role as health counselor which should not be overlooked. Many opportunities occur throughout each school day for informal counseling in regard to health practices. Observations by the teacher, pupil health records, and screening techniques may reveal numerous problems that can be alleviated by counseling. However, the most direct learning through the counseling process takes place when the pupil voluntarily seeks counsel. As pupils develop an understanding of general health problems through group guidance and group instruction, they tend to seek individual help. It is not unusual for the junior high school pupil to use devious means of seeking counsel from the health instructor, coach, physical educator, or homeroom teacher when an atmosphere permissive of such behavior exists.

An awareness of the developmental and adjustive processes of early adolescence is a primary step toward health counseling based upon understanding. In his search for independence, the young adolescent wishes to achieve adequate self-directiveness. Consequently, it becomes the task of the teacher-counselor to foster this desire by helping the pupil to draw upon his own resources for solving his problems. The teacher does not "tell," or "give advice," or direct the pupil toward a predetermined course of action. Rather, he is a skillful listener, tactfully handling the pupil's health problems with an awareness of the pupil's reactions to the teacher's personality.

The skilled counselor recognizes the pupil's difficulty in expressing his feelings, and helps him to clarify his thinking regarding the nature of the problem. Through individual conferences, the teacher may explain pertinent information, interpret significant facts, and point out the various courses of action which the pupil may select. A wise choice can be encouraged by pointing out the possible consequences of each choice, but the final decision rests with the pupil and with his parents.

It is essential that teachers who assume health counseling responsibilities be cognizant of ethical procedures in implementing the individual conferences. Ideally, individual conferences are planned, with needed data gathered in advance, and a confidential written summary made of each conference. Privacy is a requisite in all aspects of the conference. The teacher is ethically bound to observe the principle of "privileged communication" in justification of the trust placed in him. The most innocent betrayal of this trust can undo much of what has been accomplished.

Sufficient school time for individual conferences and detailed knowledge concerning significant health conditions are essential to effective counseling. These two factors impose real limitations on teacher counseling, and suggest the need for co-ordinated counseling efforts. *It is important that where the teacher sees the need for extended, expert counseling, the pupil be referred to specialized personnel who are better prepared to assist the pupil with his particular problem.*

SELECTED REFERENCES

ANDERSON, C. L. *School Health Practice.* Second edition. St. Louis: C. V. Mosby Co., 1960. 530 p.

ASSOCIATION FOR SUPERVISION AND CURRICULUM DEVELOPMENT. *Fostering Mental Health in Our Schools.* 1950 Yearbook. Washington, D.C.: the Association, a department of the National Education Association, 1950. 320 p.

COWELL, CHARLES C. "The Adolescent's World." *Developing Democratic Human Relations.* (Edited by Hilda C. Kozman.) First Yearbook. Washington, D.C.: American Association for Health, Physical Education, and Recreation, NEA, 1951. p. 219-53.

DALY, RUTH P. "Health Projects in Eighth Grade Science." *Health Education Journal* (Los Angeles City Schools) 21: 10-11; November 1957.

DENVER PUBLIC SCHOOLS. *Health Interests of Children; a Report of a Research Study*. Revised edition. Denver: Colorado Board of Education, 1954. 121 p.

GESELL, ARNOLD L.; ILG, FRANCES L.; and BATES, LOUISE AMES. *Youth: The Years from Ten to Sixteen*. New York: Harper & Brothers, 1956. 542 p.

GROSS, RICHARD E., and MCDONALD, FREDERICK J. "Classroom Methods: The Problem Solving Approach." *Phi Delta Kappan* 39: 259-65; March 1958.

GROUT, RUTH E. *Health Teaching in Schools*. Third edition. Philadelphia: W. B. Saunders Co., 1958. 359 p.

GRUHN, WILLIAM T., and DOUGLASS, HARL R. *The Modern Junior High School*. New York: Ronald Press Co., 1956. 421 p.

HAVIGHURST, ROBERT J. *Developmental Tasks and Education*. New York: Longmans, Green & Co., 1950. 86 p.

IRWIN, LESLIE W.; HUMPHREY, JAMES H.; and JOHNSON, WARREN R. *Methods and Materials in School Health Education*. St. Louis: C. V. Mosby Co., 1956. 367 p.

NATIONAL CONFERENCE FOR COOPERATION IN HEALTH EDUCATION, COMMITTEE ON SCHOOL HEALTH POLICIES. *Suggested School Health Policies*. Third edition. Washington, D.C. and Chicago: National Education Association and American Medical Association, 1956. 40 p.

OBERTEUFFER, DELBERT. *School Health Education*. Third edition. New York: Harper & Brothers, 1960. 547 p.

SASMAN, ERWIN H. "Classroom Methods: Do Laboratory and Field Experiences Change Behavior?" *Phi Delta Kappan* 39: 265-67; March 1958.

SCHNEIDER, ROBERT E. *Methods and Materials of Health Education*. Philadelphia: W. B. Saunders Co., 1958. 382 p.

STARR, HELEN M. "Today's Pupil—Health-informed or Health-educated?" *Journal of Health, Physical Education, Recreation* 25: 18-22, 58; September 1954.

STOVALL, THOMAS F. "Classroom Methods: Lecture vs. Discussion." *Phi Delta Kappan* 39: 255-58; March 1958.

the Senior High School

Health education in the senior high school includes all of the experiences in educating for health provided for older adolescents under the auspices of the school. These experiences may be obtained in a variety of school activities and programs including health services and healthful school living.* The focus of this chapter is on the learning experiences which are planned and incorporated into the high-school curriculum for the purpose of improving health knowledge, attitudes, skills, and practices. The ingredients of health education for high-school students concern us here as we explore the ways in which health education is designed, planned, administered, taught, and evaluated.

The senior high school is generally recognized today as including pupils enrolled in grades 10 through 12, although in many high schools the more traditional organization of grades 9 through 12 continues. The pupils include that group of middle and older adolescents whose ages range from 15 to 18 years. Their physical development is less diverse as compared with the early years of adolescence spent in the junior high school, although some of the young people who develop later will be experiencing rapid growth and physical maturation. There is greater maturity in the intellectual qualities of reasoning and judgment as well as in physical development, but there are still many interests to be explored, curiosities to be satisfied, emotions to be understood, and problems to be solved. The older adolescent evidences a need for education and guidance which will aid him in making intelligent choices of health behavior both for the present and the future. Education in health may well revolve around the immediate needs of the pupils plus the health problems of adult living which they soon will face.

---

* Discussed in Chapter Twelve.

ORGANIZING HEALTH EDUCATION EXPERIENCES

The principles of curriculum planning and organization have been discussed in Chapter Six, and the three major patterns of organization, namely, the separate course, the correlated approach, and the core or integrated program, have been explored. It has been emphasized that health education experiences can be organized effectively in a number of ways, and that there is no *only* way. It seems advisable to organize health education according to the curriculum pattern used by a school or school system for its over-all program. If a school operates on the basis of a subject-centered curriculum, which is the almost universal pattern in senior high schools, the health education program is not likely to operate effectively through a core program. Likewise, if the school curriculum is organized as a core curriculum it would be best not to advocate a separate course plan.

To ensure a complete instructional program in health education for all senior high school students it may be necessary to use a variety of health education patterns. Following is a brief description of the three common curriculum plans in senior high schools as they are applied to health education.

The Separate Course

Organizing health education as a separate course or courses utilizing direct health teaching is one of the most effective means of organizing experiences to change health behavior of high-school students. *Suggested School Health Policies*[1] recommends that health education at the senior high school level be organized as a separate course on a daily basis for at least two semesters, preferably during the eleventh and twelfth grades. In a doctoral study comparing three common ways of organizing health instruction, Gmur[2] studied three adequately matched populations. One school used the correlation plan of organization; the second, a core plan; and the third, a separate course or direct instruction. He found that little preference could be shown for either the correlation plan or the core plan as a means of organizing

---

[1] National Conference for Cooperation in Health Education, Committee on School Health Policies. *Suggested School Health Policies*. Third edition. Washington, D.C. and Chicago: National Education Association and American Medical Association, 1956. p. 12.

[2] Gmur, Ben. "A Comparative Study of Three Common Curriculum Plans for Organizing Health Instruction." Unpublished Doctor of Education dissertation. Los Angeles: University of California, 1959.

health instruction. However, the direct course plan showed statistically significant differences in changes in behavior as noted on pre- and post-testing using a valid health behavior inventory. He states: "All evidence in this study supports the conclusion that best results in health instruction can be achieved by direct health teaching in a daily course meeting for two semesters in the senior high school." Gmur concluded that the direct course plan is preferable for the organization of health instruction in senior high schools.

Recognition of the need for scheduling health education classes poses administrative problems which are approached in a variety of ways. Although the recommended plans of a daily class for a full semester or for a full year under the direction of a teacher trained in health education are not always possible in all high schools, these plans are to be strongly encouraged.

In a large number of senior high schools, one period a day for one, two, or three years has been reserved for a program of health and physical education. The traditional pattern for dividing the time has been to teach physical education three or four days a week and to provide health classes one or two days a week. This arrangement has been relatively unsuccessful. The inherent handicaps of a joint program can be partly overcome by (a) having a physical education teacher who is also prepared and qualified to teach health or a special teacher for health education; (b) scheduling blocks of time on a daily basis for from six to nine weeks within each 18-week semester; (c) providing a minimum of one full semester and preferably a full year of health education in a three-year program; and (d) providing classrooms, books, teaching aids, credit, and class size comparable with other academic classes in the school.

The rainy day health classes, the one or two day a week arrangements under the direction of school personnel who are not prepared in health education and who lack understanding and appreciation for the contributions of health education, should be recognized for what they usually are—a waste of time. Secondary-school administrators need to examine their offerings in health education and move toward a scheduling plan which will permit better health teaching.

A separate course alone does not provide a complete health education program. When there is a separate course there is a tendency for administrators and teachers to assume that all health education will be done by the teachers assigned to the health classes. The result is a lessened feeling of individual responsibility for the health of students on the part of other teachers. To avoid this situation it is desirable to plan carefully so that natural correlation occurs in biology or life science, the physical sciences, the social sciences, home economics, industrial arts, and other appropriate fields. Correlation of appropriate materials that are not forced unnecessarily into instructional areas supplements the experiences gained in a separate course. Likewise, the opportunities for incidental instruction and the program for sound individual health guidance should be recognized as important in the total health education offering.

The Correlated Curriculum

Correlation is a curriculum pattern of organization in which the health education materials or content are taught through another related field or course such as social studies, home economics, biology, or physical education. Oberteuffer[3] expresses this clearly and concisely when he states:

> The program of correlation aims at the breakdown of the rigid barriers which separate the subjects and areas and seeks a co-relationship between health materials and all others. Technically, correlation means the relation of parts to parts—a co- or shared relationship between them.

A number of high schools have used correlation as their major plan of organizing health education. However, there is little evidence to show that acquaintance with a balanced body of knowledge or that significant changes in behavior have occurred among students whose only experience in health education has been that organized by means of correlation.

Douglass,[4] confirms this point when he states: "Valuable contributions may be made to health education through other subjects, but these should be supplemental and never employed to evade the necessity for courses in health."

Sliepcevich and Carroll[5] outline several guidepoints of correlation. These guidepoints are as follows:

1. Correlation should be a supplement to direct health teaching, not a substitute. . . .
2. Correlation should be natural, not forced. . . .

---

[3] Oberteuffer, Delbert. *School Health Education.* New York: Harper & Brothers, 1954. p. 96.

[4] Douglass, Harl R. *The High School Curriculum.* Second edition. New York: Ronald Press Co., 1956. p. 550.

[5] Sliepcevich, Elena, and Carroll, Charles. "The Correlation of Health with Other Areas of the High School Curriculum." *Journal of School Health* 28: 285; November 1958.

3. There should be a real relationship between the ideas that are to be correlated. . . .
4. Correlated health teaching should be planned with a view of the pupils' needs and interests in mind, and in order to avoid unwanted duplication and wasted efforts.
5. Health information should not command a disproportionate part of the class time. Moderation should temper the use of this teaching device. . . .

Health education through correlation may be made more effective when two conditions occur: (a) there is a dynamic, professionally prepared health educator employed to spend a portion of his time working with teachers in other fields to assist them in achieving health education objectives; and (b) there is continuing planning and replanning on the part of the curriculum committee to ensure adequate coverage of health content, vitalized in-service education of teachers, and co-operation of community health agencies. One weakness in the correlation plan is that not all high-school teachers are competent to teach health education, nor do they wish to neglect the specific and important objectives of their own special field. Unfortunately, health objectives are usually secondary to the other subject area objectives when correlation is the only approach employed. Opportunities for correlated instruction in the secondary school are discussed also in Chapter Eleven.

Health correlation, like the separate course plan, needs to be supplemented by incidental instruction and individual health guidance on the part of teachers and health personnel. While health correlation may accomplish important objectives, it should not be a permanent substitute for the development of a separate course. Frequently, this procedure is used on a temporary basis until adequately prepared health teachers are obtained and schedules modified so that health education can be established on a more organized basis.

Health Education Through Integration

The core curriculum is an attempt to break with the traditional subject matter curriculum in the reorganization of the high school. When integration is applied to the curriculum, the single subject approach disappears, and the experiences are organized around central themes or cores. Subject lines are discarded and replaced by broad topics representative of personal and social problems. One arrangement is the establishment of a core course, frequently referred to as a basic living course. Such a course concerns the major student problems at the tenth grade including, for example, orientation to high school, personal health, self-understanding, boy-girl relationships, growth and development, and family relationships.

The basic values of the core are described as follows:[6]

. . . it helps each young person to understand himself and other people so that he develops his abilities and works well with others.

. . . it enables each young person to define his goals in terms of his aptitudes and to determine realistic ways of working toward his goals.

. . . it emphasizes the skills which every individual needs for effective living as a member of a family, as a student in the local schools, and as a wage earner.

. . . it focuses upon the knowledge which is essential for understanding how the past has contributed to the present and what the elements of modern culture are.

. . . it stresses the attitudes and habits which every person must have to be a good citizen in his community, his nation and the rapidly changing world.

The core is a comprehensive plan in itself, and includes health information and experiences that can be derived from all curriculum areas as they apply to the solution of a particular health problem chosen for study. One weakness of the core plan is the difficulty of securing teachers with the diverse competencies needed to handle the many phases of learning included. The core plan is to be found in only a few high schools throughout the country and cannot be considered seriously today as a preferred method of curricular organization.

The Team Approach to Curriculum Development

It is visionary to expect that each senior high school will employ the team approach to curriculum development in health education including a possible decision as to how health education is to be organized. Nevertheless, such an undertaking is highly desirable. As discussed in Chapter Six, one of the important principles in curriculum development is the involvement of persons concerned in the planning, implementation, conduct, and evaluation of a program. Since the contribution of the school to the health of youth is the responsibility of all school personnel, wide representation in program building is considered important.

The school health council or committee, or a health education subcommittee of this body, charged with the responsibility of

---

[6] Whittier Union High School District. *Description of the Basic Course Program.* Whittier, Calif.: the District, 1954. p. 2.

the instructional program, is a means of involving those representatives of school and community personnel who can undertake the team approach in health education.

A representative from the administration is necessary to lend official sanction to the planning and implementation of health education experiences. The school health educator, or health co-ordinator, having special professional preparation and interest in health education, is counted on for enthusiastic, competent leadership of the program.

The school nurse plays a unique role in assisting in the identification of health needs of students, recommending appropriate materials, and correlating instruction with health service procedures, as well as participating actively in curriculum planning. The school physician and the private physician representing the local medical society bring to the group the medical point of view, giving authenticity and scientific accuracy to the health content and materials used, as well as sharing their understanding of growth and development of boys and girls.

Representatives from the subject fields, such as science, social science, home economics, and industrial arts, assist in developing natural correlation of health education within their respective fields. They help to avoid unnecessary duplication of instruction. General representatives assist *all* teachers in realizing that they have responsibilities for the health of youth. Teachers of physical education can add enrichment to the group from their close association with pupils. Under capable leadership, physical education becomes a laboratory for the development of health knowledge, attitudes, and practices. Guidance personnel are particularly helpful in providing evidence of student needs and interests.

The community health educator from an official or voluntary health agency is invaluable in interpreting the health needs of the community. In addition, he assists in relating the school health education program to the community. Parent representation, such as the health chairman of the local unit of the National Congress of Parents and Teachers, is important to assure the citizens' voice in helping to plan "what to teach" for healthful living. The health chairman's interpretation of the program to parents is especially important in implementation.

Certainly, the voice of the students should be heard if instruction is to be meaningful to them and to be based on their needs and interests. Students should be represented through their student health committee, a health committee of the student government, or by selected members who work with the adult health education council or committee.

The exact make-up of this representative group varies according to the individual school situation or to the over-all district plan of co-operative curriculum development. For example, the size of the school and its location in an urban or rural area are factors which may affect the make-up of the council. Nevertheless, the principle holds true of involving a widely representative group of individuals as a team to ensure the success of the health education program regardless of the individual situation.

PLANNING THE CONTENT

In approaching the selection of content of the health curriculum, it is essential that the health education program be constructed upon as sound a base as possible. The following factors are important in developing this firm foundation: (a) a modern point of view of health education; (b) the understandings and principles found to be important through cultural experience; (c) identification of individual health needs and interests of students; (d) identification of community health needs; (e) state and local requirements; and (f) objectives to be achieved.

These factors become the criteria for determining "what to teach," "how to teach," and "the instructional goals for teaching and evaluation." A brief consideration of each factor is presented to describe the bases for planning.

Point of view. One of the first jobs for a school health council or committee or for an individual health teacher is to develop a point of view, a statement of basic beliefs concerning the purpose and functions of health education in the senior high school. The basic beliefs of the group or of the individual teacher determine the type of health education to be incorporated in the classroom instruction. For example, belief in health education as education for health with its chief purpose to change favorably the knowledge, attitudes, and practices of students for healthful living implies a problem solving approach to health education.

Knowledge of health problems. There is a wealth of published information available on problems related to human health upon which the curriculum committee or the individual teacher can draw in planning the content for health teaching. The

accumulated wisdom of the culture is available to all, and principles drawn from an understanding of the many facets of progress in protection of health and prolongation of life furnish a
sound basis for planning. Acquaintance with reputable literature
in the health sciences and knowledge of sources of sound information on health problems are basic to program planning.

Understanding the needs of students.   Discovering and understanding the health needs of students is basic to planning a sound
health education program and is a first step in successful health
teaching. The high-school teacher is charged with knowing as
much as possible about older adolescents. He should be aware of
their special concerns in order to understand the reasons for
their behavior. It is axiomatic that good teachers know their
students in addition to knowing content.

General information about adolescents.   Remmers and Radler,[7] in an opinion poll of adolescent behavior, present interesting
and informative data resulting from an intensive study of the
problems and attitudes of teen-agers representing a cross section
of the adolescent population of the country. Some of these findings are the following:

In all the surveys, teenagers revealed that the bodies they inhabit trouble
them greatly. Fifty-two per cent want to gain weight or lose it. Twenty-
four per cent would like to improve their figures. Thirty-seven per cent are
seeking to improve their posture, or, in the case of boys, their "body
build". . . .

Thirteen per cent complain of getting tired very easily. Twelve per cent
suffer from frequent headaches. . . .

And fully a third have pimples, want to get rid of them and don't know
how. Undoubtedly some of these young people have actual health problems
requiring medical attention, but most of their concern for their bodies really
stems from their own lack of understanding of physical changes, the very
natural changes, that are a part of growing up. If they knew what to
expect in the way of physical growth, the amount of flesh they will naturally put on, and the places where it naturally goes, much of their anxiety
might automatically disappear. . . .

Relationships with their parents constitute a real problem for large numbers of teenagers. Ten to twenty per cent have serious conflicts in this
area. . . .

The process of growing socially, including the tricky and emotionally
loaded area of relationships between the sexes, probably constitutes the

[7] From *The American Teenager*, by H. H. Remmers and D. H. Radler, copyright
1957 by H. H. Remmers, used by special permission of the publishers, The Bobbs-
Merrill Company, Inc.

teenagers' biggest job. That is why the high school has a serious responsibility to serve effectively as a social workshop for its students. . . .

The pervasive need for acceptance for response from other people may contribute as much as any other factor to the misdeeds that make the headlines. . . .

Sex is a continual problem. . . . Poll results reveal that our teenagers know much less about sex than they would like to. . . .

One constantly recurring question is "how far to go" on a date. . . . Some time in their teenage years about one-fourth of our high school students start asking questions about marriage. Typical of these: "What things should I consider in choosing a husband or wife?" "How can I prepare myself for marriage?" "What are the things that cause trouble between married people?" Teenagers look for the answers from their parents, from other older relatives and from their teachers. Half the time they don't get answers. . . .

. . . probably the most common problem among teenagers is determining their careers beyond high school. This is true for over half the youngsters in the national sample. . . .

To most teenagers, money is the same bugaboo that it is to adults. . . .

Undoubtedly as a direct offshoot of these tensions, our young adults often have trouble adjusting to themselves. Forty-one per cent, for example, admit they often do things they later regret. Thirty-five per cent constantly "worry about little things." . . .

This, then, is the modern teenager: a boy or girl whose energies are already sapped by the sheer process of physical growth, caught up in a whirl of school work and social activities in and out of school, confronted by decisions which will affect his entire life, confused by the shifting attitudes of parents, teachers, and society in general, all of whom doubt him and his behavior—and bewildered by the complex and rapidly changing civilization into which he must soon fit, assuming all the responsibilities of maturity.

Richardson, who has spent many years as a social science teacher and recently as a vice-principal and principal of a senior high school, has outlined the physical, emotional, and social needs of adolescents as follows:

Adequate nutrition

Adequate rest—eight to ten hours each night

A regular physical and dental check-up

Exercise and activity, preferably in the open air

Protecting individual integrity

Achieving self-direction

Having experiences of success

Reconciling inner striving with reality

Relieving feelings of guilt concerning thoughts about psychological changes

Beginning to earn money of his own

Widening interest, appreciations, and understandings of the cultural heritage

Security in trying to orient himself to adult modes of behavior and to the sudden changes in affections

Becoming emancipated from the family and yet having the security and understanding of adults

Gaining status in the group; to be accepted

Intense friendships to exchange experiences and share knowledge

Belonging to a group to which he may give loyalty

Acceptance and approval of peers

Opportunities for many types of social contacts.

HEALTH NEEDS AND INTERESTS

Rosenthal[8] thoroughly reviewed the literature on health needs and interests of high-school students to determine an authoritative list. The following are 32 health needs and interests carefully documented from at least three or more studies or other authoritative sources:

Regular physical examinations

Knowledge of eugenics and heredity

Growing normally in height and weight

Good nutritional habits

Good dental health habits

Desirable practices related to vision and hearing

Good postural habits

Good habits of personal grooming

Regular participation in exercise and activity

Participation in constructive recreation and leisure time activities

Good habits of rest, sleep, and relaxation

Practices for the prevention of illness and disease

[8] Rosenthal, Carol Lee. "Health Education Opportunities in the Physical Education Program." Unpublished, independent research study in partial fulfillment for the Master of Science degree in Health Education. Los Angeles: University of California, June 1959. p. 23-25. (With minor changes.)

Knowing good sources of competent medical and consumer advice

Knowledge of effects of stimulants and depressants

Skills for the prevention of accidents and injuries

Opportunities for expressing feelings of dependence and independence

Opportunities for making decisions

Achieving success

Gaining recognition

Giving and receiving love and affection

Developing a balance between security and freedom

Feeling a sense of belongingness

Feeling worthwhile in group and family

Making social adjustment

Gaining peer acceptance and approval

Having many types of interests and social contacts

Having a concern for the well-being of others in the home, school, community, and world

Developing a knowledge and understanding of sex relationships and attitudes

Feeling free from guilt

Being a mentally healthy individual

Preparing for marriage and parenthood

Having a wholesome philosophy of life.

Several studies have been made of health interests of high-school students, among them a study by Lantagne[9] of health interests of 10,000 secondary-school students from 26 high schools in 10 different states. Students were asked to indicate interests related to 300 specific health problems and an analysis was made of the responses. Major areas in which interest was greatest included (a) habit-forming substances; (b) safety; (c) family health; (d) mental health; and (e) exercise and body mechanics.

An analysis of the interest position of each of the 300 specific health problems revealed that the top 12 were:

1. Sex instruction
2. Cancer

3. Juvenile delinquency
4. Causes of suicide
5. Tobacco and human health
6. Problems of tooth decay
7. Causes of mental illness
8. Lifelong care of the eyes
9. Safest age to have a baby
10. How to use a gun properly
11. How to report accidents
12. Speed and accidents.

The positive response on these items ranged from 67 to 52 percent. Boys and girls showed similar responses on 89 percent of the total number of items, but girls evidenced greater interest than boys in problems relating to menstruation, childbearing, and nutrition while boys exhibited greater interest than girls in the areas of physical activity and safety. There was little variation in interests expressed by adolescents in varying sections of the country.

These and similar studies furnish important information for teachers and curriculum committees planning for health instruction. It is important to recognize that studies of interests do not necessarily provide criteria by which a deep and abiding interest can be distinguished readily from a mere curiosity or a passing whim. Selecting curricular experiences on the basis of expressed interests alone would be a decidedly questionable procedure, but properly interpreted and utilized interest studies and inventories can be of considerable value.

It should be recognized that interests can be developed through good teaching and that the curriculum should include more than the expressed concerns of pupils. Williams and Southworth[10] conducted a study in a Beloit, Wisconsin, high school in an attempt to find out whether the teaching of public health problems, which generally are rated low on the interest scale, could result in increased interest. On a test-teach-retest basis it was shown that while interest in personal health problems remained high on both inventories, there was a significant gain of interest in community health problems. This fact was revealed when

[10] Williams, Helen L., and Southworth, Warren H. "Stimulating Interest in Public Health Problems Among High School Pupils." *Journal of Educational Research* 53: 53-61; October 1959.

the second inventory was compared with the initial testing, following teaching in this area.

Individual health needs and interests within a particular class or school can be identified in a variety of ways. The following are a few examples: by teacher observation and analysis of health records; through health knowledge, attitude, and practice tests and inventories, pupil-made surveys, questionnaires, interviews, opinion polls; and data from the counseling office.

Community health needs. One of the functions of the school is to assist in the solution of social problems. Health is one of the ever-pressing social problems throughout the nation and the world. A sound health education program takes into account local, national, and international health problems and needs in determining the content of the health education program.

A representative from the community agency or agencies serving on the school health council can be of great assistance in bringing to the attention of the school the current health problems which reflect local needs. These needs may have been identified by a community survey or by consulting reports and statistics from the local or state health department. An example of this procedure in one community revealed the following to be the immediate health needs as a result of a community survey: dental health, health education, mental health, tuberculosis, school health, problems of aging, hospital and clinic facilities, health center, sanitation, maternal and child health, family life and sex education, communicable disease control, housing and community redevelopment, and occupational health.[11]

National health needs can be identified from literature and studies by national commissions and similar bodies including those of the United States Public Health Service. Some of the major health problems identified as being of importance in the United States include the following: lack of professional personnel, hospital facilities, local public health units, maternal and child care, medical care, chronic disease, mental health, dental health, nutrition, and environmental sanitation.[12]

International health needs are reviewed by Deutsch[13] in a

---

[11] West Los Angeles Health Committee. *Survey.* Los Angeles: County Tuberculosis and Health Association, 1956. p. 1.

[12] President's Commission on Health Needs of the Nation. *Building America's Health. Volume I. Findings and Recommendations.* Washington, D.C.: Superintendent of Documents, Government Printing Office, 1952. p. 11-76.

[13] Deutsch, Albert. *The World Health Organization, Its Global Battle Against Disease.* Pamphlet No. 265. New York: Public Affairs Committee, 1958.

recent publication. These needs center around the prevention and control of diseases. A priority list of international needs includes: communicable diseases including malaria, yaws, tuberculosis, smallpox, typhus, schistosomiasis, yellow fever, influenza, cholera, and typhoid fever; diseases caused by malnutrition; trachoma and other eye diseases; infant and maternal health; mental health; radiation hazards; control of epidemics.

State and local requirements. A foundation factor for curriculum planning and health teaching is the set of requirements established for the state and local school districts. Some of these are legal provisions reflecting the demands of society that health education be taught according to law, or that certain specified health content must be taught. Others are adopted by state boards of education or curriculum commissions. In some states health education or courses in physiology and hygiene are required for graduation. Where state laws or regulations have not provided for health teaching, the organization of health education is left to the local school district. In some instances local school districts have required health education as a requirement for graduation from high school.

The most frequent content specified by state law is the required instruction on the harmful effects of alcohol, with teaching about narcotics and tobacco added in a number of statutes. Fire prevention, safety education, driver education, and nutrition are other health education content areas which are specified in a number of state education codes.

State and local requirements must be ascertained before the planning committee or the instructors can decide upon the content and the scope of health instruction. The statutory provisions for instruction become one of the criteria for determining "what to teach" in the health education program.

Specific objectives or goals for health education. The objectives or goals for health education are determined from analysis of the foregoing factors, particularly, the basic beliefs, the needs of society, and the needs and interests of the students.

It has been pointed out previously that the ultimate goal of health education is to improve behavior through the acquisition of health knowledge and skills, and the changing of attitudes and practices. This implies the product of the instruction to be an individual who is health educated, not merely health informed. A description of a health-educated adolescent is presented in the following paragraphs by means of an outline of health goals stated in terms of healthful behavior. These goals may be considered as desirable outcomes of the health education program. Not only are these goals helpful in the teaching process, but they also form the basis for evaluating student progress.

The health-educated adolescent[14] is one who assumes his share of responsibility for his own health and that of his family and community. He is a person who applies his understandings of healthful, effective living to his own behavior. The following is a description of desirable health behavior—understandings, attitudes, and practices—outlined under three headings: (a) personal living; (b) personal-social relations; and (c) community relations.

In personal living, the adolescent

Co-operates in an appraisal of his health status to determine his health needs and interests; appreciates the need for periodic health examinations and screening tests

Is accepting and adjusting to a changing body; is aware that growth and development are continuous processes

Increases his poise through good body mechanics (posture); dresses appropriately for occasions and seasons; attempts to make his own appearance as attractive as possible

Keeps himself in good physical condition through a balanced program of physical activity, rest, sleep, wholesome diet, and personal cleanliness

Helps to protect himself against dental caries by regular brushing of the teeth, limitation of consumption of concentrated sweets, and periodic visits to the dentist

Desires to achieve a personally satisfying life; is developing a philosophy of life with several attainable major goals, and a plan for a useful life centered in work, play, love, and faith

Is achieving status as a person through growth in independence, yet keeps security and understanding of adults; makes decisions for himself concerning many of his affairs

Understands his sex role; expresses his emotions in constructive, socially acceptable ways

Avoids use of harmful drugs, tobacco, and alcoholic beverages during adolescence

---

[14] The following is based upon: Johns, Edward B. *School Health Education Evaluative Study. Los Angeles Area 1954-1959. An Evaluation Research Study.* Los Angeles: University of California Printing Department, 1960. p. 65-66.

Knows reliable sources of health information and appraises health information according to basic criteria

Selects health products wisely to save money and to protect health

Recognizes the common danger signals of disease and is prompt in seeking medical attention when they appear

Takes advantage of immunizations as a means of protection against disease

Takes care of himself when he becomes ill to protect his own health and that of others, and takes time to recuperate after illness

Is aware of the dangers of self-diagnosis and does not practice self-medication

Distinguishes between sound medical practice and quackery

Attempts to do things the right way—the safe, skillful way

Is a careful, considerate driver and an alert, intelligent pedestrian.

In personal-social relations, the adolescent

Is gaining status in family relations in his home

Achieves status with his peers of both sexes through effective participation in several groups

Is considerate and helpful and is growing in his concern for other people, their plans, successes, and failures

Is preparing for future family life; seeks friendship with the opposite sex; understands the responsibilities of marriage and parenthood; takes part in wholesome recreational events involving both sexes

Works easily and comfortably with people of all ages and both sexes

Understands the importance of having a family physician and dentist—personal health advisers for his own and his family's protection and care

Understands the importance of health insurance for himself and his family

Knows how to select a health adviser of the type that can best assist him and his family

Takes care of others as well as himself in unfamiliar surroundings—water, fire, forest, heavy traffic, or in an emergency

Helps to maintain an orderly home—a safe home

In community relations, the adolescent

Knows the health resources of the community—official, voluntary, commercial

Expresses an interest in promoting healthful living in his own environment

Is beginning to participate effectively in the health activities and projects of social institutions—the home, the school, and the community

Participates in group discussions of common school and community health problems

Becomes a member of school health and safety committees or councils, when opportunity permits

Reports frauds and suspected frauds in writing to the nearest office of the Food and Drug Administration or to the Better Business Bureau

Reports to authorities environmental hazards in school, neighborhood, and community, i.e., broken pavement, poorly lighted streets

Appreciates the health professions as personally and socially useful careers.

SUGGESTED AREAS OF CONTENT

The content of health courses in the senior high school will be modified by a variety of factors which make it difficult to construct a list of areas or topics which should receive attention in all schools. Much will depend on the quality and extent of previous instruction; the needs, interests, and range of individual differences of the students; the available time, staff, and teaching resources; the community needs, problems, and attitudes. The following is a composite list drawn from surveys and studies of individual and community health needs, research studies and opinions of authorities in the field. It is not intended to be complete or final and should be examined in connection with the list on pages 204-205 in order to co-ordinate the offerings in junior and senior high school.

1. Structure and function of the human body; scientific concepts relative to normal and abnormal function; contributions of scientific research and medical practice to information relative to maintenance of normal function

2. The balanced regimen of food, exercise, rest, sleep, relaxation, work, and study; evaluation of individual health needs

3. Mental health, personal adjustment, development of emotional maturity, establishment of maturing sex roles, boy-girl relations

4. Preparation for marriage, family life, child care; health implications of heredity and eugenics; food budgeting; health aspects of housing; budgeting for health insurance, medical and dental services; spending the health dollar wisely

5. Communicable and noncommunicable diseases with emphasis on adolescent and adult disease problems; prevention and control of disease and illness including heart disease, cancer, diabetes, mental illness, alcoholism

6. Consumer health education: choosing health products and services; scientific health care as contrasted with fads, quackery, and charlatanism; evaluating sources of information; awareness of nature of advertising appeals and "gimmicks" used to sell products

7. Personal and community programs and practices in accident prevention and emergency care; driver education; recreational and occupational safety; fire prevention; civil defense and disasters

8. Protection from hazards of poisons, drugs, narcotics; environmental hazards of radiation, air pollution, water contamination; chemical hazards in food production, processing, and distribution

9. Community health: local, state, national, and international; tax-supported and voluntary health agency programs; contributions of individual citizens to community health

10. Health careers in medicine, dentistry, nursing, public health, teaching, hospital administration, laboratory services, dietetics, physical therapy, occupational therapy, and allied professions.

METHODS OF TEACHING

To a great extent, effective health teaching depends upon the teacher's ability to motivate student behavior. Motivation is the driving force behind behavior, and therefore is the key to learning. Motives initiate, sustain, and direct the individual's activities. Motivation that stems from the student's own goals facilitates learning because he has the active desire to learn. Derived motivation may be accomplished by methods or techniques which relate learning to things that students want to do. For example, the field trip as a method is related to the student's desire to explore or to travel. Other motives derived from needs include competition, an important stimulus to learn; co-operation; desire for approval; desire for acceptance; desire for mastery; and desire for status.

When students are given many and varied opportunities to participate in health education activities, they are engaging in the type of health education that teen-agers need and desire. This infers that they are given situations in which they identify problems, and take part in the planning, development, and evaluation of their experiences. In short, they are given the opportunity to work out solutions to their own health problems under skillful guidance.

Functional teaching methods provide the student with something that he can do now, something that enriches his life. He may participate in the activity by constructing something; he may think through a problem and propose a solution; he may express himself orally or in writing, showing feeling or demonstrating an attitude which influences others. He may observe others in a demonstration or field trip. He may see and hear a movie and relate his observations to his particular problem. He may work with a group in planning a course of action or reaching a decision about personal, family, or community health matters. Effective health teaching results in feelings of satisfaction, success, and achievement for the student.

Some teaching methods provide greater opportunity for student participation than others. Such teaching methods promote for the student the acquisition of scientific knowledge, critical thinking, wholesome attitudes based on facts, and opportunities for action about health matters of special concern to him, his family, and his community.

Problem solving. The problem solving method is a means of applying the scientific method to instruction in healthful living. Since man is a problem solving organism, the problem solving method is a means of utilizing direct experience that has meaning and value to the student. Also, it is a method which helps to make functional any pattern of organization used in health education—the separate course, correlation, or its inherent aspect of the core program. When properly used, problem solving facilitates understanding, develops individual judgment, and promotes decision making.

The component parts of the problem solving method which have also been discussed in previous chapters are outlined clearly in a report of the Citizenship Education Study. The major steps are presented as follows:[15]

I. Defining the problem
   a. Encountering the problem
   b. Selecting the problem
   c. Wording the problem
   d. Setting up tentative solutions
II. Working the problem
   a. Recalling known information
   b. Determining need for more information
   c. Locating sources of information
   d. Selecting and organizing information
   e. Analyzing and interpreting information
III. Drawing a conclusion
   a. Stating possible conclusions
   b. Determining the most reasonable and logical conclusions
   c. Reaching a conclusion.

A fourth component needs to be added to this outline, that of applying conclusions to life situations or translating findings into individual and group behavior.

Some illustrations of health education problems are the following:

1. *Personal health problems.* Is my weight appropriate for my age, height, and body build? Should I smoke? How can I stop smoking? Should I accept a drink at a social function? How can I determine whether or not my diet is adequate? Why should I exercise regularly? How should one choose a life partner?

2. *Social health problems.* How can accidents be reduced in our school, in our community? How can dental health education reduce the incidence of dental caries? How can citizens become aware of the false advertising, quacks, and nostrums being promoted in their communities? How do the community health agencies contribute to total community health?

The foregoing examples illustrate the types of problems that may be identified in a sharing process between teacher and students. Such problems have meaning and purpose for the indi-

---

[15] The Citizenship Education Study. *Problem Solving.* Detroit: Wayne University Press, 1953. p. 4-10.

vidual student. The teacher's further role in the problem solving method is to guide and assist the student in attacking problems, gathering data, drawing conclusions, and presenting findings and conclusions together with a plan for applying the results of the conclusions. Problem solving as a method stimulates creative work, critical thinking, and provides experience in making sound judgments in health matters of personal, family, and community concern.

Discussion. In almost every phase of teaching, discussion is an oral means of student participation which stimulates thinking and provides for expression of individual thoughts and opinions. It is a medium for pooling of ideas and broadening of concepts. It is a method of student-teacher planning for solution of problems. Discussion can be entirely free in connection with a specific health education topic, but to be more effective, should be guided by the teacher or a student leader. The leader helps the group focus on the topic or problem and assures opportunity for all to participate. In effective discussion, a summary of points is made, and a definite decision is reached by the class or group as a result of the discussion. Good discussion is a great facilitator of understanding. Without understanding, a class may be completely opposed to a process such as fluoridation of the public water supply. After pointed discussion in which both sides of the issue are heard, the majority of the class may decide that fluoridation of the public water supply is an important public health procedure and that it helps to solve the problem of dental caries among children. A panel discussion in which students present their findings on a particular topic, with give and take among panel members, is an effective way to develop interest or to culminate a unit such as one on tobacco or alcohol.

Committee work. The organization of a class into committees is an appropriate way to attack certain health problems, such as investigation of the school environment or of school health service activities, or as a division of labor to study selected health problems in the community. Committee work facilitates "research" and discussion, and promotes group action and personal-social relationships.

Buzz sessions. Buzz sessions are a form of committee organization that take their name from the hum or "buzz" of group participants. Buzz groups are organized into small discussion gatherings of five, six, or seven members. The class may be divided into buzz groups to discuss one topic such as "criteria for selection of a life partner." Many ideas are expressed as a result of such discussion. Each group reports the summary of its discussion, and a class summary is made from the various group reports.

Another use of the buzz groups is to assign a different topic to each group. For example, in a consideration of health vocations, buzz groups can be organized to discuss the possibilities and potentialities of each of several vocations: medicine, dentistry, nursing, health education, medical social work, sanitation hospital administration, and others. A topic such as this cannot be discussed profitably unless the discussants have some background of information. The discussions could be preceded by reading and individual research prior to the sharing of findings and ideas. The buzz session stimulates discussion and oral participation, and fosters creative thinking in relation to identifying and attacking personal and community health problems.

Experimentation. Experimentation is a scientific method to prove or disprove a hypothesis or to provide concrete evidence to support a theory or concept. It encompasses a number of other methods including investigation, discussion, problem solving, observation, and demonstration. In conducting experimentation it is important to understand and be able to apply necessary techniques in order to carry out the experimentation. Experiments involve planning, construction, organization, ability to follow directions, exacting technique, testing and retesting, analysis of results, and interpretation of results. Nutrition experiments by the class on a good breakfast, experiments studying the growth and action of microorganisms, safety experiments, driving experiments such as reaction time or braking distance for stopping conducted in driver education are a few of the many types of activities that can apply experimentation to health instruction.

Use of resource persons. Resource persons from the school and community can contribute valuable scientific health information which may be impossible or at least difficult to procure in other ways. The best use of a resource person is to utilize an authority from the school or community when specific information is needed to help the students progress with a particular unit. The well-informed teacher should be recognized as an important resource person in the development of a teaching unit in health education. It is shortsighted to overlook the teacher's background of training and experience as a source of information for pupils.

He can contribute from his own background of scientific information and probably will be the most important and readily available resource person for the health class.

The school nurse and school physician may be invited in to prepare students for health appraisals and to interpret health service activities and procedures to students. These health personnel are employed as resource persons to discuss such problems as menstruation, overweight, underweight, acne, and endocrine gland function and malfunction. A home economics teacher is an excellent resource person to discuss personal appearance with both boys and girls. A happily married couple serves as an inspirational team to discuss marriage and parenthood.

Resource persons from the community agencies help to enrich the program, provide information about the health of the community, and bring specialized knowledge about community health problems and how community groups are organized to solve these problems. Representatives of voluntary health agencies such as the American Heart Association, the American Cancer Society, and the National Tuberculosis Association bring to the students, or make possible through interviews, the latest findings regarding the specific health problems these agencies are attempting to attack.

The public health educator is often well suited to inform students how community groups are organized to solve such problems as dental health needs, provision for additional public health services, establishment of a well-baby clinic or a class for prospective mothers and fathers, and rabies control. The sanitarian is of assistance in discussing problems of environmental sanitation and planning with the class the procedures for an environmental survey of the school. These are a few examples of resource persons whose contributions are valuable to vitalize instruction.

Demonstrations, dramatizations, field trips, and the use of audio-visual aids are effective methods frequently employed in high-school health teaching. They can be utilized for arousing interest, for development of the unit, or for culminating experiences. These methods are discussed in Chapter Twelve.

Aids to improved teaching. The successful health teacher uses a number of devices or techniques to interest students and to assist him in making methods more functional. Some examples of these techniques are the following:

Census blank. The teacher keeps a census blank of vital statistics on each student. This includes selected and pertinent information from the health record card, the counselor folder, or cumulative record folder, and usually consists of the home address, telephone number, class schedule, family data, and such information about the pupil as hobbies, activities, and service to the community. The purpose of the census is to enable the teacher to have at his finger tips information that helps him understand each student and his behavior.

The autobiography. Writing an autobiography assists the student to look squarely at his strengths and weaknesses. It gives the teacher insight into individual needs and interests. This is a valuable activity to use in a unit on mental health or one on vocations.

Teacher logs. Teacher logs of class procedures assist the teacher in objective evaluation of successes and failures. Keeping a log of methods, procedures, and techniques used in teaching health helps the teacher identify those that are successful, those that should be repeated, and those that should be rejected or restudied before future use. To keep a log it is necessary to make a note of the topic or unit, the subject matter or problems presented, steps in developing the teaching methods, the activities used, constructive criticism of results, and suggestions for the next time the topic or unit is taught.

Case history. Writing a case history of students who appear to have health problems or behavior problems is an excellent way of gathering pertinent information for referring an individual to the nurse or serving as a basis for a teacher-nurse conference. This gives the teacher valuable information about individual health needs and interests.

TEACHING CONTROVERSIAL HEALTH ISSUES

Every teacher is faced, at some time, with the question of what to teach and how to teach controversial issues. This may often present serious problems, beginning at the secondary-school level, when issues may be of the adult type and of concern to the adult community. The field of health offers no exception, and some of the problems involved are highly charged with emotion. In general, such issues can be divided into three broad categories:

1. Issues which are scientifically settled, such as fluoridation of the public water supply, but which are being debated locally and thus may be vigorously controversial in a particular community

2. Issues which are scientifically unsettled and thus scientifically controversial, such as whether there is a direct causal relationship between tobacco smoking and lung cancer

3. Issues with strong moral overtones and opposing convictions, such as whether abstinence or temperance is the best approach in alcohol education.

Policies and practices. Instruction in certain of these topics may be mandatory, as in the case of legal requirements for alcohol education. On the other hand, in some areas, certain limitations may be placed on instruction. Also, in the heat of local controversy, it may be considered desirable to postpone consideration of an issue. In any case, the teacher should be familiar with requirements or restrictions that may exist and be aware of local factors that may impinge.

Sometimes a controversial issue will be introduced by a pupil's comment or question during a discussion period. Or, the teacher himself may bring the matter into the discussion inadvertently or intentionally. A general interest among pupils and readiness to consider the issue may be quickly apparent. If not, it may be obvious to the discerning teacher that only a little follow up would be needed to create a state of readiness. At this point, it is wise "to make haste slowly"; more than ever the teacher becomes a guide and arbiter rather than a director or authority.

Teaching approaches. There is probably no one best way to teach controversial issues but there is one common element in the process. This is the maintenance of an impartial and objective attitude on the part of the instructor. Even though the teacher may have strong feelings on the subject, he is obliged to see that both sides are fully and fairly presented. Such objectivity will transfer, in some measure, to his pupils and set the stage for unbiased consideration of the issue.

Careful orientation is the first step in assuring a fair hearing for both sides of the controversy. This includes a statement of the problem, its nature and scope, and how it relates to people in general and to those living in a given community. An equally important part of the orientation is to make certain that pupils understand that the issue is controversial, why it is controversial, and that there are many intelligent people ranged on both sides. Depending upon the background of the class, the teacher may have a large part in the orientation process or merely guide discussion. When pupils are well acquainted with the problem, well-placed and judicious questions may bring out each of these points. Otherwise, it is well for the teacher to delineate them himself carefully so that there will be no reason for confusion or distortion of the problem.

Youth has an innate sense of fairness, which may be of great help to the teacher in handling controversial issues. Psychologically, therefore, a good next question is: How can we be sure that each side is fairly treated in our consideration of this problem? In class discussion other questions logically follow, such as: Where can we get the real facts? How can we tell which arguments are scientifically sound? What should be our plan of work? Perhaps the last question should be answered first.

A plan for work and study. A class that has had experience with the problem solving approach will soon come up with a plan for work and study. Again, the place of the teacher will vary, depending on the background of the class. Under careful guidance, the work plan may take form somewhat as follows:

1. Delineating the problem—its various facets and the background factors involved

2. Locating, gathering, analyzing, and evaluating available data

3. Developing and summarizing the arguments for and against the issue

4. Comparing the pros and cons, drawing conclusions, and making decisions

5. Evaluating the results and the process of work and study.

After such an outline is finished, it will be readily apparent that attention has been given not only to the last question pertaining to a plan of work but also to the first relating to a fair hearing for both sides.

Two other questions dealing with sources of data and the authenticity of the information obtained from such sources remain to be considered. A wealth of material from numerous sources is usually available on controversial issues, so that the problem for pupils is often more a matter of selecting and evaluating rather than locating and procuring materials. With appropriate suggestions from the teacher, pupils can be guided to see the need and to formulate criteria for evaluating the information found in such materials. Such criteria might develop along the following lines:

1. Are the facts in reports for the public stated in clear language that can be understood by most high-school students?

2. Are ridicule, name-calling, and appeals to fear, prejudice, and emotion omitted from supposed statement of fact?

3. Are the claims made acceptable in terms of good common sense and logical reasoning?

4. Is the practice, study, or statement approved or accepted by professional medical, dental, and public health associations?

5. If research is cited to prove a point, was the research conducted by a reputable scientific institution?

6. If research is cited to prove a point, was the research published in a reputable professional journal?

7. If opinions of scientific authorities are cited to support a statement, are these persons identified by name, position, place of residence, and professional standing?

8. Are the scientific authorities cited—individual or group—in support of a particular point properly qualified and identified with the specific issue?

Ordinarily, single criteria will not reveal the authenticity of a statement or report. But scrutinizing a statement in the light of each of these and other criteria is a good test of its validity and reliability. Guiding and encouraging youth to appraise carefully the things they read, hear, and view relating to controversial issues with such criteria as yardsticks is an important task of the teacher.

Drawing conclusions and making decisions. The gathering, sorting, sifting, appraising, and summarizing of data relating to a controversial issue involve the discriminating application of many of the teaching techniques and procedures described earlier in the chapter under the problem solving process. But these pupil experiences, as important as they are, are only a means to an end; finally, they culminate in the drawing of conclusions and the making of decisions.

To assist pupils in drawing conclusions and making decisions, it is often helpful to group summary statements on the pros and cons of an issue in double-column chart form. This is illus-

trated in the following chart, which gives some of the pros and
cons on the use of tobacco.

To Smoke or Not To Smoke

Pro	Con
The active principle of tobacco is nicotine, a sedative which acts quickly. There are times when a sedative is needed	There are other sedatives when one is really needed. A sedative sometimes is used as a crutch; this seems to be true in the case of most smokers
Social customs sometimes make it easier to smoke than not to. Smoking is very much a part of today's living	The person who dares to be different is more admired than rejected. Many persons do not need to smoke to be accepted
There may be tobacco-sensitive people who should not smoke. Many people who do smoke have no cough and show no digestive disturbances	Smoking irritates the mucous membranes of the mouth, nose, and throat, frequently resulting in "smokers" cough. Some also have unfavorable digestive reactions to smoking
Correlations of smoking with heart disease do not prove a causal relationship; there are many other factors involved	It has been demonstrated that smokers, heavy cigarette smokers particularly, have more heart and blood vessel disease than nonsmokers
The evidence against motor vehicle exhausts as a causal factor in the increased incidence of lung cancer is great	There is a strong suspicion and increasing evidence of a causal relationship between heavy cigarette smoking and lung cancer
Many persons who give up smoking substitute eating for smoking and become obese. Obesity is a major health hazard in terms of longevity and certain degenerative diseases	It has been shown that heavy cigarette smokers who give up smoking for the rest of their lives have less lung cancer than those who continue to smoke
It is careless habits of smokers and not smoking itself that causes the fires which are sometimes attributed to smoking	Smoking is the cause of many tragic fires which kill hundreds of people and cost millions of dollars each year

Pro	*Con*
The tobacco industry is highly competitive, and consequently tobacco is a "good buy" in today's market. Where else could the smoker get so much satisfaction for such a small amount?	Smoking is a costly habit; the average cigarette smoker, once this practice is ingrained, can expect to spend about $2 a week, or more than $100 a year on his habit.

Sometimes learning experiences, relating to problem solving and controversial issues, that are otherwise exemplary, lose much of their educational impact because they are not carried through to the point of decision making. An objective look at the pros and cons in the illustration indicates why this is true; the shades of difference on which a decision could be made are not too great. Some of the difficulty, however, is due to misunderstanding by pupils as to what decisions need to be made and how such decisions can be arrived at.

What are the options open to the pupils in a health class that has reached the point of decision making on an issue such as the question of smoking?

1. They may make only personal decisions on whether they as individuals will or will not smoke.

2. They may find it possible to achieve a class consensus that smoking is bad, is probably unhealthy, is questionable, or has not been proved bad.

3. They may *not* find it possible to reach a consensus as to whether smoking is good or bad. They may be evenly divided; some may feel they are undecided.

It is the last option—the option to agree to disagree—on which pupils are often inhibited. Most of the pupils' training has been oriented toward lining up definitely on one side or the other. While the teacher will want to encourage reaching a consensus whenever possible, he will not want to discourage a division of the class based on sound individual decisions. Neither will he wish to discourage individual indecision based on a feeling that the evidence is inadequate or inconclusive. There are times when the decision to be undecided is best.

EVALUATION

Evaluation is the process of assessing progress in terms of established objectives. Three approaches to evaluation in health instruction are helpful in charting progress gained. *The first type of evaluation* is appraising the program of health instruction. In program evaluation an attempt is made to appraise one's own program against a set of standards or criteria established for a recognized successful health instruction program. This entails a comparison of one's program with other programs in the district, the state, or throughout the nation. One of the major purposes of this type of evaluation is to identify gaps or weaknesses which can be remedied with replanning and further curriculum development.

The second type of evaluation of senior high school health education is an appraisal in terms of how effectively changes in behavior were accomplished. Some of these changes will not be known until the students are adults, at which time their individual health and their actions for health in their communities can be assessed. Some evidence and definite clues to changes resulting from the health instruction can be collected through appraisal of knowledge, attitudes, and practices. This is discussed in detail in Chapter Fourteen.

A third type of evaluation is the appraisal of one's own methodology of health teaching. This can be accomplished by evaluating the course or methods used as a culminating technique at the end of the term. The following steps enable the appraisal to be made:

1. List the goals established for the course or method
2. Determine to what extent these goals were accomplished
3. Determine how effectively the activities planned to meet these goals changed behavior of students
4. Revise the goals for future use
5. Summarize the value of the experience for future teaching.

SELECTED REFERENCES

AMERICAN ASSOCIATION FOR HEALTH, PHYSICAL EDUCATION, AND RECREATION. *Current Administrative Problems; Athletics, Health Education, Physical Education, and Recreation.* Washington, D.C.: the Association, a department of the National Education Association, 1960. 197 p.

AMERICAN ASSOCIATION FOR HEALTH, PHYSICAL EDUCATION, AND RECREATION. "Health, Physical Education, and Recreation in the Secondary School." *Bulletin of the National Association of Secondary-School Principals* 44: 1-206; May 1960.

ANDERSON, CARL L. *School Health Practice.* Second edition. St. Louis: C. V. Mosby Co., 1960. Chapters 11, p. 270-303; 13, p. 339-89; 14, p. 390-427; 15, p. 428-42; 17, p. 476-505.

BURTON, WILLIAM H. "Basic Principles in a Good Teaching-Learning Situation." *Phi Delta Kappan* 39: 242-43; March 1958.

BYRD, OLIVER E. "The Health Curriculum: 500 Topics." *Journal of School Health* 28: 89-96; March 1958.

THE CITIZENSHIP EDUCATION STUDY. *Problem Solving.* Detroit: Wayne University Press, 1953.

CUSHMAN, WESLEY. "Problem Solving—An Effective Method for Health Teaching." *Journal of School Health* 23: 154-58; May 1953.

GROUT, RUTH E. *Health Teaching in Schools.* Third edition. Philadelphia: W. B. Saunders Co., 1958. Chapters 2, 4, 6, 7, 9, 10, and 11.

HAAG, JESSIE H. *School Health Program.* New York: Henry Holt & Co., 1958. Chapters 23-28, p. 321-434.

HARNETT, ARTHUR L., and SHAW, JOHN H. *Effective School Health Education.* New York: Appleton-Century-Crofts, 1959. Chapters 1, p. 3-17; 3, p. 34-58; 11-14, p. 252-366.

IRWIN, LESLIE W.; HUMPHREY, JAMES H.; and JOHNSON, WARREN H. *Methods and Materials in School Health Education.* St. Louis: C. V. Mosby Co., 1956. Chapters 5-18, p. 70-349.

JOHNS, EDWARD B. *School Health Education Evaluative Study. Los Angeles Area 1954-1959. An Evaluation Research Study.* Los Angeles: University of California Printing Department, 1960. 128 p.

MEANS, RICHARD K. "Practical Instructional Methods in Health Education." *Journal of School Health* 28: 223-27; September 1958.

OBERTEUFFER, DELBERT. *School Health Education.* Third edition. New York: Harper & Brothers, 1960. Chapters 3-9, p. 51-278.

SCHNEIDER, ROBERT E. *Methods and Materials of Health Education.* Philadelphia: W. B. Saunders Co., 1958. Chapters 4-12, p. 57-302.

SLIEPCEVICH, ELENA, and CARROLL, CHARLES. "Correlation of Health with Other Areas of the High School Curriculum." *Journal of School Health* 28: 283-92; November 1958.

STARR, HELEN M. "Today's Pupil—Health-informed or Health-educated?" *Journal of Health, Physical Education, Recreation* 25: 18-22, 58; September 1954.

TRUMP, J. LLOYD. *Images of the Future.* Washington, D.C.: Commission on the Experimental Study of the Utilization of the Staff in the Secondary School, National Association of Secondary-School Principals, NEA, 1959. 46 p.

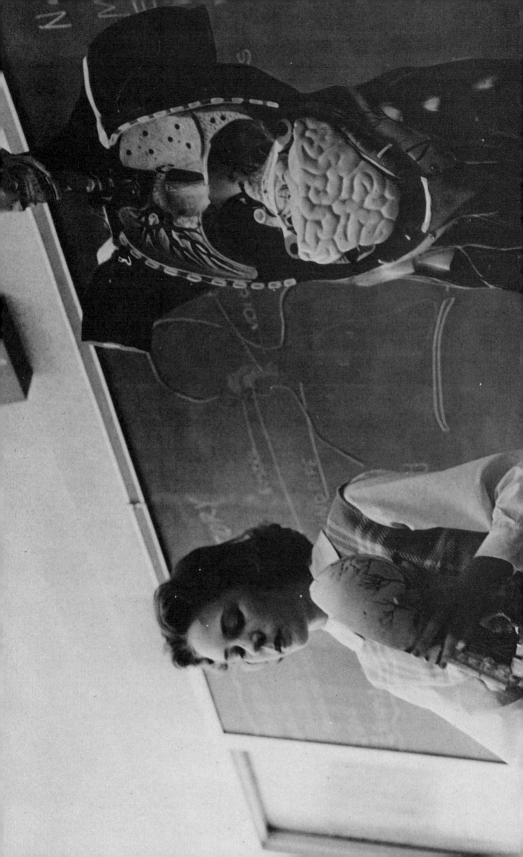

Related Areas of the Secondary School

The broad field of health includes many different areas. Nutrition, prevention of disease, physiology, dental health, family life education, safety, personal adjustment, and consumer health education are but a few. The findings of new research are being made available almost daily and add to an already extensive body of information. To encompass in one or two courses all understandings that need emphasis during the secondary-school years is difficult. Correlation and integration with other subject areas appear to be highly desirable, although this does not obviate the need for separately organized health education courses.

The universality of health. Many opportunities exist for teaching health in the secondary-school curriculum. It is important that adolescents develop the concept that health is basic to optimum living. The use of potential opportunities for health education in related areas therefore becomes meaningful. The combined impact of these learnings helps pupils to appreciate that their life goals can be more nearly approached when health is at its best. To assist them to know that many disciplines contribute to understandings about health, and that health is interwoven with all school activities, becomes the privilege of every teacher. As each teacher highlights the health implications of his courses, pupils gradually begin to generalize about the universality of health, its import to their success and happiness, and its meaning to the human race.

CURRICULUM EXPLORATION AND LEADERSHIP ESSENTIAL

Utilization of the many opportunities for health education in the various subject fields involves careful exploration and study on the part of all school departments. Each course must be analyzed to discover and to develop its potentialities for health instruction. Likewise, the various services and activities of the school need to be examined in terms of their health education possibilities. Success in utilizing the total curriculum for health education depends upon the leadership provided by the administration. Because of the degree of departmentalization in the secondary school and because of the specialization of their preparation, teachers at this level are likely to think primarily in terms of their own subject matter. Sometimes, too, they may regard with skepticism, or even with hostility, suggested changes from the traditional. The school administrator's task is to help his faculty realize that there are important contributions that each member can make to the health of his pupils, and that emphasis on the health implications in each area of the curriculum is not only their responsibility but also their privilege.

Co-ordination important. Co-ordination is the key to success of the secondary-school health program. Co-ordination helps to make desirable health behavior, as well as knowledge and appreciation of health, a vital part of all school experiences. It helps to keep these objectives before teachers. It helps to prevent excessive repetition and to fill gaps in the health curriculum. It assures parents that all teachers are working toward similar goals.

The machinery for co-ordination may vary. A school health council or curriculum committee, as discussed in Chapter Ten, may be organized for this purpose. The health education co-ordinator or consultant may be assigned leadership responsibility, with one of his functions to help committees and councils in the development of the health implications in each school subject. Different school systems have employed diverse methods. The important idea is to set up practical machinery so that co-ordination of the health program can be achieved.

Meaningful experiences the goal. The contributions of various subject matter areas to health education vary according to a variety of factors. In many classes health learnings are not great and are largely incidental. In others the concepts, understandings, and attitudes related to health are a fundamental and integral part of the learning experiences. It is reasonable to expect that music, art, foreign languages, and business education provide fewer meaningful related experiences in health education than do science, home economics, physical education, and social studies. The contributions of the former group may be considered to be largely incidental and infrequent, while the latter areas deserve serious consideration as vehicles for planned health teaching. Not every teacher needs to feel that he is a teacher of health, but each alert and interested teacher will capitalize on incidents that offer opportunity to contribute to attitudes and understandings important to health.

The old slogan, "Every teacher is a health teacher," while possessing some validity, is responsible for some rather ludicrous attempts to make every teaching and learning experience health related. Health teaching is likely to be labored and uninteresting when it is artificially inserted into unrelated subject matter or learning experiences. Singing about health, writing verses or essays about health, or basing mathematical calculations on health-related problems cannot be justified when these so-called correlations are inappropriate and forced. The teacher contributes effectively to good health education when he is sufficiently informed, and endowed with enough common sense and judgment to select suitable areas for correlation.

Ways of providing related health experiences. There are several ways in which learning experiences that influence attitudes, behavior, and concepts related to health can be made an integral part of the curriculum. The units taught in elementary schools usually transcend subject matter lines and are centered around life activities. It is often difficult to determine whether a particular sequence of experiences is organized as "science," "health education," or "social studies." This is integration at its best and can never be charged with artificiality. This same concept may extend into the core courses and broad fields curricular organization in the secondary schools.

A second way of providing related health learnings is to utilize appropriate subject matter and experiences in particular courses for purposes of health teaching as these relate to the major goals and objectives of the course. Health learnings may not be emphasized as such and pupils may be unaware that they are participating in health education experiences. Health becomes related to broader areas of experience and assumes a meaningful relationship within them.

Finally, specific units in health education may be assigned to teachers of social studies, home economics, science, or physical education. If there is no separate health course this allocation of important health units to other appropriate courses becomes imperative. When this method is utilized it is particularly important that teachers assigned to these units be appropriately prepared in the health sciences and health education. Otherwise,

they may be guilty of transmitting health misinformation, prejudice, and faddism. It is strange that some teachers and administrators share the fallacy that "anyone can teach health." The
suggestions found in this chapter for relating health teaching
to other curriculum areas can be successful only if the teacher
has the necessary training, background, interest, and insight to
make them work. Opportunities for health teaching in subjects
found in the traditionally organized secondary-school curriculum
will be found in the following section.

SUGGESTIONS FOR CORRELATION AND INTEGRATION

Physical Education

One of the major reasons for including physical education in
the school curriculum is the contribution it makes to the health
of the student. Stated another way, the superior physical education program contributes both to the personal health of the
individual participant and to his or her knowledge and understanding of life. The physical educator must apply health principles continually in carrying out activities. Students in turn are
encouraged to participate and to reinforce good health behavior
thereby.

Health education in the form of direct instruction may be
planned or incidental. Planned instruction may refer to a total
class period devoted to health teaching which replaces physical
education on a particular day or it may relate to but a few
minutes purposefully set aside for health instruction in conjunction with a particular activity. Incidental teaching is, on the
other hand, that which is unplanned and which arises spontane-
ously due to an incident in a class or around the physical education facilities. The conscientious physical educator will be continually alert to opportunities for health teaching in which the
motivations and readiness for learning in the students are high,
and in which the situation arises naturally out of regular class
activity. In addition, he should always assess the results of
these incidental experiences to determine whether or not some
planned instruction in a similar situation might be appropriate
in the future.

The following are suggested opportunities which may challenge the health and physical educator.

Relation of physical activity to organic fitness, by

Emphasizing the importance of exercise to full development of the circulatory and respiratory systems

Pointing out the importance of these fully functioning systems to total health

Relation of games and sports to health, by

Pointing up the opportunities these activities bring for increased and widened social and mental health in the present school situation

Highlighting the creative, wholesome use of time which sports entail, in contrast to possible law-breaking alternatives

Explaining the social role that tobacco, alcoholic beverages, barbiturates, and narcotics play, how their use is incompatible with competition in sports and is both symptomatic of ill health and further damaging

Dwelling further on the carry-over value of certain skills and learnings to continued enjoyment of active participation in sports beyond the school

Stressing the increasingly important role active sports play in maintaining the total health of the modern, sedentary adult

Relations among fatigue, rest, relaxation, and sleep, by

Explaining the development of fatigue and the need for balancing activity with rest

Explaining further the importance of regular hours of sleep

Pointing out that an activity may result in both fatigue and relaxation

Importance of a well-conditioned body, by

Picturing the well-conditioned body as a valuable asset which enables its "possessor" to attempt and accomplish more in a greater variety of activities than others less well conditioned

Stressing the lifelong importance of habits of body conditioning formed in the youthful years

Relations among nutrition, activity, and body weight, by

Emphasizing that the regular consumption of a well-balanced diet is essential for both ready energy and needed body growth

Explaining that calories consumed in excess of those used for heat and energy are stored as fat

Noting that a program of regular physical activity allows an individual to eat more without fat deposit

Stressing balance in diet rather than reliance on a few "fad" foods

Importance of safety in activity, by

Teaching the proper use of equipment, showing how misuse can bring about injury

Emphasizing common-sense rules and good techniques in and around swimming pools and other bodies of water

Pointing out the reasons for matching competitors for weight, size, and maturity in some activities

Emphasizing safe conduct in and about shower and locker rooms

Teaching the principles of first aid and the recognition of emergency situations

Guidance of students on individual health problems, by

Answering personal questions which students ask

Referring students to proper health personnel, as such seems appropriate

Sharing information about students with other teachers and guidance personnel

Using health records as one basis for counseling

Encouraging those students with remediable defects to have them corrected.

Social Studies

Community health protection as directed by local and state health departments:
Community sanitation
Control of disease
Health education
Maternal and child welfare
Poison control centers

Federal health protection through grants-in-aid, research, education, and the setting up of national standards concerning:
Food, drugs, cosmetics, milk, and meat
Communicable disease control
Air pollution
Radiation levels

Functions and programs of voluntary health agencies

Consumer health education

Millions of dollars spent annually in United States by people for self-medication, quack remedies, and food fads

Criteria for judging the merits of health services and products

Cost of illness to the family and community in terms of financial loss, work hours lost, divided homes, juvenile delinquency, and public assistance

Problems in dental, medical, hospital, and pharmaceutical costs and facilities

Budgeting for hospital, medical, and accident insurance

The effect of economic conditions on health

The effect of improved transportation on health

The work of the World Health Organization; implications of its program for world peace

Acquaintance with the goals and activities of the World Medical Association

Child labor regulations; how to obtain work permits

Relation of labor laws to health

Workers in the field of health; need for health personnel

Housing and health, including slum clearance

Importance of citizen interest in and support of sound health legislation

Value of vital statistics to the individual and to the community
    Reasons for birth and death records
    Vital statistics and community planning, support of public health agencies

Participation of citizens in community health projects, such as the blood bank

Citizenship and the family: understanding and appreciation that the family gives
    Shelter, food, clothing
    Health guidance and health care
    Sense of belonging, love, affection
    Pattern of moral standards

Citizenship and the community: respect for and obedience to rules and regulations related to
    Protection by police and fire departments
    Sanitary measures regarding garbage, trash, and sewage disposal
    Protection of property of others

Automobile, pedestrian, and bicycle safety

Proper use of recreational facilities including forests, lakes, streams

Protection of water supply from contamination

Citizenship and the school: understanding the importance of

Safety standards and practices

Health services available to pupils

Environmental health conditions including proper heating, lighting, ventilation, sanitation, cleanliness

Lunchroom facilities and opportunities for improved nutrition

Staying home when ill

Getting along with others; participating in school activities

Individual responsibility and citizenship

Health a factor in citizenship

Individual responsibility for maintaining health; for co-operating with health agencies; for knowing the health resources of the community; for protecting the health of his family.

Biology

Identical characteristics of all living things: movement, nutrition, respiration, growth, response to stimuli, reproduction

Identical composition of single cells: protoplasm and nuclei

Composition of protoplasm, a mixture of elements, resulting in need for a variety of foods

Comparison of food needs of man with those of other animals and plants; enrichment and fortification of foods

Knowledge of life processes in humans

Structure of body and the way it works: framework, movement, digestion, metabolism, circulation, reproduction, nervous control

Relations of activity, fatigue, sleep, rest, nutrition, waste elimination

Fighting disease

Changes in adolescence and changes of old age

Microscopic organisms helpful and harmful to man

Communicable diseases including tuberculosis and venereal diseases

Disinfection, sterilization, pasteurization

Insects as carriers of disease

Effects of alcohol, tobacco, and narcotics on living tissues

Problems of cancer, heart disease, diabetes, and other chronic and degenerative diseases.

Chemistry

Chemical constituents of living matter

The use of oxygen in the body

Air pollution

The production of energy in the body

Chemical processes in medical diagnosis, such as urinalysis and blood tests

Acid-base balance in the body

Electrolysis

Cosmetics and drugs

Conversion of sea water into fresh water.

Physics

Effects of temperature and humidity on health: results of overheating on efficiency and health

Climatic conditions and effect on health: the sea, water supply, wind, gravity

Effect of sun's rays on living tissue

Electrical hazards

Mechanics of body movement

The human eye and light
    Elementary optics and corrective lenses
    Illumination in home and school for prevention of eye fatigue

The human ear and sound

Flying and exploration of outer space
    Heat and cold in outer space and protection of life
    Effects of space flight on the body
    Effects of high-altitude flying on the body

Effects of radiation on health; use of x-ray for medical diagnosis and therapy

Use of atomic energy for health.

English

Discussion of current authoritative articles on health topics and their relationship to present-day living

Consideration of environmental hygiene as portrayed in novels of earlier times

Reading and discussion of biographies of "health heroes"

Discussion of physical and emotional characteristics as they have influenced the behavior of the main characters in novels; better understanding of human problems through literature

Writing feature stories on health topics for the school newspaper

Writing of themes on health topics such as
How health departments can protect our health
Slum clearance and health
Civic improvements and health
Recreation in our town
Health careers and health workers in our community
Health problems in our community

Oral reports, debates, panel discussions, sociodrama.

Speech

Individual reports, panel presentations, extemporaneous speaking on the importance of health to the individual, the nation, and the world

Oral reports on leading health problems in the United States, in the state, and in the community

Debate or panel discussions on current health topics, such as health insurance, hospitalization plans, cost of illness to the community

Oral reports on present-day research in medicine, including mental health, dentistry, and public health

Role-playing and dramatic skits to portray individual and group behavior patterns

Discussion of the effect on personality development, social interaction, and vocational achievement of voice quality, enunciation, fluency, and vocabulary.

History

Influence of epidemics on history

Influence of war on health

Progress in medical science
Conquest of specific diseases
Advances in surgery, x-ray diagnosis, and treatment

Influence of health on the development of governments

Influence of inventions on health: microscope, electricity, electronics (hearing aid), automobile, airplane, central heating, refrigeration

Influence of research on health: vaccines, vitamins, drugs, insulin, iodized salt, water fluoridation

Conquest of specific diseases—diabetes, venereal diseases, tetanus, polio

Famous people of each century whose accomplishments have improved the health of mankind—van Leeuwenhoek, Pasteur, Lister, Jenner, Curie, Roentgen, Clara Barton, Florence Nightingale, Banting, Alexander Fleming, Jonas Salk

History of health professions.

Mathematics

Graphs to show growth in height and weight

Family budget, with emphasis on money spent for consumer health needs

The cost of sickness to the individual, to the family, and to the community

Graphs on absence due to illness in the local school and cost in terms of loss of average daily attendance funds

Graphs on number of students in local schools who are immunized against smallpox, diphtheria, whooping cough, and polio

Morbidity and mortality rates
    Calculation of rates and ratios regarding specific illnesses, deaths, births.

Home Economics

Nutrition
    Significance to the individual
    Feeding the family
    Food during pregnancy

Preparation for marriage and responsible parenthood

Effective home living

Infant care
    Feeding (with stress on importance of breast feeding)
    Bathing
    Health protection
    Understanding of growth and behavior
    Adjustment of family to baby

Safety in the home

Home nursing

Personal appearance

Problems of adjustment
  To the family
  To friends of both sexes
  To school.

Industrial Arts

Safety education
  Safe handling of machinery and tools
  Color coding, goggles, floor marking, safety devices
  Prompt reporting of all accidents, even minor ones, to instructor
Emergency procedures in shop
  First aid kit available; plan of procedure known to all shop students
Driver training
  Conduct of driver training for pupils in schools in which this program is assigned to industrial education
Transmission of infection: close working on machines and across work benches
  Need for prompt exclusion of suspicious cases of illness to prevent further spread of infection
Emotional adjustment: learning to work with others on team projects.

Business Education

The family budget (budgeting for food, shelter, clothing, recreation, and medical and dental care)
Wasted money in the medicine chest
Health conditions in the business office
Health and salesmanship.

Art

Exhibits on health and safety topics and problems
Posters
Transmission of infection unless controls are set up in use of art facilities.

Music

Good posture
Transmission of infection through band instruments unless controls are exercised

Nutrition: need for good breakfast and lunch before band marches

Availability of first aid for band members on parade, at concerts, operettas, orchestra.

Foreign Languages

Food, housing, public health, and recreation in other lands

Development of natural resources and their relation to health

Family life in other cultures.

Related Activities

Secondary schools offer a wide range of services and activities for pupils. Some of these are of a general nature; others are offered or sponsored through specific departments. Most of these have elements which affect the health of pupils. Careful planning based on accurate knowledge is essential if these health concomitants are to enrich the classroom offerings.

The library. Library services can greatly enhance health instruction. Aside from the proper environment of a quiet, attractive, correctly lighted reading area, the library can encourage or lead pupils to additional reading on health topics as well as functioning as a resource for class assignments. In departmental planning for correlation of health teaching, the librarian has a distinct contribution to make. She can give leadership in setting up special displays on health materials. She can obtain and catalog the magazine offerings on health. She and her staff can keep the section of reference books on health up to date and gradually increase the number available. Pamphlets, bulletins, leaflets, and charts giving more recent facts than textbooks can be secured from authoritative sources. National, state, and local health reports can be added to the library. Special emphasis may be put on the use of health models, charts, graphs, and posters to be loaned for classroom use or studied by individual pupils.

In one state[1] a checklist for surveying the secondary-school health program suggests that libraries be included to see if they provide materials on the following topics to be correlated with different subject matter classes:

Public health organization and   Human growth and developproblems   ment

---

[1] Michigan Department of Public Instruction. *A Check List for Surveying the Secondary School Health Program.* Bulletin 346. Lansing: the Department.

Consumer buying
Medical care
Boy and girl relationships
Family education
Social hygiene
Grooming
Manners
Food and nutrition education
Dental health education
Exercise, play, recreation, games
Biographies of scientists and others contributing to healthful living
Disease control, including communicable and other diseases
Experiments and research in health
First aid and home care of the sick

Sanitation—community and home
Biological and bacteriological aspects of health
Sleep and rest
Immunization and health
Protective health measures
Education about alcohol
Health insurance and medical care plans
National health problems
World health problems
Mental health
Safety
Water supply
Conservation problems related to health such as water, land usage, food production, food conservation and distribution, recreation
Drugs

In addition, the librarian can provide schedules of radio and television programs which would help to enrich the health knowledge of faculty and pupils. Weekly or monthly radio and television guides showing public-service programs and programs sponsored by medical, dental, public health, and other authoritative sources could be placed in the library for ready reference. Such programs can give greater value to home-study assignments. Community events, such as lectures by health specialists, meetings of community or neighborhood health councils, schedules of community health projects, such as tuberculin testing and mobile x-ray programs, can be publicized by maintaining a bulletin board in the library.

The guidance program. Guidance and counseling services in the secondary school provide opportunities to encourage needed preventive and corrective services relating to pupil health problems. Health counseling, recording of health data, referrals, case conferences, follow through, home and community aid—all present opportunities for integration of health with guidance. Careful planning and co-ordination, on the part of the school guidance department with the health personnel including the health co-ordinator, nurses and health teachers, and with homeroom and classroom teachers, are essential if pupils are to be helped with their health problems and given sufficient and accurate health information.

Co-curricular Activities

Many secondary-school students participate in school activities in addition to those regularly included in classwork. Some of these activities involve an upset in regular routines of eating, rest, activity, and study. Long hours of practice or rehearsal found in programs of athletics, music activities, dramatics, and debate make demands on adolescent stamina and endurance. It is important that faculty sponsors of activities are aware of the additional physical and emotional demands made upon students who participate and plan schedules in accord with needs for regular and adequate meals, sufficient sleep, and time for study. Band leaders, chorus directors, drama directors, and athletic coaches have the opportunity to stress the importance of personal health practices and to motivate students toward observance of these practices.

It is likewise important that hygienic conditions associated with practice, travel, and participation be provided and that rules relative to prevention of illness and accidents be enforced. The faculty director can observe pupil health and behavior and can exclude promptly those pupils with evidence of infection or illness, thus decreasing the possibility of the spread of disease in the group. Pupils can be instructed about measures to be taken in case of emergency illness or accident. They can likewise be helped to recognize that their own health practices and their willingness to accept controls set up for their protection are of tremendous importance, not only to their health but also to their success in activities.

The Health Services

In an effort to better protect the health of secondary-school boys and girls, schools organize many health services, co-operate in arranging others, and encourage pupils and parents to obtain still others. In each instance such services offer excellent inherent opportunities for integration with health instruction. Regular classroom teaching, the homeroom period, the auditorium program, and physical education activities all can help to develop understanding regarding the need, the benefits, and the indi-

vidual's responsibility in regard to specific health services. The
weekly school paper, bulletin board displays, and special exhibits
can be utilized in interpreting health services to pupils. Films
and filmstrips provide still other media for this purpose.

Following is a partial list of health services and activities
that need to be utilized for health teaching:

Tuberculin testing (or chest x-ray)
Poliomyelitis, diphtheria, tetanus, and smallpox immunizations
Medical examinations
Vision screening
Hearing screening
Dental surveys
Survey of eating practices
School lunch programs
School safety activities
School sanitation and cleanliness campaign
Parent and student meetings on policies regarding homework
and other pupil activities
Co-ordination with community health services.

A more complete discussion of the contribution of health
services to health education will be found in Chapter Thirteen.

*Illustrative Unit Plan for Correlating Health Education
with Citizenship*

The Family

I. *Objectives*
  A. To understand that the family gives
    1. Shelter, food, clothing
    2. Care and protection
    3. Love, affection, companionship
    4. Sense of belonging
    5. Many different kinds of skills and understandings
    6. Moral and religious standards
    7. Health supervision
  B. To delineate ways in which each member can help his
  family progress
  C. To accept personal responsibility in the home
  D. To grow in human relations in the family.

II. *Problem*

In what ways does my family contribute to my well-being and happiness?

III. *Suggested Method*

Each teacher will wish to develop his own approach and his own method. The following suggested method is one approach:

A. The class, through discussion, can arrive at its own statement of problems and subproblems with teacher's guidance. The subproblems can then be used as subjects for interest groups, each pupil selecting the group with which he wishes to work. Each group then organizes.

B. The class next follows these steps:

1. Collection of information or data regarding the particular subproblem from several sources, such as

a. Reading properly selected source materials

b. Listening to recordings and tapes

c. Discussion with appropriate resource persons including parents, nurse, family physician, dentist, guidance counselor, school psychologist, other teachers

d. Viewing appropriate films and filmstrips

e. Relating and recording personal experiences

2. Preparation of a report on basis of data obtained:

a. Group decides what information to incorporate into report in light of its subproblem

b. Group decides how it wishes to present its report, who will participate, and how much time will be needed to give it. Possible methods of presentation include symposium, panel discussion, dramatization, skits

c. Group decides what visual aids to use—movies, filmstrips, still pictures, charts, graphs, posters

3. Presentation of report to rest of the class

4. Discussion of questions raised by the report or appropriate to the subproblem

5. Evaluation of results

a. Review of ways the family contributes to the well-being of all members: (1) What can each member do to build a better family? (2) In what ways does citizenship begin in the family?

b. Pencil-and-paper tests on understandings through study of unit

c. Discussion of ways in which students can improve personal behaviors related to unit.

The subproblems selected by the group might well include those listed below. Each student in the class, having selected the group with which he chooses to work, will participate in the steps listed. The reports might well stimulate some of the questions listed under each of the subproblems. For example:

Subproblem I: Of what value to me are the care and protection which my family provides?

Questions which may be raised:

1. How can we help keep our family healthy?
   a. Food
      (1) What is a balanced meal?
      (2) What foods should be included in the diet each day?
      (3) Why is breakfast important?
      (4) Why should prospective mothers be particularly careful to have a balanced diet daily?
      (5) How does the nutrition of each individual contribute to his citizenship?
   b. Sleep and rest
      (1) Why do we sleep?
      (2) How much sleep should you get?
      (3) What are the results of lack of sleep?
      (4) What are some factors which may prevent sufficient sleep?
      (5) What can you do to overcome these?
      (6) How can the amount of sleep which you get affect your ability as a good citizen?
   c. Medical, dental, and nursing care
      (1) In what ways does immunization contribute to good citizenship?
      (2) What immunizations should you have?
      (3) When should you see a physician?
      (4) How should we select a physician or dentist?
      (5) Why does having your defects corrected increase your potential service to your community and country?
      (6) What percentage of our class has visited a dentist in the past six months?
      (7) How does good nursing care for a sick family member contribute to citizenship?

2. How can we keep the home safe?

a. What do we need to know and do to protect ourselves and our family from accidents?

b. What do we expect from our parents in keeping the home safe?

Subproblem II: In what ways does my family contribute to my emotional health?

Questions which may be raised:

1. What is meant by emotional or mental health?
2. What is personality?
3. What are basic personality needs?
4. How do people react if basic needs are met? If unmet?
5. How does personality develop?
6. What is meant by, "As the twig is bent so grows the tree"; "The child is father of the man"?
7. How does heredity affect personality?
8. How does environment affect personality?
9. What effect does position in the family have on relationship with siblings?
10. How can the ill effects of living in a family which moves frequently be avoided?
11. What effect can size of the family have on a child?
12. What other environmental influences affect personality development and emotional health?
13. In what ways can you improve your emotional health?
14. What does "facing reality" mean?
15. What relationship, if any, exists between emotional health and physical health?
16. How do the skills and customs which we learn in our families contribute to emotional health?
17. In what ways is an emotionally well-adjusted person a better citizen?

Subproblem III: How can I show my appreciation for all that my family does for me?

Questions which may be raised:

1. What does your family do for you?
2. Why is the family important?
3. What problems do you have in relation to your family?
4. How do you solve these problems?
5. Of what value is a friendly family talk about differences?

6. What responsibilities do you take in the routine work of family?

7. How can you show thoughtfulness in use of telephone, bathroom, newspaper?

8. What responsibilities can you take toward younger members of your family which would help your parents?

9. What responsibilities do you have regarding such material family possessions as the television set, the car?

10. How do you budget your time?

11. What plan do you have for managing your money?

12. Where can you get help for your personal problems?

13. How does being a good family member contribute to citizenship?

14. What would you think of a school conference for parents, teachers, and pupils developed around some of your problems?

Subproblem IV: How can I further good relationships with all members of the household?

Questions which may be raised:

1. How can suggestions and criticisms be made in a helpful way?

2. How can I help my family to budget adequately?

3. In what ways does recreation with entire family help to build a closely knit family and thus better citizens?

4. What are some recreative activities which all ages enjoy?

5. What recreative activity could you introduce to your entire family which all would enjoy?

6. How can friends be made welcome in the home?

7. What are some life situations which sometimes cause difficulties in families?

8. Can you suggest a way to solve one of the difficulties and act it out in a sociodrama?

9. How can you help members of your family when they face difficult situations?

10. How can you help members of your family when they have done a good job?

11. How can you show interest in the activities of other members of your family?

12. Of what value is a hobby?

13. What are some of your hobbies?

Bibliography

ALLEN, JACK, and STEGMEIR, CLARENCE. *Civics.* New York: American Book Co., 1956.

DALY, SHEILA JOHN. *Blondes Prefer Gentlemen.* New York: Dodd, Mead & Co., 1949.

FEDDER, RUTH. *A Girl Grows Up.* Third edition. New York: McGraw-Hill Book Co., 1957.

FORBES, KATHRYN. *Mama's Bank Account.* New York: Harcourt, Brace & Co., 1943.

FOSDICK, HARRY EMERSON. *On Being a Real Person.* New York: Harper & Brothers, 1943.

GUNTHER, JOHN. *Death Be Not Proud.* New York: Harper & Brothers, 1949.

JENKINS, GLADYS GARDNER. *How to Live With Parents.* Chicago: Science Research Associates, 1948.

JENKINS, GLADYS GARDNER; BAUER, W. W.; and SCHACTER, HELEN S. *Teen-Agers.* Chicago: Scott, Foresman & Co., 1954.

KELLER, FATHER JAMES. *You Can Change the World.* New York: Longmans, Green & Co., 1948.

LINDSAY, HOWARD, and CROUSE, RUSSELL. *Life With Father.* Garden City, N.Y.: Doubleday Doran Co., 1946.

MEREDITH, FLORENCE; IRWIN, LESLIE; and STATON, WESLEY S. *Health and Fitness.* Boston: D. C. Heath & Co., 1957.

Illustrative Unit for Correlating Health Education with Business Education or Home Economics*

Planning for Health Protection

I. *Objectives*

To develop a wholesome and accurate concept of business as it affects daily living

To be aware of the need for expenditures related to health

To understand that unwise budgeting for family needs has been a frequent cause of unhappiness, marriage dissension, or divorce

To learn to budget wisely the money allotted for purchasing food

To understand factors that enter into selection of a home and the different methods of financing its purchase

To be able to budget wisely for recreational needs of the family

---

* This unit could also be taught in a health education class.

To buy first aid supplies wisely

To understand the need for providing for possible health emergencies through appropriate health and accident insurance and savings

To understand the different kinds of health insurance available to individuals and families, and to know how to secure the types of policies and contracts that will meet the needs best

To know where the tax dollars go for support of community, state, and federal health programs.

II. *The Problem*

How can I expend my money wisely for health needs?

III. *Suggested Method*

The teacher will first interest students in the need for and benefits of developing skills in managing finances for health needs. After these introductory comments, he will direct a class discussion to the formulation of the problem and listing of subproblems. Since *each* pupil needs to develop his own useful skills and realistic approach to individual and home management for health protection, there will need to be a class attack upon *each* of the subproblems.

IV. *Analysis of Problem into Subproblems*

A. What will be included in my regular expenditures to meet health needs and why is it necessary to budget wisely?

B. How do I plan to budget adequately for food?

C. What should I know about selecting a home and financing it?

D. How do I budget for recreational expenditures?

E. How shall I plan for health insurance coverage?

F. How do I plan for expenditures for health emergencies and for older age care?

V. *Procedures*

A. Collection of data on each of the subproblems through:
  1. Source materials
  2. Discussion with resource persons, such as:
    a. Parents
    b. Home economists
    c. Insurance representatives
    d. Physicians and dentists
    e. Recreation specialists

      f. Public health personnel

      g. Bank personnel

      h. Nurse serving the school.

   3. Visual aids, including:

      a. Films and filmstrips

      b. Insurance policies

      c. Charts, such as government indices of annual costs of living

      d. Magazine and newspaper advertising.

B. Individual pupil learning experiences such as:

   1. List the advantages of budgeting for health needs.

   2. Investigate the cost of a periodic health examination and of dental examinations.

   3. Itemize the cost of various accidents to individuals. Accidents in your own family might serve as examples.

   4. Compute the cost of protecting your health by having the following: smallpox vaccination; diphtheria and tetanus immunization; polio vaccine; and a chest x-ray or tuberculin test.

   5. What are the usual costs of hospitalization? In wards? In double rooms? Operating room costs? Special charges? Laboratory fees?

   6. What coverage is given in hospitalization plans?

   7. Investigate the various types of health and accident insurance, their benefits, and cost of premiums.

   8. List the common hazards to watch for in reviewing health and accident policies.

   9. Investigate the facts of a group health insurance plan.

   10. Survey the class to see which members are covered by family health insurance policies.

   11. Find out from your parents what your family health insurance coverage is.

   12. Find out what type of insurance the school carries on athletes, other pupils, and teachers.

   13. Study several types of automobile accident policies and report to class concerning benefits and risks.

   14. Develop a sound insurance plan for yourself at retirement.

15. Plan what items should be in the family medicine chest and their cost.

16. Observe the recreational expenditures of an entire family and decide whether the level of enjoyment always parallels the level of expenditures.

17. Lay out a realistic budget for yourself regarding recreation for the coming year (equipment, admittance, membership).

18. List some recreational activities that families can enjoy with little or no expenditure of money.

19. Select one health commodity (a dentifrice, for example) and decide how you would select one product over another.

20. Investigate how much tax money per capita goes for health services in your community. List the public health services your health department conducts under this budget.

21. Determine how much money is raised annually in your community through voluntary health agencies.

C. Class discussion.

D. Role-playing or dramatic skits dramatizing situations such as family councils regarding budgets, interview with an insurance agent.

E. Work out an individual budget geared to various salary levels allotting funds for food, housing, recreation, health insurance, savings, voluntary health contributions, and other health needs.

VI. *Evaluation*

A. Progress tests as subproblems are considered in class.

B. Vocabulary checks.

C. Ability of students to manage their own allowance or money earned.

Bibliography

CRABBE, ERNEST H.; ENTERLINE, HERMAN; and DeBRUM, S. JOSEPH. *General Business*. Cincinnati, Ohio: South Western Publishing Co., 1956.

WILHELMS, FRED T. *Consumer Living*. New York: The Gregg Publishing Co., 1951.

The interested reader is also advised to consult *American Business Yearbooks* (1949 through 1955).

SELECTED REFERENCES

ANDERSON, CARL L. *School Health Practice*. Second edition. St. Louis: C. V. Mosby Co., 1960. 530 p.

GROUT, RUTH E. *Health Teaching in Schools.* Third edition. Philadelphia: W. B. Saunders Co., 1958. 359 p.

HAAG, JESSIE HELEN. *School Health Program.* New York: Henry Holt & Co., 1958. 533 p.

HARNETT, ARTHUR L., and SHAW, JOHN H. *Effective School Health Education.* New York: Appleton-Century-Crofts, 1959. 421 p.

IRWIN, LESLIE W.; HUMPHREY, JAMES H.; and JOHNSON, WARREN R. *Methods and Materials in School Health Education.* St. Louis: C. V. Mosby Co., 1956. 367 p.

OBERTEUFFER, DELBERT. *School Health Education.* Third edition. New York: Harper & Brothers, 1960. 547 p.

SCHNEIDER, ELSA, and MCNEELY, SIMON. *Teachers Contribute to Child Health.* U.S. Department of Health, Education, and Welfare, Bulletin 1951, No. 8. Washington, D.C.: Superintendent of Documents, Government Printing Office, 1951. 44 p.

TURNER, C. E.; SELLERY, C. MORLEY; and SMITH, SARA LOUISE. *School Health and Health Education.* Fourth edition. St. Louis: C. V. Mosby Co., 1961.

WILLIAMS, JESSE FEIRING; BROWNELL, CLIFFORD LEE; and VERNIER, ELMON. *The Administration of Health Education and Physical Education.* Philadelphia: W. B. Saunders Co., 1958. 387 p.

Materials and Resources

"How to teach more and how to teach better" continue to be among the challenging tasks that confront the educator. Alert teachers and school administrators recognize that each succeeding generation has more to learn than did the previous one, and that not many hours can be added to the school day nor many years to a person's formal education. These conditions necessitate that education step up its methods and increase its output. In response, teachers are intensifying their use of new materials and resources. When correctly and appropriately used, these materials and resources can lead in varying degrees to greater retention of what is learned, an increased desire to learn, and improved competence in problem solving.

The variety and quality of authentic instructional materials available to the teacher are constantly improving. Each instructor is obligated to keep well informed about the availability and appropriateness of these materials for specific purposes. The school administration, on the other hand, is responsible for budgeting adequate funds to pay all rental fees and charges on equipment and materials that are used by teachers. This chapter presents brief descriptions of many types of teaching materials which have particular significance in health education.

AUDIO-VISUAL MATERIALS

Guiding Principles

Audio-visual materials usually include special kinds of communication devices and procedures such as dramatizations, demonstrations, exhibits, field trips, radio, recordings, television, motion pictures, filmstrips, graphic illustrations, and reading materials.

The use of audio-visual materials in the classroom depends on their worth to the learner. Audio-visual materials are not ends in themselves. The focus is on what can be learned more effectively through the use of these aids rather than on what knowledge can be gained from audio-visual materials alone.

Some guidelines for the use of these instructional materials may be summarized as follows:

1. All audio-visual materials are a means of helping to achieve educational objectives. The selection of these materials depends upon what is to be taught and the desired outcomes.

2. Each aid has its advantages and its limitations. For any specific situation the teacher has to select the learning aid or combination of aids which will be most helpful to the learners.

3. Audio-visual materials are not substitutes for other instructional techniques. They are an integral part of teaching, and can serve only to reinforce and supplement other forms of instruction.

4. The mere exposure to audio-visual materials will not assure learning that is meaningful. Careful planning and preparation are necessary if any kind of teaching is to serve as a channel for enriched learning experiences.

5. The skillful use of audio-visual materials encourages the pupil to assume responsibility for his own learning by helping him to organize, interpret, perceive, reflect, integrate, and apply what is being taught. These features guide the learner into an active role, rather than a passive one.

Educational Values

Research in the use of audio-visual materials offers assurance that certain values can be attributed to the use of these materials if the proper guidelines for their use are observed. Hoban, Finn, and Dale[1] summarize that audio-visual materials, when correctly used in teaching, can accomplish the following:

1. Supply a concrete basis for conceptual thinking and reduce meaningless word responses of pupils

2. Have a high degree of interest for pupils

3. Make learning more permanent

4. Offer a reality of experience which stimulates pupil self-activity

---

[1] Hoban, Charles F.; Finn, James D.; and Dale, Edgar. "Audio-Visual Materials." *Encyclopedia of Educational Research.* Revised edition. (Edited by Walter S. Monroe.) New York: Macmillan Co., 1950. p. 84.

5. Develop a continuity of thought. This is especially true of motion pictures

6. Contribute to growth of meaning and to vocabulary development

7. Provide experiences not easily obtained through other materials and contribute to the efficiency, depth, and variety of learning.

Dramatizations

Dramatizations include a wide range of experiences which provide an avenue of expression and insight for pupils. The intent of a dramatized experience is to create an opportunity for simulating or reconstructing a real situation. Although the pupils who participate in a dramatic activity may be more actively engaged, the other class members are not mere passive onlookers, for they too share in the performance by becoming emotionally involved within the limits of their past experiences.

Dramatization as an educational activity has its origin in basic and natural impulses—the desire to play, to use creative energies, and to be imaginative. Because of this point of reference, the teacher needs to make certain that the reality of the educational purposes for which the dramatization has been presented are not obscured. Dramatized experiences may take the form of plays, skits, pageants, pantomimes, tableaus, puppetry, or role playing. Akin to dramatizations are the occasional classroom preparation and presentation of mock radio and television programs.

Full-length *plays, tableaus,* and *pageants* are the more spectacular types of production, and are often parts of the co-curricular program in the school. The *shadow play,* which is a version of the tableau, can be utilized with younger children as a form of group expression in the classroom situation. *Puppets* are especially appealing to elementary-school pupils and include varying forms—finger and hand puppets, shadow puppets, marionettes, and rod-type puppets. When an interpretation is not easily adaptable to real characters, puppetry is a flexible and unique medium for portraying the desired action. The qualities of fantasy, whimsey, and subtlety are distinct characteristics of this form of dramatization.

Short versions of plays and dramatic skits are vivid ways of depicting health problems or of interpreting the social situation in which lifelike characters exist. The area of human relations is particularly suited as a subject for the classroom play.

There are some pretested play scripts[2] which have been written by outstanding playwrights, and which have been prepared under the supervision of authoritative advisory groups. These scripts have few production requirements, have little or no scenery and costumes, and can be adequately presented with the pupils reading their parts. Many of the plays are accompanied by discussion guides which serve as a springboard for exchange of ideas following the play presentation. When time is available, the pupils may choose to write their own script. This might well be a culminating activity for a unit of study in a health class.

Sociodrama or *role playing* is a popular tool for portraying social situations, mainly because it is a spontaneous and unrehearsed dramatization of some ways in which people *do* behave. A sociodrama can be followed by another role-playing episode in which the way people *should* behave is presented. Ideally, the second portrayal comes as a result of the group reaction to the first presentation, and it reflects members' suggestions for resolving the problem by improving the attitudes and behavior of the characters.

After the problem is defined, roles are assigned to volunteers or are allotted according to suggestions from class members. A brief description of the role for each character is presented in relation to the issue, but care is taken not to overstructure the situation. From there on, the pupil plays his role with empathy for the person he is portraying. Unexpressed and causal factors that affect human relations are made concrete, and the audience gains insight into the underlying dynamics inherent in the problem situation.

A word of caution is indicated here about the overuse of role playing as an educational technique. As with any other aid to teaching, it has a definite place, and its distinct contribution lies in analyzing a social situation and in helping class members to make some generalizations about behavior and attitudes that can be applied in a similar combination of circumstances.

In addition to the specific outcomes already mentioned, drama-

---

[2] A number of short elementary-school plays, particularly suited to mental health and family life education, may be obtained from Human Relations Aids, 1790 Broadway, New York 19, N.Y. Other health plays and dramatic sketches are available from American Theater Wing Community Plays, 351 West 48th Street, New York 36, N.Y.

tizations make a concomitant contribution to learning. They provide a setting in which the self-conscious or shy pupil can forget himself and divert his attention to problems shared by others in the class. At the same time, by proper casting, pupils who demand attention or who show overt characteristics may find satisfaction. The group involvement and co-operation necessary for any type of dramatization tend to develop a cohesiveness and a high degree of rapport among the performers and the audience.

Demonstrations

The teacher frequently uses a demonstration, or visualized explanation, to show how something operates, how it is done, or to show cause-effect relationships. In the demonstration he draws upon many other teaching materials that are available to illustrate a given concept. A step-by-step procedure for applying artificial respiration, a comparison of pulse count at rest and following varying degrees of activity, clarification of the parts and functions of the human ear with a cutaway model, a chronological explanation of the menstrual cycle with a chart or model, an experiment to show the conditions under which disease-producing organisms thrive—all these are examples of demonstrations.

The teacher may tell a class how something is constructed or how it functions. To add reality, he illustrates his explanation with a demonstration. Whenever appropriate and practical, he allows the pupils to perform the demonstration. This opportunity for "doing" on the part of the class is especially desirable in health and safety education where the learning of a skill or pattern of behavior is a primary goal. First aid and driver education are almost wholly dependent upon individual practice by the pupils following the teacher's demonstration, if learning is to be reinforced and lasting.

The successful demonstration demands simple design, clarity of explanation, and advanced preparation of materials to be used. In addition, the teacher needs to be thoroughly familiar with the subject, to communicate well during the demonstration, and to be cognizant of the salient points in the demonstration. It is necessary, of course, that the demonstration be clearly visible to all pupils. The quality of the questions and class comments during the demonstration and following it are gauges of the degree of relevant learning which is taking place.

Exhibits

When time and distance present limitations to the widening of educational horizons, the teacher considers ways of providing the learner with a replica of the real situation or environment. Exhibits, which rely upon arrangements of objects, models, specimens, or mock ups (scale models), are planned to convey a specific message to the viewer.

When an object or specimen of the real thing is not available, or is impractical for display purposes, a three-dimensional likeness or model, scaled up or down, can be constructed or obtained from commercial sources. Such representations are best when authentic, but sometimes a simplified version is necessary. In these instances the teacher points out to the class the omission of certain parts of the original, so that inaccurate impressions will not be formed.

The *cutaway model* has advantages as a learning aid in that it enables pupils to view the interior structure or workability of some specific organ that is not outwardly visible. For example, a model of the eye or ear, with removable parts, lends itself to examination and broader understanding of the importance of each part in the total functioning of the organ.

The *diorama* is relatively new to the classroom. It is a three-dimensional representation of a scene with the objects and models positioned in proper perspective within a replica of their natural environment. In a unit of study devoted to community health, there are many phases of this topic which lend themselves to presentation through the use of a diorama. A comprehension of the potential hazards which confront a driver on the highway and in congested traffic centers can be gained readily from a realistic arrangement in a diorama. The instructional value of the diorama in health education, if pupil made, is found primarily in the study of the finished scene rather than in the construction process.

There are many things that contribute to the efficacy of an exhibit. Motion, viewer participation, accuracy of detail, location of the exhibit, brevity and clarity of captions, illumination, and color are points to be considered. Although the exhibit is often placed within the school environment, real advantages may accrue by locating the exhibit in a community setting to help citizens appreciate the civic-minded concern of pupils for some health problem.

The educational *health museum,* which has had an amazing period of growth and expansion in recent years, enriches school curriculums. Pupil observation in the museum needs adequate time and expert guidance, for a hurried and unorganized museum tour leads to confusion and misunderstanding. The exhibits in a legitimate health museum are authentic, attractive, and dynamic, and they cover a wide range of topics in personal, family, and community health. Some of the exhibit materials are available for loan to schools. The health museums provide additional services such as the orientation of teachers for the optimal use of museum facilities, preparation of resource materials, lectures, and group discussions.

Field Trips

A field trip is a vitalized experience in which the classroom is extended into the community. It may be a planned visit to some place within the school building or its environs, or a journey to some point within the community. The latter is particularly significant for the contribution it can make to narrowing the gap between school experiences and community life. More extensive field trips may require traveling a considerable distance and may last a period of several days.

Many school systems issue a guidebook which has been developed for teachers on the basis of past experiences with field trips. The teacher will find this item a valuable reference. It lists the available resources in each community, together with suggested procedures for planning the field experience. Usually the guide also classifies the trips which are suitable for various age groups, and helps to eliminate duplication of trips experienced at other grade levels.

In most communities there are numerous opportunities that can be assessed for their potential contribution to health and safety education. Visits might be made to laboratories, food processing plants, produce markets, water purification plants, sewage disposal plants, governmental agencies, traffic centers, pharmaceutical firms, industrial establishments, research centers, museums, and clinics and hospitals during open house or at other appropriate times. The maturity level and intellectual background of the pupils will govern the type of visit to be made. Although the large metropolitan areas are richer in the resources they have to offer, studies show that the school systems located in smaller communities utilize the available resources to a greater extent. Obviously, the complexity of the administrative arrangements, particularly transportation and the time factor in the larger cities, serves as an obstacle to more frequent field trips. However, once the values of field trips are recognized, it is believed that these obstacles can be overcome. For example, when field trips are administratively difficult, small groups or individuals making the excursion and then reporting to the class serve as a fair substitute.

The field trip is often used as a motivating device, and in this sense it serves as a good introduction to a unit of study. It may be planned during the unit to enhance the learning and clarify some specific segment of a unit, or it may be selected as the procedure which will serve best at the termination of a unit to recapitulate the learning experience.

Essentially, the same educational principles that underlie the use of other teaching aids apply to the field trip as a learning activity. It is imperative that the reason for the field trip be clear to both the teacher and the pupils, because what is learned through the experience depends largely upon the purpose and planning agreed upon at the outset.

In a successful field trip, the need for the trip usually comes as a natural outgrowth of classroom study, and pupils develop an awareness of the purposes and values of their trip. The use of other teaching materials during the stages of preparation helps to enhance the value of the experience. Pupils and teacher share in formulating the observations they hope to make and the questions they want to have answered. Since a guide is usually assigned by the host group, he needs advance notice of the class' expectations, so that the visitors and the personnel at the community resource are in accord with each other's purposes.

Preparations for a field trip prior to the community visit are perhaps more extensive and detailed than those for use of other teaching procedures. Often in this learning situation an entire class of pupils goes to the scene of learning activity rather than bringing the learning aid into the classroom. This type of field trip requires meticulous attention to administrative details, transportation, arrangements with the community resources to be visited, parental permission, appropriate clothing, standards of behavior, time allotment, changes in class schedule, safety factors, and adequate supervision. However, when carefully planned and conducted, a field trip can:

1. Encourage exploration and interest
2. Develop pupil curiosity
3. Cultivate careful observation
4. Provide accurate, firsthand information
5. Clarify concepts and give additional meaning to previous classwork, especially for pupils whose background of experience is very limited
6. Provide opportunities for vocational guidance through direct contact with work opportunities
7. Promote intelligent citizenship through experiences in social living
8. Form new ties between the pupil and his community
9. Arouse the interest of parents and other citizens in what schools are doing.

The follow-up activities that result from this field experience include creative projects, class discussions, and the use of other evaluation instruments to measure the understandings gained and the attitudes acquired. The teacher will want to review for himself the mechanical and administrative aspects of the trip so that he can minimize the difficulties and increase the educational features of future community visits by his classes.

Radio

Radio supplies an endless amount of resource material which is timely and vital, and which has dramatic appeal for the listener. The school broadcast usually is a carefully planned audio learning experience which utilizes resources beyond those readily available in the classroom. Broadcasts are prepared under the supervision of excellent teachers who consult school personnel and subject experts about information which lends itself to this means of communication. Many topics of personal and community health are in this category. Wittich and Schuller[3] have identified three rather consistent characteristics of educational radio broadcasts:

1. The expert teacher and subject authority participate to bring an appropriate and enriching experience into the classrooms in the reception area.

---

[3] Wittich, Walter A., and Schuller, Charles F. *Audio-Visual Materials*. Second edition. New York: Harper & Brothers, 1957. p. 276-80.

2. Educational radio broadcasts provide an immediate awareness of and an opportunity for "listening participation" in current history.

3. Educational radio programs make it possible for experts to visit classrooms.

In spite of the desirable features of radio in the classroom, it has some definite limitations. Among them are:

1. *One-way communication*—During the broadcast there is no opportunity for pupils to ask the radio teacher questions.

2. *Timing*—Adjustment of broadcast time to the specific schedules of schools and classes, and adjustment of classwork to the actual broadcast time is difficult. This is particularly true for the high-school level.

3. *No prehearing or reusability*—The teacher is unable to prehear the broadcast. At best he can study the advance announcements and the teachers guide for a particular broadcast.

4. *Lack of nationwide coverage*—Not all schools have radios or are located within the range of stations which broadcast educational programs.

5. *Poor reception areas*—Some schools are located in areas where radio reception is usually of poor quality.

Recordings taken directly off the air or purchased from commercial sources can be used to overcome most of these limitations. With a disc or tape recording of a radio broadcast, the teacher does not run the risk of questionable content, or the inconvenience of set program schedules. He is able to control these factors and he can use the teaching material when it is most desirable and appropriate.

As a first step in the classroom use of radio, the teacher explores the radio resources which exist in his community, and he selects those programs for classroom or home listening which have a direct bearing on current classwork, and which have potential for contributing to educational outcomes. The subjects of school radio broadcasts are usually announced well in advance, and preliminary study guides are often provided for teachers so that pupils can be oriented to the experience of listening. Passive listening to radio broadcasts in the classroom without preplanning, selectivity of the content, and subsequent follow up can be a waste of valuable time.

The significance of radio for teaching discriminative listening has not been fully appreciated. Pupils can be encouraged to seek out and critically appraise the various elements that make up a good radio program, or carefully analyze the accuracy of programs and advertising which contain health information. In the preplanning stage the teacher points up clues for listening, and the follow-up activities, which come as a result of the listening experience, reflect the effectiveness of the broadcast. In addition to classroom listening, pupils can be encouraged to listen at home for radio announcements about current health problems, and to give brief résumés to the class of what they have heard about new advances in medical science, safety precautions, or the work of local health agencies.

The teacher also seeks out opportunities for pupils to participate in actual broadcasts from local stations. When time is granted, the pupils can engage in meaningful activities as they do research, prepare the script, and produce a broadcast based on a health or safety theme. Often a pupils' pleas to an adult audience, urging them to take action on some community health problem, bring favorable and immediate response. When time for preparation is limited, excellent radio scripts[4] prepared for wide distribution are available free of charge through various local or national groups interested in health promotion and maintenance.

Recordings

Tape recording invites exploration as a useful approach to many areas of health and safety education. In some schools, pupils check out tape recorders for class assignments, and return the next day to share the results of a planned interview with a group of health officials. The tape recorder also may be taken on a field trip to the local health department and a recording made wherever possible of the explanations given during the guided tour. A pupil may choose to record all radio and television commercials with health implications, or programs of health quackery, which can be played back to the class in conjunction with a unit on consumer health education.

A narrative can be recorded on tape to enhance the showing of a set of school-made slides or a filmstrip on some health or safety

---

[4] One source of free radio scripts is the Bureau of Research in Education by Radio, University of Texas, Austin, Texas. The educational kit for classroom teachers includes a teachers manual, a promotion brochure, an evaluation manual, a production manual, and a pamphlet for parents.

topic. A continuous loop of tape can be used by placing on a strategically located recorder and play-back machine a message about some health or safety campaign which grows out of a classroom activity.

Many states have duplication centers, each with an extensive collection of permanent recordings on master tapes. A school which orders any of the available recordings sends an appropriate number of blank tapes to the nearest center together with a list of the recordings which are desired. It is an easy process to transfer any recording from one of the master tapes to a school tape. Where outstanding classroom radio programs have been prepared throughout the country, school systems are utilizing tape recordings to exchange programs and to improve the quality of their school-on-the-air broadcasts. Other sources are listed in *The Educators Guide to Free Tapes, Scripts, and Transcriptions*[5] and in the *National Tape Recording Catalog.*[6]

Television

A program may be televised: (a) as a "live telecast"; (b) via video tape, which instantly records both sight and sound on magnetic tape and is ready for immediate use; and (c) on kinescope, which records the live program on motion picture film and which requires processing before it can be used. Video tapes and kinescopes serve much the same purpose for television as recordings do for radio. The main advantage of video tape is that a "live" program or event can be recorded and played back, with no appreciable loss of quality, a minute, a month, or a year later.

Some telecasting is done on closed circuits. In these instances the televised information is transmitted by wires, or by microwave, from cameras to private receivers that are located in nearby rooms, buildings, or even at greater distances. This type of television is often employed for teacher observation, for teaching manual skills, or to transmit lecture-demonstrations in technical and science courses.

Open-circuit telecasting utilizes the television channels which are controlled and assigned by the Federal Communications Commission. As defined by the Commission, there are two major

---

[5] *The Educators Guide to Free Tapes, Scripts, and Transcriptions,* published annually by the Educators Progress Service, Randolph, Wis., classifies educational scripts and recordings by sponsor, title, running time, subject, content, and suggested uses.

[6] *National Tape Recording Catalog,* published by the Department of Audio-Visual Instruction, National Education Association, Washington, D.C., lists and describes content of tape recordings for teaching.

varieties of television, commercial and educational. Commercial television refers to network programs or those initiated by broadcasting stations which are operated by private organizations primarily for profit. Some of the commercial telecasts have a fairly high educational value, and occasionally they can be used to good advantage in the classroom. Examples of public service programs on commercial television which could be used in a health education class are televised meetings of the World Health Assembly, an illustrated report by a sanitary engineer, a Civil Defense telecast illustrating a new method of resuscitation, and an on-the-spot telecast of antibiotic drug production in a pharmaceutical laboratory.

In 1952 the Federal Communications Commission reserved 242 television channels for noncommercial use by educational interests in the United States. Later, other channels were assigned to education so that by 1957 the number totaled 258. This legislation is similar to the Morrill Act of 1862 which set aside part of the public domain (land) for educational purposes—the land-grant colleges. Applied to television, the same principle gives a portion of the broadcasting spectrum to education.

Of the programs broadcast on educational channels, some are for out-of-school viewers, while others are for in-school reception and use. Today, school-planned television is a reality, particularly in the centers of heavy population. The programs are planned and produced by qualified and experienced teachers who work in direct co-operation with school personnel. The programs are developed on topics which have been requested by teachers. Well in advance of each telecast, a copy of the program schedule and its content in the form of teacher and pupil guides is sent to all the teachers so that they may prepare their pupils to obtain full benefit from their television experiences.

The designs of educational telecasts vary. Some, especially those for out-of-school viewing, are planned to do the total job of teaching a specific unit of instruction. More frequently, for classroom viewing, the studio teacher provides some basic instruction on a given subject for many pupils in many classrooms. Then, immediately after the telecast, each classroom teacher continues with the same subject, building upon the foundation established by the studio teacher and adapting the experience to the needs of individual pupils.

Occasionally a telecast is used to supplement the regular classwork. For example, by closed circuit, a class which is studying about microorganisms could view a demonstration of an electron microscope in a nearby laboratory. This arrangement enables all of the class members to see the demonstration simultaneously, whereas a field trip to the laboratory would consume far more time and the pupils would have to view the microscope in small groups.

Most often a live, kinescoped, or video-taped television program is used to enrich classwork. As in selecting any audio-visual material of instruction, the basic questions are: Does the telecast make a contribution to the learning situation beyond that made by instructional materials already in use? Is the general level of the program keyed to the age of the group that will see it? Will the content promote better understanding of the subject? Does the program include useful supplements to the unit of work or the general curriculum area? In answering these questions the teacher is confronted with the impossibility of previewing a live telecast. In this case, teacher judgment will have to be based upon previous experience with the program, the reputation of the sponsor or producer, the caliber of the expert authority or demonstrator who appears on the program, and the care taken in organizing the telecast. These items will help the teacher to decide the probable usefulness of current telecasts and those that may be produced in the future. Fortunately, kinescopes and video tapes can be previewed prior to classroom use.

Some of the characteristics of television as a teaching device are:

1. *Concreteness of the real and the immediate*—Through the avenues of vision and hearing, television brings the pupil into contact with contemporary events in exciting and clarifying ways.

2. *Uniformity of communication*—Through a television broadcast, teachers, parents, pupils, and citizens may share a common experience *at the same time*. At least some essentials may be shared in common. Beyond that, the influence of the experience depends upon the education, experience, and interest levels of the individuals.

3. *Succinctness of explanations*—Television has developed a new, compressed form of communication, whose very succinctness brings clarity. On the other hand, there is always the danger of oversimplification.

4. *Versatility*—Any telecast may use a carefully combined battery of audio-visual materials such as models, charts, diagrams, exhibits, and chalkboards. These add variety and interest, but they can only be *viewed* by the pupil in the classroom; he cannot handle and examine the materials in a televised exhibit.

5. *One-way communication*—Television is primarily a one-way form of communication. The pupils cannot ask questions except where a closed-circuit installation provides microphones in each classroom which permit pupils to communicate with the studio teacher. Such talk-back arrangements cannot be made with broadcast television.

6. *Reinforcement of existing understandings*—Television tends to stimulate and reinforce ideas, beliefs, and tendencies already possessed by the viewer.

Through the Fund for Adult Education, an Educational Television and Radio Center has been located at Ann Arbor, Michigan. Among other purposes, the Center provides consultation on the production and use of kinescopes and telefilms. As increasing progress is made toward using the full potential of television in education, it becomes apparent that this medium of communication, like any other, is not the answer to all educational problems. As is true of other media, its worth as an educational tool is dependent on many factors, of which the user is an important one.

Motion Pictures

The educational motion picture is of standardized 16mm width and may be silent or sound, black-and-white or in color. Although the motion picture film is undoubtedly the most frequently used teaching tool in health education, like all teaching methods and materials, it can be misused.

In selecting a motion picture for a particular unit of study from the thousands which are listed in film guides,[7,8] the teacher needs to identify clearly beforehand the purposes for which the film is to be used. Sound motion pictures can:

[7] *Educational Film Guide*, published by the H. W. Wilson Co., 950 University Avenue, New York 52, N.Y., is the most complete listing of educational films. It includes health education films. It is kept up to date with periodic supplements. Information on each film includes type, length, cost, producer, synopsis of content, grade level, and an evaluation of the film by expert reviewers.

[8] *Educators Index of Free Films*, published annually by Educators Progress Service, Randolph, Wis., contains sources, titles, and descriptions of free educational films.

1. Present certain meanings involving motion, sound, narration, and color (when it is useful)

2. Compel and focus attention

3. Increase interest and retention of learning

4. Influence specific attitudes

5. Bring a variety of places and past and current events into the classroom

6. Speed up or slow down time

7. Present the same audio-visual record over and over again, without forgetting

8. Bring hazardous and difficult demonstrations into the class

9. Reduce the size of large objects and, through photomicrography, enlarge things which are too small for the naked eye to see

10. Visualize a concept through animation

11. Clarify relationships among things, ideas, and events

12. Provide a satisfying aesthetic experience.

Sound motion films have their limitations, too. Some of them are as follows:

1. The film may contain inaccuracies of fact.

2. The content of a film may go out of date.

3. It is sometimes difficult to obtain a film from a library at the time it would be most helpful.

4. The film may create incorrect concepts of time and size.

5. The film may be too brief or oversimplified.

6. Few films are suitable for all grade levels.

7. The high cost of films prevents many schools from developing their own film libraries.

8. With most projectors, once the film is started it continues to the end without opportunity to stop for prolonged projection of an individual frame.

However, films can present skills, action, background information, and facts. In addition, when used by a skillful teacher they can build attitudes, stimulate emotions, motivate discussion, and promote critical thinking.

There are many commercially sponsored films available for use by schools and colleges. Although these materials need careful checking for objectionable advertising and other forms of bias, many are informative and authentic, and cannot be overlooked as possible resource materials. The policy of the local school system, critical appraisal by the teacher, and the opinions of health specialists can serve as guides in the use or rejection of these materials.

There is a trend to produce films which may be correlated with high-school and college textbooks. At least half a dozen authors and publishers mention films in their textbooks or teachers guides which make specific contributions to better understanding of the contents.

It is best if the teacher can preview a film before showing it to the pupils. Sometimes, because of tight shipping schedules, the teacher may not be able to do so. Study of the excellent teachers guides which accompany many films will substitute in part for the actual preview, but the teacher is never on safe ground unless the film has been previewed. Sometimes it might be well to omit the use of a film if the teacher has not received it in time for a preview. Some films contain material which the pupils, and possibly the community, are not prepared to view.

Class preparation is necessary before the film showing to help pupils know what to look for in the film. Otherwise, their purpose in viewing may not be in harmony with the outcomes the teacher hopes to achieve. This is another reason why it is so important for the teacher to preview each film. It is recommended, too, that discussion immediately follow the showing. This may well lead to a variety of other follow-up activities. A greater part of the learning activity follows the film showing. Wittich and Schuller[9] present evidence that the level of achievement with a group of upper elementary-grade children was increased almost 60 percent when a film showing was preceded by an introduction and followed by a review. The achievement level was influenced approximately 48 percent with only the introduction and showing, but no follow up, and the level dropped to less than a 30 percent increase when both the introduction and review were omitted.

Although the one-reel, 400-foot film, which has a running time of 11 minutes, is perhaps the most popular for use in the average class period, there are other helpful films which may range from six minutes to over an hour in length. Whatever the length of the film, the steps in getting the most out of an educational film are:

1. Establish purposes.

⁹ Wittich and Schuller, op. cit., p. 403.

2. Show the film (under conditions to be described).

3. Discuss the film as a fulfillment of purposes, and as a stimulus for other learning activities.

4. Reshow the film when necessary to clarify items that may have been missed or only partially comprehended through the initial viewing.

One modification of this procedure consists of stopping the film at a predetermined point and immediately involving the class in discussion of a problem, question, or situation which has been presented by the film. Following adequate discussion, the rest of the film is shown. Some films are specially designed for this purpose. Another modification is that of individual or small group use of films by pupils. As pupils mature and become experienced in the use of films, under the teacher's guidance, they can conduct previews, develop introductory activities, and plan follow-up procedures.

The *loop film*, which is approximately 5 to 25 feet of motion picture film, is particularly helpful in teaching difficult skills, and may be utilized with areas of content in which the practice of a given skill is desired while viewing the film. A simple attachment facilitates adaptation to any projector so that a sequence action may be repeated. This technique is particularly useful in teaching first aid and specifically in demonstrating methods of artificial respiration.

The physical setting and conditions under which a motion picture is viewed determine to a great extent the value of this teaching medium. The regular classroom is a preferred location. It is best if all equipment is set up and ready before the class period begins. Careful attention to the seating arrangements, the ventilation, black-out facilities, the angle of the screen, and proper sound adjustment is required along with advance assurance that the projector mechanism is in good working order. All research indicates that note taking during film viewing interferes with attention and learning.

One of the criteria for the selection of any teaching aid is that it meets the needs and interests of the particular group with which it is being used. Films prepared for a general audience may not be as effective as those prepared for an audience and a setting of defined characteristics. The magnetic sound projector makes it possible to add a sound track to a locally produced film, to record the commentary, and then to play it back.

Every teacher will find of practical value a film evaluation file which he can keep for future planning and ready reference. The information for each film might be placed on a 3″ by 5″ card, and include a brief summary of the essential points outlined in the sample evaluation form on page 296.

There are over 3000 educational film libraries in the United States. However, the alert teacher acquaints himself first with sources of health films, such as the local and nearby school systems, the state department of education, the local and state health departments, the public library, nearby colleges and universities, and the voluntary health agencies. By studying a variety of film listings, the teacher will find that many films are available at no cost or on loan with only the charge of a return shipping fee. Films obtained from commercial libraries, on the other hand, charge varying rental fees. Since films from local and state sources will usually be in great demand, it is wise to make arrangements well in advance of the showing date.

Projected Still Pictures

The *filmstrip* provides a 35mm film of transparent still pictures or drawings in sequence which may range from 10 to 100 frames on a subject. It is a carefully prepared sequence of teaching material. Filmstrips are available in the silent version and are accompanied either by brief explanatory captions or by a script which the teacher can read as each frame is projected on the screen. The sound filmstrip is developed with appropriate commentary and sound effects recorded on a disc. A separate filmstrip projector and a dual-speed record player set at the proper speed will meet the requirements for this type of projection. A special compact projector is available which includes both the projector and record player in one unit. This piece of equipment may also provide for automatic advancing of each frame to correspond with the sound. Both 33⅓rpm and 78rpm records are used; however, the former is more popular because its use reduces the number of record changes.

The filmstrip has some advantages in that it is compact, relatively inexpensive, can be shown in a semidarkened room, and can be produced locally or within the school to meet a specific need. If the silent version of a filmstrip is used, the teacher is allowed more flexibility since he can easily adapt the material to the pupils in his class. Further, with very little cost, a school or school system can build up its own filmstrip library.

Film Evaluation Form

Title_____Date of Production_____

Running Time_____Color_____Black and_____Sound_____Silent_____
                             White

Producer_____Available from_____

Purchase Price_____Rental Charge_____Free on Loan_____

Grade Level:

                                          Junior   Senior
Primary_____Intermediate_____High_____High_____

General   Teacher
College_____Preparation_____Adult_____Other_____

Purpose of Film_____

_____

_____

A. *Scientific Accuracy:* General rating (based on content, continuity of information, technical consultants, date of release)

Excellent_____Good_____Fair_____Poor_____

B. *Teaching Potential:* General rating (based on level of comprehension, presentation of new ideas, suggestions for *action*, positive approach)

Excellent_____Good_____Fair_____Poor_____

C. *Technical Quality:* General rating (based on photography, casting of characters, sound quality, realistic action, lighting, appeal to "aesthetic" sense)

Excellent_____Good_____Fair_____Poor_____

Other Comments (such as suggested uses)_____

_____

_____

Date of Evaluation_____Evaluated by_____

There are an increasing number of filmstrips in health and safety education, many of which are particularly useful at the elementary-school level. Like the motion film, many filmstrips are being developed to correlate with textbooks. Several good indexes[10, 11] are available which will guide the teacher in selecting filmstrips on various topics in health education.

Transparent slides of the 2″ by 2″, or miniature, size, and glass or cellophane slides of the standard $3\frac{1}{4}″$ by 4″ size are other examples of projected still pictures. The slide has characteristics similar to the filmstrip, but provides an added advantage in that the material projected can, but need not, be shown in sequence. Thus, it is possible to select one or two slides to add emphasis or clarity to a particular point in a lesson. Slides can be purchased commercially or they can be school made easily and with little cost.

The standard size slide has an added instructional advantage in that the larger surface enables the teacher or pupil to utilize it for producing more detailed graphic materials such as charts, diagrams, and tables. Although in most instances the teacher's voice satisfies the need for necessary explanatory comment, sound can be recorded to accompany the slides.

When a teacher has single copies of material or flat objects which he wishes to show to a class, he will find *opaque projection* a useful technique. There is an unlimited variety of opaque material which can be used with this medium of projection. If a permanent enlargement of some material is desirable, the opaque projector can be used to project the material onto the chalkboard or a large piece of paper. Window shades with a white cloth water base can be used as a background for projecting a small detailed diagram of some physiological function or body organ. By tracing the outline which is magnified several times, and adding appropriate color and descriptive labels, the teacher will be able to reproduce quickly an artistic chart or diagram in a convenient roller-type form. Window shade fixtures can be affixed permanently above the chalkboard for quick insertion of the specific chart which may then be installed as needed.

New improvements in opaque projection make it possible to

[10] *Filmstrip Guide*, published periodically by the H. W. Wilson Co., 950 University Ave., New York 52, N.Y., classifies, describes, and cross references 13,000 filmstrips. It is kept up to date with annual supplements.

[11] *Educators Guide to Free Slidefilms*, published annually by the Educators Progress Service, Randolph, Wis., lists sources, titles, types, descriptions, and other pertinent data on free educational filmstrips.

accommodate materials up to 8½″ by 11″ in size. Mounting of the material is recommended, and more continuous projection can be achieved if materials are mounted on a long strip of paper which can be pulled through the projector.

Refinements in the opaque projector have eliminated to a great extent some of its disadvantages in regard to intensity of the light, the cooling system of the apparatus, and the bulk of the projector. Experimentation with the opaque projector will reveal some ingenious and versatile uses for this type of teaching aid.

Other types of still projection include the *overhead projector* which is simple to operate from the front of the room. It enables the teacher to write or draw on a plastic surface with a special pencil, the markings of which are easily erasable. This type of projector will accommodate many kinds of transparencies, and has an added unique feature in that development of a sequence or a sectional view is possible by the use of cellophane or plastic overlays similar to those found in many modern textbooks. This is a handy device and a great time saver. By using a cellophane roll the teacher can prepare up to 100 frames of material in advance, or as required, to illustrate some points in a discussion.

Microprojection, as an instructional technique, makes it possible to project on a screen enlargements of bacteria, cellular structures, various kinds of tissue cultures, and similar microscopic material. It reduces the need for individual microscopes, and increases the similarity of what each pupil sees. It is essential that care be exercised to avoid damage by heat of the wet or dry slides which are used. Also, the room has to be sufficiently darkened to assure good projection. A separate type of apparatus with a self-contained microscopic lens or an attachment for a microscope is available.

Before selecting any of the techniques of still projection described here, the teacher will need to determine whether or not motion is essential to the learning situation. The degree of flexibility which characterizes most still projection can be a distinct advantage in adapting material to the requirements of the group with which it is to be used.

The remainder of this chapter continues the description of some types of teaching materials and their application in health education. It also presents a summary of how and where teachers can obtain assistance, information, and materials for health teaching.

GRAPHIC MATERIALS

There is an abundance of graphic material from which the teacher can select posters, charts, graphs, maps, diagrams, pictures, comic strips, and cartoons to make his teaching more effective. The majority of these materials are available free or at little cost. Perhaps the greatest problems confronting the teacher in the use of these materials are filing and cataloguing them so they will be readily accessible, and evaluating them to ascertain their scientific accuracy and educational soundness.

These media of communication are relatively simple, and have optimal usefulness when the focus is on one fact, concept, or theme. Because of the degree of abstraction involved, their meaning to the pupil will often be in proportion to the background of experience and information to which he can relate what he sees in these pictorial representations.

Besides providing information, such graphic materials as cartoons and posters can be powerful forces in attitude formation. The choice of a specific type of graphic material depends on the goal which the instructor expects to achieve. The intent may be to motivate pupils to action, to arouse interest or curiosity, to stimulate thinking, to provide factual or comparative data, to influence pupil opinion, or to add humor to a problem situation. It is not enough merely to display these materials and leave to chance whatever learning might take place. It is the teacher's responsibility to make certain that the material can be related to something concrete in the learner's experience. If this condition exists, the impact on the observer can be instantaneous and lasting.

There are certain limitations to graphic materials just as there are to all teaching materials. Again, the teacher's competence in selecting and using graphic materials is the guard against misrepresentations, stereotypes, bias, oversimplification, and vague symbolism which may confuse rather than clarify. The potential value of these materials is unlimited if pupils can be involved in their production and use. They afford an opportunity for pupils with varying degrees of skill and imagination to express their creative talents. The media on which graphic materials can be displayed are the tackboard, chalkboard, feltboard, and magnetic board.

Modern and well-planned classrooms reflect consideration for adequate *tackboard* and *chalkboard* space. These teaching devices

have long been a part of every schoolroom, but teachers often
have neglected the possibilities offered by these items either
by rare or haphazard use in which the principles of good display
techniques were violated. It is essential that materials placed on
display be pertinent to the subject, up to date, and have eye
appeal for the viewer if they are to stimulate thought, clarify
concepts, and maintain interest. Pupils quickly lose interest in
displays that are not attractive, stimulating, and kept current.

Rapid advances in the medical and health sciences provide a
continual flow of dramatic and scientific articles and photographs which can become the subject of tackboard displays. The
use of three-dimensional objects adds reality to the display, and
clever captions or slogans give it continuity and enhance the
communication level of this medium.

The modern versions of the chalkboard have prompted teachers to experiment with an infinite number of uses for one of the
oldest instructional devices. Patterns will save time, especially
patterns of the more complicated drawings and diagrams which
are repeatedly used in health teaching, and which cannot be
retained for an extended period on the chalkboard. When a
portion of the chalkboard can be set aside for permanent diagrams or illustrations, a method described by McCloy[12] can be
adapted to meet the needs of the health education instructor.

A unique technique for attracting and holding pupil attention
is to place a series of items on the board in advance of the
class period and cover each unit with a strip of paper and mask-
ing tape. Then, when each is needed for illustration during class,
the instructor removes the paper strips one by one and exposes
the individual parts of the chalkboard display. This procedure
has three advantages. It arouses pupil curiosity and stimulates
interest, it focuses pupil attention on a particular illustration,
and after successive exposure and discussion of each item, the
entire display can be seen as a unified, meaningful whole.

The *feltboard* is another display device which receives popular
acceptance today, especially in the elementary grades. The
principle of the feltboard is that wool, flannel, felt, or similar
fabrics adhere to like surfaces. Feltboards and the materials
for display on them may be purchased commercially, but many
useful cutouts can be made easily and inexpensively in school.
Letters, words, and objects may be cut out of felt, and magazines

[12] McCloy, C. H. "Simplified Methods for Anatomical Drawings." *Journal of Health, Physical Education, Recreation* 29: 56; February 1958.

may be the source of an endless variety of pictures and other illustrations. In the latter case, small pieces of felt, sandpaper, or flocklite are pasted on the back of the cutout so that it will adhere when placed on the board. Colorful and realistic food models can be made from these cutouts for use with a teaching unit on nutrition.

The use of the feltboard needs practice and planning by the teacher to make sure that there will not be distractions caused by materials that frequently slip out of place. A prepared script helps to maintain continuity and adds much to the presentation.

The *magnetic board* is still another technique which has possibilities for use in health education. In some schools a small portion of the wall space has been set aside for a permanent magnetic board. Other schools have chalkboards with steel backing which also serve as magnetic boards.

Today's teacher strives for well-organized and functional displays of graphic material. The principles outlined previously for the use of projected audio-visual materials also apply to the display of graphic materials.

TEXTBOOKS

Textbooks in health education have changed markedly in recent years. From an early content of facts and details about the human body, adroitly summarized, but with little functional explanation, the content now includes much more usable and realistic information. In contrast to the formerly limited scope of physiology and hygiene, many of the best books now range far into the behavioral, social, and physical sciences to aid the reader in finding solutions to his own health problems.

Educators generally agree that with the remarkably rapid growth of knowledge, a body of scientific health information is essential as the core of any health textbook. At the same time, they also agree that the mere statement of authoritative health facts on the printed page is not assurance that the information will be translated into desirable attitudes and health behavior. Textbooks need to be more than encyclopedias. For effective learning, the health information is accompanied by problem solving experiences in which the knowledge is brought to bear upon real life situations.

The teacher plans and prepares to teach with a textbook just as he does with any other instructional tool. One of his first concerns is the selection of textbooks which are suitable to the achievement levels of the pupils. Rather than assigning copies of the same health textbook to all pupils, he may prefer to use a variety of textbooks which can be assigned to pupils on the basis of their individual reading abilities and comprehension. Further, he gives thought to such questions as: What new concept is the pupil expected to acquire from his reading? How does the new learning transcend his past perceptions? What further experiences will supplement the reading and help make certain that the learning will endure?

Authors and publishers give attention to the format and other technical features of the textbook to make it attractive and to capture pupil interest. Photographs and other illustrations are carefully selected according to the maturity level and the life context of boys and girls for whom the book is written.

Teachers manuals or guides provide a wealth of helpful suggestions which the teacher can modify and adapt to his classes and pupils. Neither the textbook nor the accompanying guide is a crutch upon which the teacher relies. The focus always remains on the pupils and their health needs. *Pupil workbooks* need to be used with caution, lest they become a form of "busy work" or rote copying from the textbooks. Some current high-school workbooks contain health education activities which demand reflective thought by pupils. Wise selection of workbooks is based upon their potential motivational power.

As mentioned previously, there is a trend among publishers to correlate films and filmstrips with health textbooks at the elementary, secondary, and college levels. The colored transparencies and plates of body systems and organs which appear in modern health textbooks are further evidence of efforts to clarify and enrich the content. "Problems to be solved," which appear at the conclusion of a chapter or section of a text afford opportunities for pupils to explore and investigate personal and community health problems, and to relate new learnings to situations in their own communities.

In spite of the development and improvement of other instructional materials, the increase in the scope and amount of what is to be learned makes the textbook even more significantly a basic tool in health education. The acknowledged role of books in our society is reflected, too, in the vast selection of paperback volumes that are available in virtually every field of knowledge, including health science. The economical feature of these paperback books makes it possible to enrich the health course immeasurably, and encourages the pupil to do extensive reading on his own and to build a library on related topics.

CRITERIA FOR SELECTING PRINTED MATERIALS

The following criteria are guides for the selection of textbooks and other printed teaching materials. How each applies in a given instance depends upon the specific teaching objectives which have been set up to meet particular needs.

A. Content

1. Are the facts scientifically accurate?
2. Does the material present what needs to be taught?
3. Is all of the information pertinent?
4. Do the selection and arrangement constitute good coverage?
5. Are the ideas essential, significant, and important to clear understanding?
6. Is the content worthy of time and attention in a crowded curriculum?
7. Is the content free of unsound or untrue claims?

B. Psychological values

1. Is the interest-appeal strong enough to capture and hold attention?
2. Is the mixture of familiarity and newness such as to foster growth?
3. Is the material suitable for the level of comprehension currently possessed by the pupils?
4. Does the manner of presentation neither "talk down" to nor "go over the heads" of the intended readers?
5. Is the degree of action-urge sufficiently potent?
6. Is there educationally objectionable propaganda in the appeal?

C. Technical attributes

1. Are the type size, boldness, and spacing adequate for easy reading?
2. Is the paper stock good from the standpoint of color, contrast, and lack of glare?

3. Is the artistry of design and illustration attractive and effective?

Obviously, from among the wealth of proposed materials,[13, 14, 15] those acceptable for use will score quite well in all three major groups of criteria. Any appreciable failure in content, psychological values, or technical attributes will undermine or completely negate the "instructional quotient" of a given item.

Those responsible for the selection of textbooks and other printed materials are urged to study them carefully for scientific accuracy. Because of the rapid advancements in medical research and allied fields, health education materials need periodic re-evaluation with an eye toward elimination and replacement of obsolete items, and selection of those supplementary materials that provide completeness and exactness. Representatives from official, professional, and voluntary health organizations can be helpful to teachers in the task of judging health education materials for their adherence to currently accepted facts.

SOURCES OF ASSISTANCE, INFORMATION, AND MATERIALS

The health teacher is expected to help his pupils understand how the latest discoveries in the medical and health sciences relate to their behavior. This requires more than imparting knowledge. The teacher's task is to influence how pupils feel about health and what they do about their health. Health teaching necessarily draws on many sciences for the best information on how to live, and on the broad field of education for skills to make this information meaningful. Thus, the teacher looks to others for specialized knowledge and enrichment materials which will strengthen his teaching. *He looks first within the school, next within the community, and then outside the community.*

---

[13] *Elementary Teachers Guide to Free Curriculum Materials*, published annually by Educators Progress Service, Randolph, Wis., lists about 1200 items with a brief description of each.

[14] *Free and Inexpensive Learning Materials*, published annually by the Division of Surveys and Field Services, George Peabody College for Teachers, Nashville, Tenn., lists pamphlets and other printed materials with annotations about content, timeliness, format, educational features, publisher, and distributor of each piece.

[15] *Free and Inexpensive Health Instruction Materials*, edited by John R. LeFevre and Donald N. Boydston, and published by Southern Illinois University Press, Carbondale, Ill., lists health instruction materials which cost a dollar or less and which are suitable for use in schools and colleges.

Resources Within the School

Many schools have developed *teachers guides*[16] which include classified listings of the audio-visual materials, resource persons and agencies, textbooks, pamphlets, and other health education resources which are readily available. The teacher needs to know what materials and equipment, such as projectors, charts, and models, are in his building and what may be secured through the central office.

Many school systems provide health education materials through the *school or public library*. Periodicals, pamphlets, films, slides, and recordings as well as books are provided. Many libraries carry current catalogues of audio-visual suppliers and listings of films, posters, and exhibits that are available locally. The teacher can locate further "leads" in the card catalogues; indexes such as the *Education Index, Readers' Guide to Periodical Literature, Educational Film Guide, Catalogue of Free Teaching Aids, Selected United States Government Publications;* and other sources for locating up-to-date information and audio-visual materials. The school librarian is a helpful resource person for teachers who are seeking aids to better teaching.

School Staff Resources

Some school systems have a *director of curriculum* or a *co-ordinator of audio-visual materials* who heads a centralized service apart from the library. One function of such a director or co-ordinator is to assist teachers in securing curriculum materials for classroom use.

A *specialist in health education* may be employed. He may teach some health classes and devote part of his time to the promotion of a complete school health program. His title may be health consultant, co-ordinator, supervisor, or director of health education. Sometimes a specialist in health and physical education is employed. Each elementary school and high school may have a teacher appointed to serve as co-ordinator of health education. The helpfulness of these people in providing source materials and information depends on their qualifications, interest, time, and assigned responsibilities.

There may be a variety of *health specialists* working on the school health team who can be called upon from time to time

---

[16] The Association for Supervision and Curriculum Development (NEA) prepares an annual list of new curriculum guides which have been produced by school systems, state departments of education, and colleges engaged in teacher preparation.

to help teachers with special problems. The school medical adviser, the nurse who serves the school, the dentist, dental hygienist, nutritionist, and speech and hearing therapist expect to serve as resource persons. The teacher may ask these people to help him find materials and to keep him informed about the newer knowledge of their health specialties. There may be times when it is desirable to have these specialists serve as resource visitors to the classroom.

Resources Within the Community

Within the community the teacher will find official and non-official health agencies such as city or county health departments, voluntary health associations, and professional organizations such as the local medical and dental societies.

The *local health department,* if a fully qualified unit organized at the county or city level, is a most helpful source of information and materials. The modern health department recognizes education as a means for solving many of today's community health problems, and it is usually staffed to carry on a public health education program. Many health departments employ health educators who assist in the schools when they are invited to do so. In some instances a health educator is employed jointly by the departments of education and health with the school health education program as his major responsibility.

Ideally, the full-time local health department has at least a medical health officer, a sanitary officer, a laboratory technician, a clerk, and public health nurses on its professional staff. Larger units may have health educators, public health dentists, dental hygienists, nutritionists, and other specialists. The clerk can usually direct the teacher to proper personnel for the help he needs. The health department often provides the school health services. Where this is done, a public health nurse makes periodic visits to the school. At this time she is usually willing to discuss with the teacher health instruction materials as well as the health problems of certain children. The teacher cannot afford to overlook other branches of local government, such as the police and fire departments, as sources for materials and consultants in certain aspects of health and safety education.

Voluntary health agencies provide education and service as part of their programs. The better known agencies are well organized at either the city or county level. Voluntary health agencies have been active in the development of public health programs in this country since the early part of the present century. Each is concerned with special health problems. They raise money for research and experimental programs, and support the activities of official health agencies. A major objective of these organizations is the education of the community about certain specific health needs. The teacher usually will find local chapters of the voluntary health agencies concerned with cancer, tuberculosis, heart disease, hearing conservation, and other specific health problems. Often they can furnish him with films, filmstrips, teaching guides, and up-to-date printed information concerned with their special areas. These materials usually have been developed by the state or national offices of the agencies, but can be secured more quickly and at less cost through the local units.

Voluntary agencies have served the schools well by furnishing teaching aids, helping in the preparation of teachers guides, assisting with short-term projects, promoting the in-service education of teachers, providing speakers and consultants for pupils and teachers, and participating on school health committees. Considerable attention has been given to the ways through which voluntary agencies may work co-operatively in the school health program. These methods are described in a formal report.[17]

Local medical, dental, and other *professional societies* are interested in school health education and services, and in recent years many of them have formed school health committees to help schools improve their programs. Most of the materials available through the local professional organizations have been developed at the state and national levels. Resource people from these organizations can assist in special areas of health instruction such as home nursing, quackery, and sex education. Representatives from these groups can also be helpful in the scientific evaluation of health education materials, and as members of the school health council.

In recent years, schools, colleges, and communities have formed *health councils* to mobilize their health resources in ways which will best serve school and community. The detailed organization and functions of a health council are discussed in Chapter Sixteen. The council provides opportunities for lay

---

[17] American Association for Health, Physical Education, and Recreation. "How Schools and Voluntary Agencies Can Work Together To Improve School Health Programs." *Journal of Health, Physical Education, Recreation* 26: 35-36; October 1955.

and professional people to exchange ideas and information. Through studies and surveys the health council can determine the most important health needs of a school or community. The chairman of a health council can advise the teacher where to get help on certain problems.

Resources Outside the Community

When the health teacher seeks health education assistance, information, and materials outside the school system and local community, he finds a large number of sources which lead to a hard core of authentic and reliable enrichment materials.

Most *state departments of education* have consultants in school health. These people are employed to help school systems improve their health education programs. Also, most states have minimum standards and legal requirements for health and safety instruction in schools. Usually the state department of education provides guides for elementary and secondary health teaching, as well as pamphlets, films, and other teaching materials on health topics.

State health departments have specialists in maternal and child health, disease control, dental health, sanitation, nutrition, mental health, and health education. Films, bulletins, pamphlets, and other materials are available for school use. The state health departments generally prefer that school personnel channel requests for materials or consultant services through the school superintendent and the local health department or district office. Both state and local health departments can be helpful in securing teaching materials from national sources.

Services for schools from state departments of health and education have been improved in recent years by joint planning between the two departments. Such planning permits the employment of specialists to serve both departments, provides coordinated services, eliminates duplication of materials, and avoids confusion by following common policies for school health programs. Some states have planning committees or councils which not only include representatives from the state departments of health and education, but also from voluntary health agencies, professional societies, and the colleges which prepare teachers.

The *U.S. Department of Health, Education, and Welfare* at the national level houses the Public Health Service (the official health agency), the Children's Bureau, and the Office of Education. The Public Health Service publishes *Public Health Reports*, a periodical of value to public health personnel. *School Life*, a journal dealing with general school problems, is the official publication of the Office of Education. The Children's Bureau issues *Children*, a bimonthly interdisciplinary journal concerned with the growth, development, and problems of children. The Superintendent of Documents, Government Printing Office, Washington 25, D.C., will send free to teachers or the school library the biweekly listing, *Selected United States Government Publications*, and the annual price lists, PL31 *Education* and PL51 *Health and Hygiene*.

The *National Education Association* is a professional organization of educators. It works with other groups to improve education through better schools and advancement of the professional, economic, social, and civic status of teachers. Through its affiliated state associations, the NEA represents the concerns of 1.5 million teachers. It publishes the *Journal of the National Education Association* and hundreds of other journals, bulletins, books, and pamphlets devoted to the interests of teachers and the promotion of better education at all levels. One of NEA's departments, the *American Association for Health, Physical Education, and Recreation*, publishes the *Journal of Health, Physical Education, Recreation*, the *Research Quarterly*, and numerous other bulletins, pamphlets, and books in school health education and related fields. Requests for consultative assistance and teaching materials may be sent to the National Education Association or directly to the American Association for Health, Physical Education, and Recreation, at the same address.

The *Joint Committee on Health Problems in Education* of the National Education Association and the American Medical Association is a committee of representatives from both the medical and education professions which has functioned since 1911. In addition to this publication, *Health Education*, the Joint Committee has published two other books, *School Health Services* and *Healthful School Living*. *Answers to Health Questions in Physical Education* and *The Health Appraisal of School Children* are among the many reports of this Committee. These publications can be secured from the American Medical Association or the National Education Association.

The *American Medical Association* and its state, territorial, and county medical societies have a deep interest in school, college, and public health education. The Association publishes the *Journal of the American Medical Association* for its members and *Today's Health,* which interprets to lay people medical opinion on health problems. *Today's Health* is a most valuable resource for teachers at all levels and for health classes at the secondary and college levels. The AMA has a Department of Health Education which is staffed by consultants in school and public health education. Through this and other departments, and in conjunction with other organizations, the Association has developed valuable resource materials. The AMA prefers to have schools and teachers make requests through local and state medical associations.

Among the best avenues to reliable, current information and new materials are the American Association for Health, Physical Education, and Recreation; the American School Health Association; and the School Health Section of the American Public Health Association. These professional organizations are concerned primarily with school health. They publish journals which, besides having articles on various aspects of health education, carry book reviews, news from the field, annotated bibliographies, notices of new teaching materials, and advertising of reliable commercial products. These groups have annual meetings at which members gather to discuss new knowledge in health science and health education. They have affiliated state and, in some instances, district or regional organizations that also meet periodically.

School health problems are of interest to many of the numerous sections of the *American Public Health Association,* but since its organization in 1942, the School Health Section has attempted to bring together those with particular interests in school health education. The Section functions throughout the year by means of committees which are appointed to study and report on certain health problems. Committee reports, many of which have direct implications for health teaching, are published in the *American Journal of Public Health* or in the *Section Newsletter.*

The *American School Health Association* holds an annual meeting in conjunction with the American Public Health Association. Its membership includes physicians, dentists, dental hygienists, school nurses, nutritionists, health educators, and school administrators. The Association has many study committees which prepare recommendations and reports on all phases of school health. The committee reports and a variety of health education articles are published in the *Journal of School Health*.

Since 1931 the *American Academy of Pediatrics* has had a Committee on School Health which gives special attention to school health services. Reports of the Committee are printed in *Pediatrics,* a monthly publication of the Academy. This has encouraged the active participation of pediatricians in school health services, and has given schools the benefit of their thinking on health education problems. Reprints of the Committee's reports are available on request.

The *American Dental Association* has a strong interest in health education of the public. Its Bureau of Dental Health Education has developed excellent resource materials for schools and offers consultant services. A listing of its literature, special publications, and audio-visual materials is available free of charge.

The *voluntary health agencies* at the state and national levels are interested in health education. At state and national levels the programs of these associations are similar in organization and methods of education, while local level programs are varied to meet community needs. These associations develop and distribute excellent pamphlets, teaching guides, plays, charts, and posters for school use. As previously indicated, teachers can save time and sometimes money by securing these materials through the local units.

Commercial organizations have developed some most worthwhile and attractive health education materials. Many life insurance companies and industry-sponsored associations produce extensive amounts of enrichment material which is accurate and free of objectionable advertising. Many private companies supply materials of excellent quality at no cost and with no more advertising than an identifying label. On the other hand, some manufacturers and distributing companies mislead the public in order to sell their products. Their educational materials are not suitable for classroom use.

The following criteria are helpful in evaluating the health instructional materials prepared by commercial organizations:

1. The material shall bear a clear, but modest, label identifying its source.

2. It shall be free from advertising.

3. It shall be scientifically accurate.

4. It shall be consistent with modern educational methodology.

5. It shall not promote products, services, or concepts which are contrary to accepted good health principles and practices.

Consultants from the local health department, voluntary health agencies, and the county medical society can be helpful to individual teachers and to teacher committees in applying these criteria.

The *World Health Organization,* a specialized agency associated with the United Nations, is dedicated to promote the highest level of health for all peoples. WHO publishes pamphlets and newsletters which describe what it is and what it does. It issues reports of its committees that work on certain aspects of the school health program. The Columbia University Press serves as WHO's publications outlet in the United States. *Chronicle of the World Health Organization,* giving special information about WHO's activities, is published monthly in English, French, Spanish, Russian, and Chinese.

Whereas WHO is an international governmental agency, the *World Medical Association* is a professional organization of the national medical associations in some 50 countries. It is dedicated to the improvement of medical education and care throughout the world, improvement of health standards in industry, exchange of medical information among physicians throughout the world, and development of an international Code of Medical Ethics. The World Medical Association publishes special reports in addition to the *World Medical Journal* which appears six times a year.

RESOURCE FILE OF TEACHING MATERIALS

If the health teacher is going to make full use of the tremendous amount of available reference and teaching materials, it becomes necessary for him to develop a simple, flexible resource file. As the teacher reads articles, pamphlets, and books that are valuable to him, he makes notations of certain information on filing cards. The use of separate cards permits alphabetical arrangement by topics. Each card carries a brief résumé of the contents, merit, and use of a given item. For books and pamphlets the essentials include: author's name, complete title, place of publication, name of publisher, date of publication, and cost. For periodicals indicate: author's name, title of article, name of journal, number of volume, date of publication, and numbers of the pages on which the article appears.

A card file on films and other audio-visual materials can be developed. Here, each card contains how, where, and the time needed to secure the material, as well as its cost. Other useful information to note depends on the nature of the material. Through annotation of lesson plans, the teacher can note how any one item is used and how it might be used again. It is important to replace notations on out-of-date materials, especially pamphlets and films, with current ones on more recent items.

The health teacher cannot keep all of the materials that come to his attention. However, he can develop the ability to scan and recognize what is useful, according to the guidelines presented in this and other chapters. A resource file is basic for good planning and efficient use of teaching materials.

SUMMARY

Audio-visual materials are integral parts of teaching. They do not take the place of the teacher or the textbook, nor do they relieve the pupil of responsibility for his own learning. They can be, when properly used, both teaching and learning tools. The increasing variety and continual improvement of teaching equipment, materials, and techniques place an obligation on the teacher to become thoroughly familiar with resources in the school, within the community, and outside of the community. Local, state, and national agencies and organizations, both official and nonofficial, provide assistance in the form of audio-visual materials and consultant services. A resource file with appropriate notations can be a helpful and time-saving device in aiding the teacher to screen out teaching materials for future use by himself and other staff members.

There is a wealth of instructional material in the area of health education. More and more school boards are making budgetary provisions for current and scientifically accurate texts, library materials, and audio-visual supplies. The extent to which these materials are utilized, and the effectiveness of their use depend in large measure upon the resourcefulness, skill, preparation, and alertness of the teacher.

SELECTED REFERENCES

ALLEN, WILLIAM H. "Audio-Visual Communication." *Encyclopedia of Educational Research*. Revised edition. (Edited by Chester W. Harris.) New York: Macmillan Co., 1960. p. 115-37.

BARNOUW, ERIK. *Mass Communication—Television, Radio, Films, Press*. New York: Rinehart & Co., 1956. 290 p.

BROWN, JAMES W.; LEWIS, RICHARD B.; and HARCLEROAD, FRED F. *A-V Instruction Materials and Methods*. New York: McGraw-Hill Book Co., 1959. 554 p.

DALE, EDGAR. *Audio-Visual Methods in Teaching*. Revised edition. New York: Dryden Press, 1954. 534 p.

DEKIEFFER, ROBERT, and COCHRAN, LEE W. *Manual of Audio-Visual Techniques*. Englewood Cliffs, N.J.: Prentice-Hall, 1955. 220 p.

ESTVAN, FRANK J., and OTHERS. "Instructional Materials." *Review of Educational Research* 26: 113-97; April 1956.

FAUST, CLARENCE H. "Educational Philosophy and Television." *Educational Record* 35: 44-51; January 1958.

FINN, JAMES D. "Automation and Education." *Audio-Visual Communication Review* 5: 343-60; Winter 1957.

GROUT, RUTH E. *Health Teaching in Schools*. Third edition. Philadelphia: W. B. Saunders Co., 1958. 359 p. Chapter 5, "Audiovisual Materials and Their Use in Health Education."

HAAG, JESSIE HELEN. *School Health Program*. New York: Henry Holt & Co., 1958. 533 p. Part IV, "Community Resources."

IRWIN, LESLIE W.; HUMPHREY, JAMES H.; and JOHNSON, WARREN R. *Methods and Materials in School Health Education*. St. Louis: C. V. Mosby Co., 1956. 367 p. Part II, "Methods and Materials in Teaching Health."

KINDER, JAMES S. *Audio-Visual Materials and Techniques*. Second edition. New York: American Book Co., 1959. 592 p.

MCCLUSKY, F. DEAN. *The Audio-Visual Bibliography*. Dubuque, Iowa: William C. Brown Co., 1955. 218 p.

NATIONAL SOCIETY FOR THE STUDY OF EDUCATION. *Mass Media and Education*. Fifty-Third Yearbook, Part II. Chicago: University of Chicago Press, 1954. 290 p.

NICHOLS, RALPH G., and STEVENS, LEONARD. *Are You Listening?* New York: McGraw-Hill Book Co., 1958. 236 p.

SANDS, LESTER B. *Audio-Visual Procedures in Teaching.* New York: Ronald Press Co., 1956. 670 p.

SCHNEIDER, ROBERT E. *Methods and Materials of Health Education.* Philadelphia: W. B. Saunders Co., 1958. 382 p. Part IV, "The Materials of Health Education."

THOMAS, R. MURRAY, and SWARTOUT, SHERWIN G. *Integrated Teaching Materials.* New York: Longmans, Green & Co., 1960. 545 p.

TRUMP, J. LLOYD. *Images of the Future.* Washington, D.C.: Commission on the Experimental Study of the Utilization of the Staff in the Secondary School, National Association of Secondary-School Principals, NEA, 1959. 48 p.

WILLIAMS, CATHERINE M. *Sources of Teaching Materials.* Teaching Aids Laboratory Pamphlet No. 1. Revised edition. Columbus: The Ohio State University, Bureau of Educational Research and Service, 1958. 37 p.

WITTICH, WALTER A., and SCHULLER, CHARLES F. *Audio-Visual Materials.* Second edition. New York: Harper & Brothers, 1957. 570 p.

WOELFEL, NORMAN. *How to Reach Your Teaching Goals with Teaching Aids.* Teaching Aids Laboratory Pamphlet No. 2. Columbus: The Ohio State University, Bureau of Educational Research and Service, 1955. 12 p.

Health Education
Experiences

Health service experiences provide an excellent opportunity for health education. When a pupil is participating in an activity such as a tuberculosis case-finding program, a dental health survey, or a vision screening test, his interest is easy to capture and his potential level of learning from the experience is high. The quality of the experience in terms of beliefs or attitudes, knowledge or information, and subsequent motivation of behavior depends upon (a) the nature and worth of the experience itself; (b) the accompanying instruction and interpretations; and (c) the quality and degree of pupil participation. Such participation needs to be on an intellectual and attitudinal level as contrasted with mere physical participation in which the pupil is nothing more than the "subject" in the program.

The basis for pupil interest is evident. Everyone is interested in himself. When he takes a hearing test, he is curious about the outcome. When he has a positive tuberculin reaction he will wonder what this means. When a physician examines him, he wants to know if he is "fit." As one third-grade pupil phrased it at the conclusion of a Snellen eye test, "Did I pass?" Capitalizing upon this interest in self and one's abilities and disabilities, the teacher, physician, nurse, or technician can provide the information and understanding which make the experience truly educational.

The Quality of the Experience

Learning takes place with reference to health service experiences whether or not such learning is planned or intended. The influence of the experience on attitudes toward physicians, nurses, dentists, and other health personnel will be determined in part by the quality of the experience itself. If health examinations are conducted at school in routine fashion on an assembly line basis, with little attention paid to needs and questions of those being inspected, the attitudes of pupils toward medical

317

services are likely to be negative. Physicians, nurses, or dentists may be seen as cold, impersonal automatons rather than as professionally trained advisers who can help with problems or give assurance that health and well-being are commendable.

Conversely, when examinations are unhurried, adequate, and adapted to individual needs, pupils gain more favorable attitudes toward health services. Removing routine examinations from the school setting to the private physician's or dentist's office has provided greater opportunity for better medical and dental supervision and consequent greater appreciation of the value of such service by pupils and their parents. In those situations in which examinations are performed at the school, every effort must be made to provide the type of experience for the pupil which will have a desirable influence on his attitudes toward medical and dental supervision. The quality of the experience has profound educational significance.

Individual Instruction and Guidance

The most direct and meaningful health education of the individual probably occurs on a person-to-person basis. When a patient seeks guidance and assistance from his personal physician, he has motive, interest, and readiness to learn. His motive sometimes may be one of fear or concern, but if it has impelled him to seek professional guidance, he has established a threshold of interest. The skill with which the physician answers questions, gives advice and support, and explains the situation in terms of ability of the patient to understand will help to determine subsequent behavior on the part of the patient.

Similarly, in school situations pupils will learn from participation in health service experiences when there is opportunity for individual questioning, counsel, and interpretation which meet individual concerns. There is opportunity also to help meet the need which parents of young children feel for individual health education with respect to their own children. When health service experiences are conducted in rapid, routine fashion with little or no opportunity for individual participation beyond supplying the body for purposes of the test, survey, or examination, the experience has little medical or educational value.

Group Instruction Relating to Health Services

One of the justifications frequently used to support health service experiences in schools is that they have educational goals.

If such goals are to be realized in fact as well as in theory, there should be conscious planning for the development of favorable attitudes, beliefs, and understandings of pupils with reference to the experience. Group instruction both prior to and following a health service procedure will help to achieve educational objectives.

There are numerous examples of the need and opportunity for this type of health teaching. Preparation of groups of pupils for vision screening, audiometer testing, health examinations, or immunization procedures can be carried out most effectively by the teacher working with her class. Teaching will involve more than making an announcement concerning the impending procedure. There may be an opportunity for development of a teaching unit with reference to health service experiences, providing this is appropriate, profitable, and within time limits. The least that can be done is to provide opportunity for information giving, discussion, questions, and possibly a demonstration if the procedure is unfamiliar. Fears can be removed, interest quickened, and voluntary participation markedly increased by good teaching prior to the event. After the experience there will be further questions, need for interpretation, and evaluation of what occurred. In many school districts the nurse, because of her professional training, helps the teacher in preparing pupils for these special health activities or procedures, making the occasion a profitable health education experience for the teacher as well as for the pupils.

OPPORTUNITIES IN SPECIFIC EXPERIENCES

While each health service procedure possesses similar potential for influencing health attitudes, understandings, and behavior, there is value in exploring several activities in greater detail to emphasize their value as tools for health education. Some of these experiences and their possible utilization are discussed in this section.

Screening Tests

Vision screening is a common school practice; in some schools it is conducted on an annual basis. The first time vision screening is performed with a particular group of children, the class needs careful instruction, including demonstration and practice in the method of testing. Assuming that the first experience occurs at an early age, that is, in kindergarten or first grade, little instruction on the nature of vision and the significance of testing will be given at that time. Later, in the third or fourth grade, a specific unit on vision might be taught and the vision testing included as a part of the unit. Each time tests are given there should be opportunity for questions, interpretation of findings to individual children, and some instruction on care of eyes and of glasses. During the secondary-school period, when some boys object to wearing glasses because of their fear that they will not be able to participate in athletics and when girls are concerned with the effect of glasses on appearance, another unit on vision needs to be taught and the vision screening made a part of it.

Although the experience occurs less frequently, similar teaching is accomplished easily in connection with audiometer testing in the schools. When growth records are kept in connection with weighing and measuring at school their potential value for health education is evident. Children are vitally interested in their growth, and adolescents have major concerns relating to size, physical development, weight, and body build. Perhaps the greatest value of the weighing and measuring program in schools is its educational potential. Unless used as a means of interpreting normal variations in growth or of motivating better eating, activity, and rest practices among pupils, the procedure loses much of its value.

Health Inventories

Prior to the health or medical examination, history sheets or health inventory forms often are utilized to secure information from parents and pupils with reference to past illnesses and operations, immunizations, present health conditions and practices, and similar matters. In the secondary schools the pupils themselves are often asked to complete their own health inventories. This offers a unique and significant opportunity for health education. Pupils need to recognize the importance of an accurate record and to accept the assignment seriously. There will be many questions raised as teacher and pupils review the nature of the forms together. In fact, the health inventory may well become an index of pupil interest as well as of health status and behavior. Effectively used, a truly functional health education unit may well evolve.

Health Examinations

Preparation for health examinations, whether performed in the private physician's office or in the school situation, is an important constituent of the total experience. Group discussion prior to the examinations may be helpful in influencing pupil attitudes toward the procedure, and in some instances, a demonstration of examining techniques by a physician in person or utilizing a series of slides may enhance the meaning of the examination. This is particularly true for older pupils and can be used as a basis for discussion of the values of medical supervision and the importance of individual responsibility for follow up on recommendations made by the physician.

During the examination itself the physician has an unexcelled opportunity for health education of the pupil. Attitudes toward physicians and toward medical supervision can be influenced by an expertly conducted examination and conference. Understanding of individual health assets and limitations can be developed and confidence of the pupil elicited by willingness of the physician to answer pupil or parent questions and his effort to interpret his findings. Recommendations for follow up must be clearly understood if action is to ensue. The nurse may contribute to the educational value of the experience by her participation in the examination and her subsequent individual guidance toward solution of important health problems.

Dental Surveys

Although dental inspections and examinations are more frequently performed in private dental offices and clinics, there are many instances in which dental surveys are carried out in the schools. These may be conducted for several reasons, such as discovering the nature and extent of dental problems in a school population, encouraging dental follow up and corrections, and comparing dental caries experience with levels of fluorine content in the water supply. Whatever the objective, the dental survey can be a rich source of health learnings if properly utilized. Teaching should be done in the group both prior to and following the survey, and individual guidance may be conducted while a pupil is being seen by a dentist or dental hygienist.

Physician's Contributions to Health Education

The physician, although seldom a regular member of the school staff, has significant opportunities for health education of pupils, parents, and teachers. The physician has contact with parents and children in his private practice and, in addition to providing health supervision of the child, guides parent and child in the development of better health attitudes and practices. When health supervision and guidance are maintained continuously from infancy, the child is better fitted to meet the demands of entrance to school and to profit from the experiences provided in the educational program.

The physician operating in the school situation has similar opportunities to work with children and parents in the areas of health guidance and health education. Health problems often are identified first in screening tests and health examinations conducted at school. In some situations the physician interprets findings to parents and pupils, recommends steps for action, and joins with the nurse and teacher in guiding health attitudes and understandings of pupils.

The physician is an important resource to the school in the adaptation of school procedures to the health needs of particular children, and his judgment and advice should be respected and followed. The school staff needs to realize the importance of the interchange of information deemed necessary for the health or adjustment of pupils and also needs to recognize the professional ethics involved in maintaining relationships with private physicians. Education of the school staff may be needed to establish the desirable climate for co-operative activity of physician, teacher, and administrator in the interest of the child.

Nurse-Pupil-Parent Contacts

The nurse operating in the school has significant opportunities and responsibilities for the health education of individual pupils and often of their parents. In fact, the school nurse of today is often considered as a health consultant to pupils, parents, teachers, and administrators, and supplies the information and guidance which not only result in the solution of individual health problems but also in an improved health program in the entire school.

The pupil who comes to the nurse for emergency care may be sent away with nothing more than a routine service or he may be helped to help himself and to prevent or solve further health emergencies. The adolescent who has many unanswered questions about himself and his emotional and physical needs may mask his concerns under a veneer of teen-age bravado.

The discerning and skilled nurse may be able to help him express these concerns and consequently be in a position to render assistance. The fifth-grade class may request the nurse to visit their group and help them with their unit on vision or hearing. Parents will be grateful for individual help with a child's problem or for assistance in a parent-study group. The nurse has many opportunities for health teaching which should not be underestimated or overlooked.

Immunizations; Tuberculin Testing

Participation in immunization and tuberculin-testing procedures by children of school age is usually on a voluntary basis. There is need for education of both pupils and parents regarding the importance of these disease prevention measures. The immunizations and tuberculin tests may be conducted in the private physician's office, in the clinic of the local health department, or in the school itself according to the policies of varying schools and communities. Whatever administrative procedure is followed, the participation of pupils should be preceded, accompanied, and followed by opportunities for education. Two examples are appropriate.

During the original trials of Salk poliomyelitis vaccine in the schools of the nation, first- and second-graders were enlisted for the program. In those schools in which an educational program for parents was undertaken before the trials, participation was higher than in areas where this was omitted. In those primary-grade classrooms in which children were taught what was to be done and why it was important, the enthusiasm of the children carried into the homes and convinced some doubtful parents that their children might participate. To be a "polio pioneer" became important. Teaching made the difference between participation and nonparticipation.

An example of the need for education of pupils in a tuberculin-testing program for ninth- and tenth-graders was noted in a visit to a high school at the time a physician and nurse were observing and recording the results of the test performed two days previously. As the pupils filed by the table and heard only the words "positive" or "negative" as the physician examined the reaction, one could not help but note the look of consternation on the faces of those pupils identified as "positive." Inquiry revealed that no teaching had been done prior to the experience, that pupils had little understanding of the significance of the results, and that parents were likewise confused when a few pupils reported that they had "positive TB." *

Emergency Care

Sudden illnesses or injuries often present unexcelled opportunities for health teaching. Pupils are interested in what happened, what was done, and how similar emergencies might be avoided. For instance: a high-school pupil becomes ill with acute abdominal pain. He is taken to the nurse who immediately gets in touch with one of his parents. The nurse advises that no food, water, or medication be given, and that he be seen by his physician as soon as possible. The parent arrives and takes the pupil to the physician's office. Within a short time the pupil is in the hospital and is undergoing surgery for appendicitis.

The classmates of this pupil will undoubtedly ask many questions of the teacher, some of which he will be able to answer while others may need to be referred to a physician or nurse. Why did the nurse suggest that the pupil should have no food, water, or medication? Is surgery the only treatment for appendicitis? Can appendicitis be prevented? What is a ruptured appendix? Is all pain in the abdomen caused by appendicitis? Discussion of these questions and others presents an opportunity for pupils to learn that appendicitis is a serious emergency that requires prompt medical attention, that sudden severe pain in the abdomen may be a sign of appendicitis but only a physician can make a diagnosis, and that administration of food, water, or medication can aggravate the condition of the person who may have appendicitis.

Appendicitis is used here only as an illustration.[1] Any sudden illness or injury provokes similar interest. A case of insulin shock, unconsciousness following a head injury, an accident in the chemistry laboratory—these and many other incidents need to be discussed with pupils, their questions answered, and their knowledge extended with relation to causes, prevention, and care of emergencies. Care must be taken that the pupil involved in

---

* NOTE: A positive reaction to a tuberculin test indicates that the person has been exposed to tuberculosis and may or may not have developed an active case. Positive reactors are advised to have a chest x-ray in order that a more accurate evaluation of the case can be made. The majority of positive reactors do not have active tuberculosis.

[1] The preceding material in this section adapted from: National Education Association and American Medical Association, Joint Committee on Health Problems in Education. *Healthful School Living.* Washington, D.C. and Chicago: the Associations, 1957. p. 270.

the incident is not embarrassed or hurt by the teacher's handling of the experience.

Attitudes Toward Handicaps and Illnesses

The recognition that people differ from one another is a fundamental fact which all children should be taught. This is especially true of children who have a visible handicap. The nonhandicapped child accepts his crippled playmate if he has been given an objective, factual explanation, within his comprehension, of the reasons for and nature of the handicap, and how it modifies the crippled child's activities. A frank and matter-of-fact approach by the teacher obviates the possibility that the nonhandicapped child will react toward his unfortunate fellow pupil with pity or ridicule, but instead engenders a healthful attitude of acceptance of the situation. This is even more true in the case of the child who has an epileptic convulsion in the classroom, the child who faints, or the child who has an attack of asthma or of vomiting.

If the teacher shows distress, panic, or distaste when such an incident occurs, serious and lasting emotional reactions can develop in classmates who are not familiar with these symptoms. However, if he adopts an attitude of calm and sympathetic helpfulness, and later promotes a discussion of the condition in the class, he will have taught the pupils several valuable lessons. They will have learned some fact of physiology and the manifestations of disease; they will have learned to accept without fear or horror evidence of body malfunction; the afflicted child, by the understanding attitude of his classmates, will have been helped in living with his disability.

HEALTHFUL SCHOOL LIVING AND HEALTH EDUCATION

Excellent opportunities exist in the experiences involved in living healthfully at school to influence pupils' practices, attitudes, and knowledge relating to health. Classroom and school environments and procedures affect health attitudes and behavior either for good or for ill. Sometimes these influences are subtle in their effect; at other times they are direct. The effective use of the health education opportunities provided by the school environment and regimen is a challenge to those who teach.

Some of these opportunities are explored without reference to appropriateness for specific grade levels. The effective teacher will select those experiences adapted to the needs of his group and pertinent to his program of health teaching.

Guidance and instruction concerning health will often be incidental, or be directed to the needs of an individual child. Nevertheless, situations constantly arise which should be recognized for their value in health education. This type of health education extends throughout the school day and the school year.

Getting Acquainted with the School

When children enter kindergarten or first grade, the school building and grounds are an unfamiliar and complex new world. New behavior patterns must be learned and puzzling adjustments made. Learning how to use toilets, handwashing facilities, and drinking fountains properly requires teaching and supervision. Lunchroom and playground behavior which is healthful, safe, and socially acceptable must be established. Safety factors involved in bus transportation and pedestrian behavior are imperative. The teacher of newcomers to school will, of necessity, help pupils understand and practice health and safety skills in the use of the school environment. Helping children to live healthfully at school constitutes a major goal of health education in the primary grades.

A tour of the building and grounds may be a first step in this orientation process. Children will feel more secure and sure of themselves if the teacher takes them around and introduces them not only to the physical facilities of buildings and grounds, but also to the people who are new to them, such as the principal, nurse, lunchroom manager, and custodian. During the tour, they can be taught how to use the drinking fountains, toilets, urinals, and washing facilities. Playground apparatus can be observed and discussion initiated concerning the proper use of slides, jungle gyms, "tricky" bars, and other equipment.

Observation and acquaintance with the environment is only the first step in the development of the skills, attitudes, and understandings necessary for safe and healthful living at school. Supervision of pupils and help in developing acceptable behavior patterns should continue as long as there is evidence of need.*

The Classroom Environment

Management of the classroom environment is a joint responsibility of the custodial staff, teachers, and pupils. Movable

* See Chapter Seven.

school furniture is rapidly replacing stationary rows of seats. The arrangement of seating can be changed in accord with the variety of activities which normally occur in the elementary-school child's day. There may be a tendency to move seats around with little regard for advantageous lighting unless the teacher is aware of the importance of visual comfort. Even though seats are movable they should be assigned individually on the basis of varying sizes to ensure comfort and good body position for each child. Pupils can discuss good seating and be made conscious of its relationships to comfort, correct sitting posture, and the prevention of fatigue.

Management of classroom lighting and ventilation can become a shared responsibility of teachers and pupils. The age of pupils and the types of mechanical controls of heating, ventilating, and lighting are factors in determining the kind and degree of responsibility which pupils may be expected to assume. An awareness of the importance of light and ventilation for comfort and health can be developed through discussion as well as through practice in classroom management.

The care of plants and animals (fish, white rats, hamsters, etc.) which are often part of a classroom environment involves health practices and understandings. The needs of living things for food, water, air, sunlight, and temperature regulation can be learned by pupils as they assume responsibility for the care of ferns or guppies. Health learnings are inherent in such experiences even though they may be incidental. At times, the teacher may wish to utilize the interests of children in a classroom aquarium or conservatory to develop a health education unit which leads to an understanding of the similar life needs of human beings.

Housekeeping practices in the classroom which promote safety and order should be learned early in the school life of the child. Proper storage of lunches brought from home and of coats, caps, and boots is an aspect of classroom housekeeping. Provision of storage space which is adequate and properly ventilated is important in teaching pupils to store their belongings in orderly fashion. Name tags on the outdoor clothing of young children facilitate order and system.

The emotional climate of the classroom is of tremendous importance in its influence on the health of children, and permeates the entire teaching process. In a discussion of healthful school living as a basis for health education, one should not lose sight of the fact that the personality of the teacher, teaching methods, and methods of classroom control are of paramount importance in the development of sound emotional health.

USE OF THE ENVIRONMENT

Health education involves a variety of approaches to development of the practices, attitudes, and understandings important for healthful living. In addition to the more or less incidental opportunities for health teaching discussed in the preceding paragraphs, teachers can develop a series of related learning experiences which utilize the school environment as a basis for study. Interest can be increased and health outcomes more readily achieved in the setting of reality provided by the school facilities in which children live and work together.

Studying Lighting

A sixth-grade class, as part of a unit on the care of the eyes, considered desirable conditions for reading and studying. The project included learning how to use the light meter and measuring the amount of light in different parts of the room. As a result, the classroom seating arrangement was reorganized so that pupils were able to utilize the best light for reading and for other work requiring good illumination. Less desirable areas of the classroom, from the standpoint of light, were used for discussion groups. Each pupil had a vision screening test followed, if needed, by a conference with the nurse. Pupils were advised regarding the best seat for them in the classroom if they had a particular vision problem. One goal of this counseling was to help the pupil to recognize the importance of having the best place for him to see well in relation to his particular vision problem. The teacher encouraged pupils to select a good place at home for reading, writing, and other activities requiring good illumination.

In another instance, the study of lighting by a combined seventh- and eighth-grade class in a rural school resulted in the renovation of the entire school building. The pupils borrowed a light meter from the public health nurse and measured the illumination of their classroom. The amount of light proved to be inadequate in all parts of the room. They studied standards for good lighting and decided that their room should be painted a light color and that new blinds and light fixtures were needed.

Under the guidance of the teacher (who was also the principal of the school) a committee was organized to consult a member of the school board who agreed to present their recommendations at the next board meeting.

The school board authorized the purchase of paint, and parents agreed to help in the painting job. A school social was arranged to raise money for new blinds. The local farm bureau agreed to finance new lighting fixtures and an electrician in the neighborhood agreed to install them. The project extended over several months. When the room was renovated, the parents of the pupils were invited to inspect it during a parent-teacher meeting. The reaction of the parents was not only one of approval and appreciation, but they also asked, "Why shouldn't the other three classrooms be similarly improved?" During the summer, renovation of the rest of the school was authorized and financed by the school board.

Learning About School Sanitation

Various aspects of sanitation can be taught through observation and study of school facilities and procedures. Pupils can learn about heating and ventilation by becoming familiar with the way these matters are handled in their own school, including a visit to the boiler room. What type of fuel is used? How is classroom temperature regulated? Who regulates it? If there is a mechanical ventilating system, how does it operate? These and numerous other questions that come to the minds of pupils are means of furthering understanding of certain aspects of health.

Similar opportunities for realistic health education are provided by study of the school water supply. If the school has its own water supply, as is the case in many rural schools, pupils should learn what precautions are taken to assure its safety. Where does the water come from? Where does the water go? Study of school water supplies in cities will lead naturally to consideration of public water supplies, including their adequacy, methods of treating water to make it safe, advantages of fluoridation in prevention of dental decay, and how communities finance their water supply programs. School drinking fountains should be observed and their sanitary characteristics discussed. Demonstration of the proper use of drinking fountains may be appropriate and desirable. The same is true of handwashing facilities, including instruction in the proper use of soap and towels. Instruction should also be given concerning the reasons for handwashing at appropriate times, especially after use of the toilet and before eating.

Pupils may learn how the school disposes of sewage, garbage, and rubbish, thus gaining understanding of these important sanitary measures. The alert teacher will point out the significant characteristics of proper disposal measures and, if appropriate, point out deficiencies that exist and suggest how they may be corrected.

A visit to the school kitchen, planned in advance with the school lunch manager, affords opportunities for high-school pupils, or even younger pupils, to gain firsthand information concerning sanitary procedures for food handling and storage. Analysis of regulations relating to the health of food handlers will assure pupils that the school administration is concerned with protecting them from food infections which come from poor food handling. They will be interested in the standards used for dishwashing and in methods used to keep flies, rats, roaches, and other undesirable bugs and animals out of the kitchen and dining room.

SAFETY AT SCHOOL

A school accident prevention program has many facets which can be related to classroom instruction. From kindergarten through high school, there is need for concern that children be protected and learn to protect themselves and others from accidental injuries.

Safety in Physical Activities

School accident statistics reveal that playground and gymnasium activities constitute the greatest cause of accidents occurring at school. There are many administrative and supervisory controls which must be exercised to reduce playground accidents, but these need to be supplemented by teaching if pupils are to learn and practice safety skills. The playground, gymnasium, and athletic field are the laboratories in which such skills and their concomitant attitudes are developed.

The teacher of young children will concentrate his efforts on helping them learn how to use playground apparatus, to follow rules and directions in play activities, and to develop skills and co-ordinations which enable them to use their bodies easily and well. Awkwardness and poor co-ordination of themselves can be causes of accidents. Some classroom activities may develop out of needs evidenced on the playground. Children should discuss why they should maintain order and not push or shove or throw stones or snowballs; they should learn to take turns and otherwise conduct themselves in an orderly manner.

Older elementary-school pupils and high-school students may use the physical education and athletic program as a basis for classroom study related to safety. Many projects can be initiated which will enhance understandings and attitudes relating to safe behavior in vigorous activity. Some suggested activities include:

Investigating accidents which occur in the school physical education and play programs and discussing how they may be reduced in number and severity

Studying proper first aid for accidental injuries occurring during activity

Making a survey of equipment and facilities for physical education to determine their adequacy for safe use

Setting up a playground safety patrol, if this seems advisable

Studying safe behavior in a variety of recreational pursuits such as skating, skiing, swimming, boating, bicycling, mountain climbing

Surveying the use of bicycles for transportation to and from school and setting up rules relating to their storage and use on the school grounds

Investigating hazards in athletics and reasons for requiring certain equipment and enforcing rules of play; comparing the hazards of different sports

Discussing reasons for varying rules in girls' sports and boys' sports.

The utilization of actual accidents for teaching purposes requires skill and tact on the part of the teacher. An accident frequently is due to an error on the part of one or more persons. Teaching should be constructive, pointing out how similar accidents may be prevented rather than humiliating the one who committed an error.

Some accidents are emotionally traumatic for all concerned, making the teacher's task that of restoring emotional equilibrium as soon as possible. The most important factor in relieving anxiety, fright, or even panic on the part of pupils is the calm, efficient handling of the situation by the person responsible for administering first aid in case of a serious accident. The training of all school personnel as well as of pupils in the fundamentals of first aid is therefore of major importance.

Safety in Shops and Laboratories

The safe use of laboratory materials, equipment, tools, and machinery should be an integral part of teaching in those activities requiring their use. There are several departments in the secondary school in which teachers and pupils need to be particularly alert to problems involved in working with equipment and materials that may be dangerous. The safe disposal of radioactive isotopes and bacteriological specimens used in school laboratories is a case in point. Departments particularly concerned with problems in this area include the various metal and wood shops, home economics classes, chemistry and biology laboratories, ceramics and leather classes, construction of stage scenery in drama classes, and similar curricular activities. Each teacher in charge of such a program is responsible for teaching and supervising the proper use of the equipment used in his class or group. Appropriate first aid measures for accidents which may occur in the particular shop or laboratory should be studied, demonstrated, and practiced when necessary.

Fire Prevention

The primary responsibility for fire prevention is administrative and involves building construction, maintenance, and inspection. The reasons for fire regulations should be explored with pupils and their responsibilities discussed.

The fire drill is a protective measure practiced routinely in schools. Pupils need instruction and practice in orderly evacuation of the building and, in addition, a discussion of the reasons for holding such drills. It is important to build proper attitudes relating to fire drills, particularly among high-school students. Older pupils are likely to consider such drills as a joke unless there is positive instruction regarding them. Some teachers may reveal attitudes toward such routine procedures which have an undesirable influence on pupil attitudes.

The visit of a fire marshal to the school can be capitalized upon as a learning experience for pupils. He may be invited to talk with a group of pupils about the work of fire protection personnel and to answer questions concerning fire prevention in schools. Often, the interest in fire prevention at school can be extended to include fire protection in the home and in the community. National losses in life and property and the importance of fire prevention in woods and forests can be dramatized. A unit on fire safety can be developed from an initial interest in school fire protection.

A similar approach can be made in the area of disaster protection. Older pupils particularly should understand the civil defense program of their communities and be willing to participate in appropriate procedures. Even the younger pupils should be sufficiently instructed in civil defense measures so that they will not be frightened by reference to atomic bombs and ionizing radiation. School alerts and drills for disaster defense should be approached in the businesslike manner previously advocated for fire drills.

There are other areas of safety in the school which can be used for teaching. Safety in the classroom, proper use of stairs and ramps, movement through the halls, and avoidance of crowding around drinking fountains are additional examples of experiences which can be utilized in classroom teaching. Pupils may wish to examine the school accident report form developed by the National Safety Council[2] to help them focus on the particular problems of their school environment.

THE SCHOOL LUNCH AND HEALTH EDUCATION

Perhaps no phase of the school day offers greater possibility for establishing important health practices than that provided by the school lunch period. Whether or not this opportunity becomes significant depends on the interest and skill of the teacher in utilizing school lunch experiences for health education.

Mere provision of a well-balanced meal at school is no assurance that all children will benefit thereby. Food habits vary; food dislikes are common; cultural preferences may limit consumption of nutritionally desirable foods. By observing children and studying their eating behavior, teachers can discover areas in which health education relating to food and nutrition is needed.

Teaching can center around the lunch experience, although an effort should be made to encourage good nutritional practices throughout the day. The teacher should recognize that not all

---

[2] A copy may be obtained from the National Safety Council, 415 North Michigan Avenue, Chicago, Illinois.

children need to conform to the same eating pattern in order to be adequately nourished, and that it is nutritionally desirable for people to consume a wide variety of food to learn to accept and include new foods in the diet. Based on the nutritional needs and interests of pupils, activities can be developed around:

Considering the relation of adequate nutrition to general health and its effect on appearance, vitality, and athletic performance

Learning to try and like a variety of foods

Analyzing the nutritional value of the noon meal and determining the foods to be included in other meals to balance the daily dietary intake

Planning meals for the school lunch and working with the lunchroom manager in having student-planned meals served periodically

Studying sanitary food handling and storage practices

Observing and evaluating eating practices in the lunchroom to determine the kind and amount of food waste

Surveying the lunchroom environment and making suggestions for more pleasing and comfortable eating arrangements

Learning to select foods wisely, being careful to include essential nutrients in appropriate amounts

Co-operating in maintaining a clean, pleasant, attractive lunch environment

Evaluating the effect of the availability of soft drinks, candies, and other sweets on participation in the school lunch program

Developing proper eating behavior, including leisurely eating, proper use of eating utensils, and practice of table courtesies.

These and many other activities can be initiated around the school lunch experience for the purpose of improving nutritional knowledge and practice. Eating together at school can be a significant and effective experience in health education.

MENTAL HEALTH EDUCATION

A school environment includes people as well as buildings, grounds, and equipment. The interaction of personalities in a variety of situations at school is a constant yet varying process. Incidents occur which cause anger, frustration, or fear; other situations engender courage, co-operation, and confidence. Pupils interact with each other and with teachers and other adults at school. Problems arise; discussion and interpretation are needed; decisions must be made. Around the many situations, incidents, and procedures originating in the school, valuable mental health education can be built.

Individual Guidance

Since the experiences and needs of pupils vary, much teaching for mental health will be accomplished on an individual basis. As the teacher helps a child or an adolescent to understand himself, to face reality, to gain a basis for self-respect, or to improve his group relationships, he is contributing to the goals of mental health. This type of teaching goes on more or less continuously and often unobtrusively day by day. Upon occasion there is need for individual conferences with certain pupils to discuss and evaluate particular problems, and sometimes teachers need assistance from specialized guidance personnel, the physician or the nurse, in reaching a solution. However, the individual guidance which the teacher provides as a part of his daily work is an important aspect of mental health education.

Group Experiences

School situations and occurrences which provide opportunity for classroom discussion and decision bearing on pupils' emotional health are legion. An incident on the playground may lead to discussion of appropriate playground behavior and the importance of learning to control one's temper or to respect the rights of others. The littered lunchroom or school grounds may be the stimulus for a discussion revolving around the acceptance of responsibility by each person in maintaining a healthful environment for all. An impending game with a rival high school may furnish the setting for consideration of the nature and importance of sportsmanlike behavior by a group of high-school students. Planning for a school field day may involve discussion of ways of working together and emphasis on the idea that each person must do his share in a group project in order for it to succeed. Illustrations of mental health teaching inherent in the activities of the school are too numerous to list; there are personality interactions in every situation. The teacher with insight and understanding will recognize readily the many opportunities for promoting emotional health which occur as each day goes by.

Planned Units of Instruction

Individual and group experiences at school can often be utilized for more extensive and related instruction than that which occurs in one discussion or is limited to one experience. The experience or situation at school may be the point of departure, but the projects and learning experiences that teachers and pupils plan together may lead them into many and diverse facets of mental health education. The following examples are sufficient to illustrate this point.

Considering the ways in which the school can be a happier place for all

Analyzing the club and activity programs of the high school to determine their relationships to social adjustment and to the provision of opportunity for participation by all

Formulating a code of behavior for school dances, parties, and athletic events

Studying the ways in which different persons contribute to the achievement of a common goal

Evaluating the social life of the high school in terms of democratic ideals

Setting up a schedule for the individual which provides a balanced day of class, study, work, recreation, and rest

Evaluating the reasons why balanced living is important.

There seems to be little doubt that the school experiences of children and young people are fertile opportunities for mental health education—individual, incidental, or planned. Good teachers are constantly utilizing them.

SELECTED REFERENCES

AMERICAN ASSOCIATION OF SCHOOL ADMINISTRATORS. *Health in Schools*. Revised edition. Twentieth Yearbook. Washington, D.C.: the Association, a department of the National Education Association, 1951. 477 p.

ANDERSON, C. L. *School Health Practice*. Second edition. St. Louis: C. V. Mosby Co., 1960. 530 p.

ASSOCIATION FOR SUPERVISION AND CURRICULUM DEVELOPMENT. *Fostering Mental Health in Our Schools*. 1950 Yearbook. Washington, D.C.: the Association, a department of the National Education Association, 1950. 220 p.

NATIONAL EDUCATION ASSOCIATION AND AMERICAN MEDICAL ASSOCIATION, JOINT COMMITTEE ON HEALTH PROBLEMS IN EDUCATION. *Health Appraisal of School Children.* Washington, D.C. and Chicago: the Associations, 1957. 64 p.

NATIONAL EDUCATION ASSOCIATION AND AMERICAN MEDICAL ASSOCIATION, JOINT COMMITTEE ON HEALTH PROBLEMS IN EDUCATION. *Health Aspects of the School Lunch Program.* Washington, D.C. and Chicago: the Associations, 1956. 31 p.

NATIONAL EDUCATION ASSOCIATION AND AMERICAN MEDICAL ASSOCIATION, JOINT COMMITTEE ON HEALTH PROBLEMS IN EDUCATION. *Healthful School Living.* Washington, D.C. and Chicago: the Associations, 1957. 323 p.

NATIONAL EDUCATION ASSOCIATION AND AMERICAN MEDICAL ASSOCIATION, JOINT COMMITTEE ON HEALTH PROBLEMS IN EDUCATION. *The Nurse in the School.* Revised edition. Washington, D.C. and Chicago: the Associations, 1955. 56 p.

NATIONAL EDUCATION ASSOCIATION AND AMERICAN MEDICAL ASSOCIATION, JOINT COMMITTEE ON HEALTH PROBLEMS IN EDUCATION. *School Health Services.* Washington, D.C. and Chicago: the Associations, 1953. 486 p.

NEMIR, ALMA. *The School Health Program.* Philadelphia: W. B. Saunders Co., 1959. 428 p.

OBERTEUFFER, DELBERT. *School Health Education.* Third edition. New York: Harper & Brothers, 1960. 547 p.

WHEATLEY, GEORGE M., and HALLOCK, GRACE T. *Health Observation of School Children.* New York: McGraw-Hill Book Co., 1956. 488 p.

Chapter 14

Evaluation in Health Education

Does health education work? Does it pay? Does it produce measurable, meaningful results? The answer to all three questions is "yes." The difficulty lies in *proving* what is often self-evident but does not easily yield to objective evaluation in terms of numbers, letters, grades, and scales. In health education the proof of the teaching is in the living. Further, many of the attitude and behavior changes that are commonly sought in health education develop slowly and, for many individuals, may not be clearly discernible until long after school days are over. Yet, evaluation is worthwhile even within the limited range of the school's ability to observe, test, grade, and appraise its pupils and itself.

Evaluation is related to all objectives of the health education program, but its primary focus is upon the growth and development of boys and girls. It takes into account the judgments of teachers, parents, health specialists, and community agencies concerning the influence of the program. Direct observations, interviews, anecdotal records, and a variety of tests and rating scales are all useful procedures.

Active curriculum development is promoted to the extent that new criteria and techniques of evaluation are used. Evaluation and curriculum development mutually support and modify one another; a change in one usually stimulates a change in the other. Evaluation is important for determining progress and for helping to point toward future developments.

PURPOSES, SCOPE, AND INSTRUMENTS

Evaluation is the process of determining to what extent a program has accomplished its objectives. The task of evaluation in health education, as in any other field, is much broader than finding out how much factual knowledge is retained by a group of pupils after their exposure to a specified amount of health instruction. As summarized by Grout,[1] whether the evaluation deals with pupil progress and achievement or primarily with the program itself, it serves the following purposes:

1. It helps the teacher to know where to place emphasis in a teaching program. It may show which behavior patterns and which home, school, and community conditions have been improved as a result of the program, and which need further attention.

2. It helps to show strengths and weaknesses in teaching procedures. When a teaching program has produced results, evaluation may reveal which procedures have proved worthwhile. Conversely, when a program has failed, it may show which procedures have been ineffective.

3. Evaluation made by the pupils themselves may help them to find out their own progress in health behavior.

4. Evaluation may be used as a basis for marks. This statement would apply only to systematic health instruction and in schools where marking systems are used.

5. Evaluation aids health committees and other groups in curriculum planning. It gives information that should help to determine content and methods.

6. Evaluation gives data of value in "selling" a program to administrators and to the citizens of the community.

One of the byproducts of the evaluation process is the inevitable review of the objectives of the total school program, of the pupils' needs and interests, of the experiences provided in the curriculum to meet these needs, and of the environmental conditions in the schools, homes, and community. Another byproduct is the positive influence on human relationships that are involved in the co-operative teamwork of continuous evaluation.

Relationship to Objectives

A major objective of the school health education program is to bring about changes in what pupils know or understand, what they do, and how they feel about health. At the same time, schools increasingly are recognizing their broad community responsibilities in sharing efforts for school, home, and community health improvement. Evaluation of school health education includes not only procedures through which the school finds

---

[1] Grout, Ruth E. *Health Teaching in Schools*. Third edition. Philadelphia: W. B. Saunders Co., 1958. p. 270-71.

out how far its objectives are being realized in respect to health improvement among the pupils themselves, but also takes steps to determine its influence upon school, home, and community life.

It is imperative that the objectives of school health education be consistent with the general objectives of education, and that the general objectives, in turn, be consistent with health education objectives. This interrelationship is particularly clear in the elementary school. Here, much of the health teaching is through guided experiences which involve practices of living rather than a subject matter approach. For example, the teacher sees that boys and girls are appropriately dressed before permitting them to go out to play, or he checks to see that they wash their hands after the finger-painting period and again before they go to the lunchroom.

In such situations, the evaluation process involves observation of the types of experiences to which boys and girls are exposed, and the carry-over of such health practices into their lives when they are away from the guidance of the teacher, as well as a check on the pupils' awareness of the reasons for such actions. The factual material learned in the process is important and is a segment for evaluation, but the broader application of these facts in living is of still greater importance. It represents the translation of knowledge into action.

Studying the Program

Evaluation may be directed toward the health education program itself to find out to what extent it is in accord with sound educational principles. Practices that are in harmony with generally accepted policies can be expected to produce better results than those that are not. This approach is justified inasmuch as results in terms of changes in pupils and their environments often do not become evident for some time. As mentioned earlier, there is a lag between health education and its measurable application.

The American Association of School Administrators, in its twentieth yearbook,[2] recognizes the importance and scope of health education in the secondary school, and suggests the following practices as a simple checklist for administrators in evaluating health education in their schools:

---

[2] American Association of School Administrators. *Health in Schools*. Revised edition. Twentieth Yearbook. Washington, D.C.: the Association, a department of the National Education Association, 1951. p. 180-81.

1. All school personnel understand the philosophy of health education and make positive contributions to it.

2. One staff member is responsible for coordinating the total health education program.

3. Health teachers are healthy themselves, mentally and physically, and are prepared academically to teach health.

4. A progressive, flexible course of study is followed.

5. There is a minimum time allotment equal to two semesters of health instruction for five days a week, at least one semester in junior high school and one semester in senior high school, in addition to any integrated or correlated instruction.

6. Health teaching is done, preferably in separate courses on a five-days-a-week basis, in classes no larger than those in other subjectmatter areas.

7. The teaching materials provided include texts, library materials, and audio-visual aids that are current and scientifically accurate.

This example clearly indicates that evaluation of the school health education program is as broad as the whole school, and that determining its success requires the co-operative efforts of school administrators, classroom teachers, health specialists, parents, and the pupils for whom it is planned.

Since a complete evaluation of health education covers all parts of the program, it is required that an attempt be made to measure the degree of success in accomplishing *each* of the objectives of the program. Inevitably, a prerequisite to adequate evaluation is school-wide understanding of the health education program, and crystal-clear listing and describing of its objectives. Certain phases of this process involve the entire school staff. Ideally, a system-wide program of school health education develops out of co-operative planning, and evaluation of the plan follows its introduction and use in the school.

Evaluation Instruments

Even though he may not be particularly conscious of the fact, a teacher is constantly evaluating his pupils. When teaching plans are carefully made in advance, the teacher's purposes are clarified and his choice of experiences or subject matter is more appropriate. By the same token, if the methods of collecting information for evaluation in health education are planned in advance, the collection of such data is more orderly, more complete, and probably will portray more accurately the situation as it really exists.

Some of the more common procedures or methods of collecting evaluation information used by teachers are:

1. *Observations*—These may include teachers' observations of pupils' health behavior, of particular skills, or of events in the home or community.

2. *Surveys*—At periodic intervals surveys may be made of various health conditions or of parts of the program. Surveys are usually based on predetermined standards.

3. *Questionnaires and checklists*—Pupils, and sometimes parents, may be asked questions about various health matters or invited to express their interest, or lack of interest, in different topics.

4. *Interviews*—Conferences with pupils, parents, teachers, school health personnel, and community workers may be conducted in the classroom, health office, or principal's office as well as during home visits.

5. *Diaries and other autobiographical records kept by pupils*—These records give subjective accounts of the pupils' own accomplishments or opinions.

6. *Health and growth records*—Periodic measurements of height and weight, findings of health examinations, records of defects corrected, and of immunizations performed provide objective evidence of needs and accomplishments.

7. *Records of other health conditions or improvements*—Here may be included such records as the sale of protective foods in the cafeteria; sanitary improvements in the school, in homes, or in the community; and vital statistics from the health department.

8. *Samples of pupils' work*—Examples of creative work which show pupils' ability to apply health principles are included in this category. These may be drawings, charts, models, other exhibits, reports, and the like.

9. *Case studies*—Detailed study of an individual pupil may show changes in health behavior in relation to other factors that influence his total life.

10. *Health knowledge tests*—Oral or written tests of health knowledge or understanding are among the most frequently used evaluation instruments.

Each of these instruments or techniques can be used to good advantage. The resourceful teacher will not limit himself to the use of only one, but will become skillful in using many of them.

EVALUATING PUPIL PROGRESS

Although some may argue that the purpose of education is to teach facts, and that determining whether such information is put into actual use is not the function of the school, there is general agreement among health educators that merely measuring knowledge is an inadequate and incomplete approach to evaluation in health education. In spite of this idea, there is a tendency to overemphasize the acquisition of knowledge in evaluating pupil performance in health. A realization of this tendency suggests three bases for the evaluation of pupil health achievement:

1. The pupil's health status and his willingness and success in having needed remedial treatment or in adjusting to irremediable conditions

2. The pupil's health behavior and actual improvement in health habits and attitudes

3. The pupil's knowledge about and interest in health.

Pupil Health Status

If groups of pupils are involved in the evaluation, some appropriate questions include: How does the health status of one group match that of another? How does an experimental group, for example, compare with a control group? How do the groups compare at the beginning of an experimental program and after the program has been in operation?

In appraising the health status of an individual pupil, some of the questions would be: Is it in accord with his particular needs for optimum growth and development? In general, does it follow what is considered acceptable for this age group? Does it indicate a particular practice, interest, understanding, or attitude that suggests program emphasis? How does it compare with his previous status? These questions can be answered adequately only through consultation with the school medical adviser or with the pupil's private physician.

Personalized objectives can be set up for each pupil based on the needs revealed by his health examination record and in conference with the health specialists who serve the school. With this information the teacher will have the needs of his particular group clearly in mind. At appropriate times progress toward improvement of individual health status can be checked with relative ease. *Typical questions are:* Has the weight problem been controlled? Is the pupil receiving dental treatments, or have his cavities been filled? Is he wearing the glasses that were prescribed for him? Has indicated surgery been obtained? *For the pupil with an irremediable condition:* How well is he adjusting physically and emotionally to his problem? Does his problem interfere with his academic progress, his relationships with fellow pupils, and his participation in any school activities? If the objectives have not been accomplished, what effort has been made by the pupil (and his parents) to reach them? If such questions are carefully considered co-operatively with the pupil and his parents, a relatively objective evaluation of efforts to improve his health status can be made. Furthermore, it provides a means of motivating the actual application of knowledge and of making the health examination meaningful to each pupil.

It is not proper to penalize a pupil for failure to correct conditions which are beyond his control. Environmental or financial conditions, or even parental indifference, may have hampered his efforts. Furthermore, a failure need not be charged against him. To a certain extent, the teacher may have failed. The true spirit of evaluation would be to discuss what both teacher and pupil can do the next time so that the desired result might be achieved. In this way the emphasis is removed from the failure and transferred to finding a possible way of succeeding. Evaluation thus becomes the discovery of a way to reach success.

Pupil Health Behavior

Admittedly, the measurement of health habits and attitudes is difficult and largely subjective. Many health practices take place in the home and their observance is difficult to determine. Furthermore, real changes in attitude and behavior may be slow, and demonstrable indications of such changes may be infinitesimal, or may be a long time in appearing. Granted all these points, one still can continue to try to measure such outcomes.

In fact, a study of health practices is not too difficult in itself; the problem is to relate these changes to the educational program. Direct services to the individual boy or girl, quite unrelated to teaching activities, may bring about improvements in health practices. Children may be immunized against diphtheria merely because they were lined up, willingly or unwillingly, for the injections. Parents may cause children to follow some health procedures, such as going to bed at a certain hour, without the influence of the school program. Boys and girls are influenced

by their playmates and by people they admire, often quite apart
from the school program. The health attitudes and behavior of
pupils result from a number of influences. Although this limits
the claims for accomplishments through health instruction, it
does not make less important the need for evaluation.

Informal *daily observation* may reveal much about pupil health
practices. Good working posture, for example, is a manifestation
of health, and is influenced by such factors as vision, nutrition,
and fatigue. Whether or not a pupil covers his cough or sneeze
with a handkerchief or disposable tissue can be directly observed,
as can his personal cleanliness and the way he uses school sanitary facilities.

A more formal approach to the observation of pupil health
behavior as a basis for evaluation is the preparation of a checklist. This may be done co-operatively by the pupils and their
teacher, and can be patterned after the following:

Teacher's Checklist of
Pupil's Health Habits Observable at School

Has clean face and neck: Always____Usually____Seldom____
If eating at school, washes hands before meals: Always____
    Usually____Seldom____
Fingernails are clean: Always____Usually____Seldom____
Hair is combed: Always____Usually____Seldom____
Sits erect in seat____Leans over work____Slides down in seat____
Stays at home when he has a cold: Always____Usually____
    Seldom____
Covers mouth and nose when coughing or sneezing: Always____
    Usually____Seldom____
Uses drinking fountains properly: Always____Usually____
    Seldom____
Keeps fingers, pencils, and other inappropriate objects out of
    his mouth: Always____Usually____Seldom____
Shows fatigue: Slowly____Somewhat readily____Quickly____
Irritable: Frequently____Seldom____Never____
Bodily movements are: Quick____Graceful____Average____
    Slow____Awkward____

This is not an inclusive list of all physical and emotional health
behavior that reflects what has been taught or what needs to be
taught, but it is suggestive of what teachers may observe.

In some instances, teachers substitute "performance" for
"habits" and find that it is a less formidable word. An example

of a simple test of health performance would be to determine the percent of class members who volunteer for immunizing shots following a unit of study on poliomyelitis. Other examples might include observation of the number of pupils making proper food selections in the lunchroom, dressing properly for weather conditions, or covering their mouths when coughing and sneezing.

A *personal inventory or self-appraisal form* may be helpful in an attempt to measure health behavior and its improvement. When used for pretesting purposes, individual objectives can be established for each pupil. Comparison of the findings at the beginning and at the end of a period of study will indicate progress toward desirable goals. A number of personal inventory forms are available, but the development of a single form for a given class may be a worthwhile experience which has value in itself both as a learning experience and as an evaluative procedure.

Checklists, although valuable for rough screening of health practices, have their limitations. What may be a satisfactory "standard" for one individual, community, or section of the country may not be desirable for another. Moreover, teachers who use an untested questionnaire need to make certain that the standards they use have a sound health basis. Typical items on a checklist are:

Do you eat some fruits and vegetables every day?

Do you take a shower or bath after vigorous exercise?

Do you wash your hands before handling food?

Do you budget your time and try to stay within this plan?

Do you visit your dentist at least once a year for examination and necessary repair work?

Checklists and questionnaires about health practices must be used skillfully if accurate results are to be obtained. It is well to inform pupils that the procedures are only for obtaining information and are not designed to test their knowledge or to provide a basis for grades. Unless this is done, pupils will give answers which they think are wanted. For best results with young children, the questions should refer to recent, specific practices, rather than to usual or general practices. A third-grade pupil, for example, can give correct answers to such questions as "What did you have for breakfast this morning?" or "What time did you go to bed last night?" but would have difficulty with questions worded "What do you usually eat for breakfast?" or "What time do you usually go to bed?"

Health and medical records provide objective evidence of certain health behaviors. As suggested previously, they should be used cautiously in evaluating the influence of a particular educational program. A study of these records by teacher and nurse may give assurance that the health education program is producing results, or it may show weaknesses not previously recognized. For example, health examinations are likely to reveal a large number of pupils with uncorrected visual defects.

If the number of pupils with uncorrected defects as shown on the records is greatly decreased following an intensive educational program, or gradually decreased year by year through less intensive efforts, then it may be assumed that the educational activities are producing results. If, however, the percentage of uncorrected defects remains constant or even increases, something is wrong. If, following a study unit on dental care, dentists report a great number of pupils coming to their offices for treatment, then health education so far as it relates to this problem is an influencing factor.

One of the measures for success of health teaching in the school which has probably been somewhat neglected is its impact on the *attitudes and behavior of parents*. This effect may come indirectly through the children or directly from the school through parent-teacher contacts. Co-operation of parents is essential if change in pupil health habits is to result, since many of these habits are learned and practiced largely in the home environment. Some indication of parents' behavior and attitudes toward health can be gained from observations, parent-teacher-nurse conferences, and interviews.

Pupil Health Attitudes

Measurement of attitudes depends upon subjective evidence as shown through observation, interviews, and pupil diaries. However, attitudes as expressions of opinions may be studied also through questionnaires or checklists. In such a questionnaire for high-school boys and girls, numerous statements are made, and each pupil responds by indicating whether he agrees, is uncertain, or disagrees with each statement. Examples of items include:

If one is going on a diet, he should do so under a physician's guidance.

A drunken driver should have his license permanently taken away.

An individual should be entirely responsible for his own health.

Health articles appearing in magazines and newspapers provide reliable health information.

This device is helpful when the viewpoints expressed form the background for discussion of related topics, and is followed, when necessary, by a presentation of the different factors which require consideration in formulating a viewpoint.

Pupil Health Knowledge and Understanding

Knowledge testing may be very helpful in evaluating the outcomes of health teaching. It is particularly helpful when combined with pretesting to determine what a group knows about a given topic at the beginning of a period of study. Actual progress as a result of the teaching can then be determined, and unnecessary repetition of material already mastered can be avoided.

Pretesting need not necessarily be in the form of a written test or examination. It may take the form of an impromptu discussion or an informal question-and-answer period. It has the added value of stimulating interest and motivating a group to improve its performance. Pretesting also assists in pinpointing objectives so far as knowledge is concerned. This promotes more specific teaching, for the goals are more clearly understood by both teacher and pupils.

In knowledge testing, the error is often made of confining test items almost exclusively to an inventory of factual material. Questions can be asked which indicate ability to apply health information. Examples of test questions which indicate factual material learned are:

A bulge in a can of food is likely to indicate spoilage. (true) (false)

Alcohol is primarily a (a) food; (b) depressant; (c) medicine; (d) stimulant; (e) poison.

Examples of questions which show the pupil's ability to apply knowledge in answering are:

1. A group of children were playing barefooted in a yard. One boy stepped on a nail and received a deep puncture wound from

which a small amount of blood flowed. What care should he be given? Choose the best answer.

a. Put fingers on the nearest pressure point until the bleeding stops.

b. Soak the foot in a solution of Epsom salt.

c. Get the child under medical care within a few hours.

d. Paint the wound with iodine.

2. A variety of foods is available in the school cafeteria. Which of the following would provide the best balanced lunch?

a. Roast beef, bread, pie.

b. Vegetable soup, cheese sandwich, and milk.

c. Ice cream, chocolate layer cake.

d. Vegetable salad, crackers, iced tea.

The development of problem situation questions based on "What would you do if . . .?" or "How do you feel about . . .?" reactions are recommended. While answers to such problems are still paper-and-pencil reactions, they at least sample the ability to marshal factual material in solving particular problem situations.

A number of *standardized health knowledge* tests are available which may be used to find out how one group of pupils compares with another or with a national norm. One of the advantages of such tests is that they usually have equivalent forms which may be used for pretesting and post-testing for purposes of exact measurement of outcomes in terms of knowledge learned over a given length of time. A brief description of selected health knowledge, behavior, and attitude tests appears in *Measurement and Evaluation Materials in Health, Physical Education, and Recreation.*[3]

Pupil Interests

Every teacher desires to see active interest in health arise from health teaching. Interests are the spark plugs to action in health education. The most suitable instruments for detecting and measuring interests are observations, questionnaires, checklists, interviews, diaries, and autobiographical records.

Observations reveal pertinent evidence of interests. One may observe, for example, whether or not the pupils put themselves

---

[3] American Association for Health, Physical Education, and Recreation. *Measurement and Evaluation Materials in Health, Physical Education, and Recreation.* Washington, D.C.: the Association, a department of the National Education Association, 1950. p. 81-84.

wholeheartedly into the study of a particular problem. Do they take initiative in bringing illustrative material to class? Do they ask questions that show genuine interest? Does the degree of interest appear to increase as study of a given health topic progresses?

Questionnaires or *checklists* are often helpful in discovering interests. Pupils are given a series of questions about health and asked to indicate whether they would be interested or uninterested in studying the scientific facts behind each question. Typical questions include:

What causes pimples?

Is suntan healthful?

Is there any relationship between housing conditions and disease?

What effects might war have on the health of a country?

Can a mother "mark" her unborn child by her thoughts or emotions?

High-school pupils usually will show a definitely greater interest in items pertaining to personal health than in questions about community health. However, one study[4] reports that through health teaching, the interest of high-school pupils in community health problems can be appreciably increased without reducing their concern for the personal aspects of health.

When high-school boys and girls are given an opportunity to submit anonymous, *written questions* which they would especially want to have answered in a health course, a large percentage of questions are apt to ask for specific medical advice. Here is evidence of a need for instruction about wise individual use of community medical resources and selection of family medical and dental advisers. An analysis[5] of the health questions from a population of 10,000 high-school pupils shows that 70 percent of their questions relate to the following health instruction topics:

Nutrition	Chronic disease, especially
Posture and exercise	heart disease and cancer

[4] Williams, Helen L., and Southworth, Warren H. "Stimulating Interest in Public Health Problems Among High School Pupils." *Journal of Educational Research* 53: 53-61; October 1959.

[5] Southworth, Warren H.; Latimer, Jean V.; and Turner, Clair E. "A Study of the Health Practices, Knowledge, Attitudes, and Interests of Senior High School Pupils." *Research Quarterly* 15: 118-36; May 1944.

Oral hygiene	Acute disease, especially the
Care of hair	common cold
Care of eyes	Mental health
Care of skin	Use of tobacco
Body weight and height	Sex education

Interviews, likewise, may be used to discover interests and their implications for health teaching emphases. For example, a teacher may talk with individual pupils and parents, or with a class group, about things which they like or dislike about what is being taught. In informal interviews, it is common to have pupils make such comments as, "I couldn't see any point to what we were doing at first, but now that I've tried it out at home, I've become so interested I'd like to go on and do more."

Students' diaries and *autobiographies* may reveal interests which are outgrowths of an instructional program. The pupils in one school had been studying about the way people live in India and the effects of industrialization on their population, food supply, and economic growth. When a boy who recently had lived in India enrolled in the school, several pupils recorded in their diaries that they had asked him to tell about health problems in India.

Test Construction

The value of tests in health, as in any other field, is probably directly proportional to the thought and effort expended in developing them, and in grading and discussing their outcomes with pupils. When objective tests are made, use of several types of questions is preferable to reliance on any one type. Among the possibilities are multiple choice, particularly of the "best answer" type; matching questions; completion questions; and the more common true-false variety. Rating-scale questions are valuable for collecting certain types of information, particularly in the listing of attitudinal responses. If carefully developed, instructions preceding each variety of objective questions will help to avoid misunderstandings which might invalidate results.

Essay questions have a place in health education evaluation, particularly when facts are to be organized in new relationships, when general insight or understandings are to be determined, or if problems are to be solved. Too often essay questions involve trivial answers or can be answered by a short statement of fact or by a simple "yes" or "no."

Regardless of the type of test used to measure knowledge and understanding in health science, it will contribute much more to the learning process if it is graded and returned to pupils promptly so that misunderstandings can be cleared up and correct answers learned. If this opportunity is denied pupils, much of the potential value in the test situation is lost. Such "post-mortems" may also help the teacher in improving his methods so that greater learning results the next time he covers the same material.

EVALUATING CHANGES IN SCHOOL, HOME, AND COMMUNITY

Improvements in school health conditions frequently can be traced to the health instruction program. Efforts to improve the school environment provide an interesting teaching activity. Likewise, the daily adjustment of the school's program for healthful living is an area for which pupils may be given some responsibility. Their efforts often show tangible results.

The School Environment Survey

A common device for studying surrounding conditions at school is the environmental survey. When used periodically by school and public health personnel, it may give evidence of actual improvements attributable to the education program. Typical of the points which may be noted in such a survey are:

1. Are the window shades adjusted for the best light?

2. Are toilets kept clean?

3. Are the school grounds kept free from debris or obstructions which may be safety hazards?

4. Are room temperatures checked regularly during the winter months?

Similar types of questions may be asked in regard to the school's arrangements for healthful living. For example:

1. Are there appropriate rest or relaxation periods for young children?

2. Is there opportunity to wash hands before eating and after using the toilet?

3. Do boys and girls appear happy, cheerful, and interested in their work?

4. Are activities adapted to the capacities of individual pupils?

Home and Community Problems

As the school extends its activities to include attention to home and community health problems, there is increasing need to take stock at intervals of the worth of such efforts. Since, under ordinary circumstances, the school will be only one of several community forces exerting influence in these spheres, evaluation from the standpoint of the school's contribution often will be difficult to make.

In the realm of parent education an opportunity is present for direct evaluation of the school's program. In rural communities it is observed that parents, or other members of the community, soon copy at home sanitary improvements that have been made at school. Also, when the pupils enjoy new recipes which are tried in the lunchroom, requests for the recipes are received from the homes.

In urban areas influences of the school are not so readily seen. Nevertheless, certain changes can be evaluated when there is contact with the homes through teachers, nurses, or other community workers, or when pupils report back what their parents are thinking and doing.

In the last analysis, many of the behavior changes in the boys and girls themselves can be traced directly to the homes and to response of parents toward educational programs at school. This is particularly true in connection with such matters as health examinations in the family physician's office or having physical defects corrected.

There are some indices of community health status which may be helpful. They include vital statistics, housing surveys, and special surveys and studies of health services and conditions. In addition to providing evaluation information, they may suggest interesting, localized content for health instruction, and may help to awaken the school to its responsibilities for sharing with other community agencies in the solution of community health problems.

Sometimes the schools are able to trace community improvements to their own doors. In a number of communities the addition of fluorides to the drinking water supply as a means for reducing dental decay in growing children has come about after an intensive educational program which included classroom study, discussion by the school health council, and presentation of facts to the parent-teacher organization.

EVALUATING THE WHOLE SCHOOL HEALTH PROGRAM

This chapter consistently emphasizes the importance of behavior or practice as the ultimate test of success in health teaching. An evaluation of the total school health program, therefore, might well be considered a rigorous measure of the effectiveness of health instruction. If the instructional phase is successful, its teachings will be reflected in the total school health program. In other words, a school which has unusually successful health instruction is a school which inevitably has an adequate health service and a continually improving school environment from a health standpoint.

Obviously, neither the health instruction, school health service, nor the healthful school living aspects of the program can function independently of each other. They are closely related and interwoven. It is recommended that they periodically be evaluated separately, as well as together. Successes and weaknesses of any one of the three parts are a measure of the worth or lack of merit of the other two in a school.

A list of evaluation instruments in school health education has been developed[6] which includes general survey forms as well as criteria and techniques for dealing with special phases of the total program or with certain grade levels. A collection of appropriate forms might well be made in a given situation in which evaluation is contemplated. Quite often state education departments prepare survey or appraisal forms which are helpful in evaluating local programs.

The best results probably will be secured if a survey form is developed locally through co-operation of the entire school staff. This procedure has the added advantage of furnishing valuable in-service education for the staff as well as providing a measure of the success of the general health education program.

In addition to the use of a survey form, a list of questions might be prepared to help in the evaluation of the total program. The following questions are typical:

1. Is the program based on an understanding of child growth and development and on the needs that are inherent in this development?

---

[6] Joint Committee on Evaluation; American Association for Health, Physical Education, and Recreation; American Public Health Association (School Health Section); and American School Health Association. "Evaluation Instruments in School Health Education." *Journal of Health, Physical Education, Recreation* 26:13; November 1955.

2. Does the program deal with significant health problems as revealed through studies of the health status of individuals, schools, homes, and community?

3. Is the program properly related to other health education efforts both within the schools and in homes and community?

4. Is health instruction a planned part of the total school health program?

5. Are opportunities for health education provided in the procedures for control of the school environment?

6. Are opportunities for health education provided in the health appraisal plan and in health counseling?

7. Are the health education and the physical education aspects of the program interrelated?

8. Are sound psychological principles used in the organization and application of health teaching?

9. Is health teaching a definite part of the school curriculum?

10. Is there well-balanced health instruction at both elementary and secondary levels with adequate time allotment, suitable teaching materials, and well-prepared teachers?

11. Is there a planned program of adult health education on a community-wide basis?

12. Are all possible sources of help being used?

A common error is to consider evaluation a separate phase of the teaching process which is undertaken only after a period of study and learning. Real evaluation is part of the total educational process and is carried on continuously from the inception of a program, during the establishment of its objectives, and throughout the development of the project, as well as at its culmination. It requires the combined efforts of all school personnel—administrators, teachers, and special service and custodial staffs—as well as the co-operation of parents and community agency workers if it is to be complete and operational in realizing the outcomes of health education.

SELECTED REFERENCES

AMERICAN ASSOCIATION FOR HEALTH, PHYSICAL EDUCATION, AND RECREATION. *Measurement and Evaluation Materials in Health, Physical Education, and Recreation*. Washington, D.C.: the Association, a department of the National Education Association, 1950. 138 p.

AMERICAN ASSOCIATION FOR HEALTH, PHYSICAL EDUCATION, AND RECREATION. *Your Community: School-Community Fitness Inventory.* Washington, D.C.: the Association, a department of the National Education Association, 1959. 40 p.

CLARK, H. HARRISON. *Application of Measurement to Health and Physical Education.* Third edition. Englewood Cliffs, N.J.: Prentice-Hall, 1959. 528 p.

EDWARDS, RALPH. "Approach to Health Attitude Measurement." *Journal of School Health* 26: 215-19; September 1956.

FRASER, ELLEN D. "Looking Back on a School Health Program." *Journal of Health, Physical Education, Recreation* 25: 29-30; December 1954.

GROUT, RUTH E. *Health Teaching in Schools.* Third edition. Philadelphia: W. B. Saunders Co., 1958. 359 p. Chapter 10, "Evaluation."

HAGEN, ELIZABETH P., and THORNDIKE, ROBERT L. "Evaluation." *Encyclopedia of Educational Research.* (Edited by Chester W. Harris.) New York: Macmillan Co., 1960. p. 482-86.

JACKSON, C. O. "Let's Rate Your Health Education Program." *Journal of Health, Physical Education, Recreation* 26: 29; September 1955.

JOINT COMMITTEE ON EVALUATION; AMERICAN ASSOCIATION FOR HEALTH, PHYSICAL EDUCATION, AND RECREATION; AMERICAN PUBLIC HEALTH ASSOCIATION (SCHOOL HEALTH SECTION); and AMERICAN SCHOOL HEALTH ASSOCIATION. "Evaluation Instruments in School Health Education." *Journal of Health, Physical Education, Recreation* 26: 13; November 1955.

JOINT COMMITTEE ON EVALUATION OF SCHOOL HEALTH PROGRAMS (SCHOOL HEALTH SECTION), AMERICAN PUBLIC HEALTH ASSOCIATION. "Evaluate Your School Health Program." *Journal of School Health* 26: 167-74; June 1956.

KNUTSON, ANDIE L., and SHIMBERG, BENJAMIN. "Evaluation of a Health Education Program." *American Journal of Public Health* 45: 21-27; January 1955.

LARSON, LEONARD A., and YOCOM, RACHAEL D. *Measurement and Evaluation in Physical, Health, and Recreation Education.* St. Louis: C. V. Mosby Co., 1951. 507 p.

MOSS, BERNICE. "Guide Posts for Evaluating Health Classes." *Journal of Health, Physical Education, Recreation* 23: 12; March 1952.

NATIONAL STUDY OF SECONDARY SCHOOL EVALUATION. *Evaluative Criteria.* 1960 edition. Washington, D.C.: the Study, American Council on Education, 1960. 376 p.

ROSS, C. C., and STANLEY, JULIAN C. *Measurement in Today's Schools.* Englewood Cliffs, N.J.: Prentice-Hall, 1954. 485 p.

RUGEN, MABEL E., and NYSWANDER, DOROTHY. "The Measurement of Understanding in Health Education." *The Measurement of Understanding.* Forty-Fifth Yearbook, Part I. National Society for the Study of Education. Chicago: University of Chicago Press, 1946. Chapter II, p. 213-31.

SHAW, JOHN H. "Evaluation in Health Teaching." *New York State Journal of Health, Physical Education, and Recreation* 8: 18-20; December 1955.

SHAW, JOHN H. "Evaluation in the School Health Instruction Program." *American Journal of Public Health* 47: 582-86; May 1957.

TRUMP, J. LLOYD. *New Directions to Quality Education.* Washington, D.C.: Commission on the Experimental Study of the Utilization of the Staff in the Secondary School, National Association of Secondary-School Principals, NEA, 1960. 16 p.

Colleges and Universities

At the peak of the American educational pyramid stands the college or university. What these institutions do, or fail to do, about health education has a direct bearing upon what is done, or not done, in the broad areas of health education at the elementary-school, secondary-school, and community levels. College and university graduates and former students are in positions, and often possess the skills and leadership, to exert a favorable influence on the health of the nation.

The major purpose of general education is to prepare the individual for responsible citizenship and productive living. According to the President's Commission on Higher Education,[1] it is the task of general education to provide the kinds of learning and experience that will enable the student to attain certain basic outcomes:

1. To develop for the regulation of one's personal and civic life a code of behavior based on ethical principles consistent with democratic ideals
2. To participate actively as an informed and responsible citizen in solving the social, economic, and political problems of one's community, State, and Nation
3. To recognize the interdependence of the different peoples of the world and one's personal responsibility for fostering international understanding and peace
4. To understand the common phenomena in one's physical environment, to apply habits of scientific thought to both personal and civic problems, and to appreciate the implications of scientific discoveries for human welfare
5. To understand the ideas of others and to express one's own effectively
6. To attain a satisfactory emotional and social adjustment
7. To maintain and improve his own health and to cooperate actively and intelligently in solving community health problems
8. To understand and enjoy literature, art, music, and other cultural activities as expressions of personal and social experience, and to participate to some extent in some form of creative activity

[1] The President's Commission on Higher Education. *Higher Education for American Democracy*, Volume I. Washington, D.C.: Superintendent of Documents, Government Printing Office, 1947. p. 50-54.

9. To acquire the knowledge and attitudes basic to a satisfying family life

10. To choose a socially useful and personally satisfying vocation that will permit one to use to the full his particular interests and abilities

11. To acquire and use the skills and habits involved in critical and constructive thinking.

Several of these goals are specifically related to personal and community health. They place upon each college and university a responsibility for the health and health education of its students. Any program which will help students to achieve these goals is founded upon the needs, interests, and abilities of the students whom it serves. What, then, are some of the health needs and interests of college and university students?

STUDENT HEALTH PROBLEMS

Expansion of the American educational enterprise during the past 50 years has been phenomenal. More students are attending college, with an increasingly greater enrollment anticipated for the future. They come to college from a wide range of socioeconomic backgrounds and with varying abilities and preparation. They present strikingly diverse understanding of personal and public health and, when given the opportunity, reveal the widest range of interest in and need for health education.

From many studies of the health problems among college students, it may be gathered that the college student has a startling variety of personal problems for which he seeks solution. He is generally eager to learn about mental health, nutrition, marriage and reproduction, and about the control of all forms of disease. He is probably more particular than his less well-educated, less "sophisticated" brothers about the selection of his medical adviser and the kind of treatment he is willing to undergo. He, along with other millions, is the victim of numerous superstitions and prejudices about health, but he demonstrates a willingness to discuss, argue, and formulate new opinions or plans of action. In comparison to high-school pupils, it is clear that the college student has just as many health problems, is just as articulate about them, and is just as impatient with "glittering generalities" or "background material" offered in answer to them.

In some ways, the college student's health behavior is contradictory. Because of the availability of services and changing attitudes, he is more than likely to seek medical care for apparent physical and mental health problems. On the other hand, when well, his concern for health is a remote consideration.

A summary[2] of responses from 200 college presidents indicates what they believe are the major health problems of their students. Emotional problems and accidents lead the list, and poor food and living habits are a close second. "Mononucleosis, the 'occupational disease' of the college student; emotional problems; accidents; poor food habits; very little sleep; too much work and play or too much of one and not enough of the other; upper respiratory infections; and gastrointestinal disturbances—these are some of the more prominent items in the catalogue of health problems noted by the college presidents." The incidence of dental caries in students entering college is high, if the experience of two eastern universities can be considered typical.[3]

The health problems of college and university students cannot be ignored. A healthful environment, health services, and health instruction must be interwoven into a program which positively affects the health knowledge, health attitudes, and health behavior of all students.

ORGANIZATION

There is wide variation in the programs through which colleges and universities fulfill their obligation to protect and promote the health of their students. The type and extent of the program in each educational institution is influenced by such conditions as (a) the size, location, and financial resources of the institution; (b) the composition of the student body, i.e., proportion of men and women students, number of dormitory and commuting students, number of married students; (c) the professional health personnel on the staff; (d) administrative philosophy and attitudes toward student health; and (e) available community resources.

As the chief administrative officer, the college president is responsible to the board of trustees for the health program. It is common practice for the president to delegate this responsibility to a vice-president or dean. Some colleges and universities have a health director or co-ordinator as the administrative officer responsible to the president.

---

[2] Ginsburg, Ethel L. *The College and Student Health.* New York: National Tuberculosis Association, 1955. 102 p.

[3] Farnsworth, Dana L., and Thorndike, Augustus. "Health in Colleges and Universities." *New England Journal of Medicine* 255: 949-55, 992-96; November 1956.

Health Committee or Council

Authorization and appointment of an advisory health committee or council is one way to establish objectives and to help gain co-operation and support from administration, faculty, nonacademic personnel, students, and community leaders for the college health program. Its primary function is to identify, define, and make recommendations for solution of college health problems. The problems for consideration and study by the council may range from campus safety hazards to ways of improving student eating habits. Recommendations of the council are sent to the president, or his delegated representative, who makes the necessary decisions and implements the recommendations.

Objectives

The ultimate aim of the college health program is the meeting of all health needs on the college or university campus. The major objectives are presented in the Report of the Third National Conference on Health in Colleges:[4]

1. To create a healthful environment and atmosphere in which students may develop physically, mentally, and socially and in which they may learn to live more happily as health-minded citizens in their personal lives, in their homes, in their communities, and as members of a world society

2. To provide means whereby administrators, faculty, and all other college employees may be enabled to work together cooperatively for the total health of all

3. To facilitate the practical application of health knowledge to daily living in the medical clinic, the classroom, on the campus, and in the community

4. To safeguard the health of students, faculty, and nonteaching personnel through the prevention of communicable diseases

5. To develop well-adjusted students and graduates who possess information, attitudes, habits, skills, and ideals favorable to efficient and healthful lives for themselves, their families, and their communities

6. To assist college students to assume responsibility for their own health, so that they will know when they are in good physical and emotional condition, will recognize deviations from the normal, and will know when and how to seek expert assistance to meet their health needs

7. To provide scientific knowledge through a well-integrated plan of health education, so that students will be able to evaluate pseudoscientific reports and advertising campaigns regarding health and disease nostrums

---

[4] National Tuberculosis Association. *A Health Program for Colleges.* Report of the Third National Conference on Health in Colleges. New York: the Association, 1948. 152 p.

8. To prevent loss of study time and promote the development of efficiency in pursuing college work by insuring maximal personal and community health

9. To assist students who are moving from their homes to an unfamiliar college environment to find competent and adequate medical care when they become ill

10. To develop a working arrangement among members of the college community to promote a single policy of healthful living on the campus.

Specific Health Responsibilities

Any college health program will have cultural values which arise from acquainting students with the scientific, historical, and social significance of individual and community health problems. Relatively few students will become physicians, nurses, or teachers. However, many of them will have opportunities in later life to apply the results of health education, both as individuals guiding their own and their family's health and also as community leaders serving on boards of education, boards of health, community planning commissions, or as board members or lay workers in voluntary agencies and hospitals. Some will participate eventually in health programs in business and industry. Preparation for these important activities is a legitimate part of higher education.

Teacher-training institutions have further responsibilities in health education. Each teacher will be expected to participate in his school health program, and he needs preparation for this phase of his work. Most teachers need to be prepared as "generalists," but some will become specialists in health education.

In summary, each college and university has at least three distinct responsibilities in the health field:

1. To safeguard the health of students through provisions for healthful living within the institution and through appropriate health services

2. To provide health instruction for all students, regardless of their academic or professional interests

3. To organize and conduct the college health program in proper relationship to the total community health program.

Institutions that prepare teachers have additional responsibilities:

4. To provide prospective teachers with adequate preparation for their functions in school health programs

5. To prepare health education specialists.

The balance of this chapter presents some recommendations for meeting these responsibilities. Through vigorous application of the recommendations, higher education can make a great contribution to the health progress of the nation.

SAFEGUARDING STUDENT HEALTH

College and university life is rich with opportunities for development of self-assurance, resourcefulness, and independence. At the same time, the relative freedom from parental and other restraints often results in confusion, uncertainty, and excess. This is particularly true for the student who has not been given previously the opportunity and responsibility for developing intelligent self-direction. In accepting students the college or university becomes obligated to provide certain safeguards, supervision, and services to protect and promote the health and welfare of its students. The responsibilities for safeguarding student health fall into the main areas of healthful living and health services.

Healthful Living

The college and university have a legal and moral responsibility to provide an environment which ensures to every student an opportunity for healthful living. This requires recognition and control of conditions which may be deleterious to physical, mental, or social well-being. Pertinent problems of the physical environment include water supply; food service; garbage and waste disposal; sanitation of swimming pools; housing, including heating, lighting, ventilating, and crowding; housekeeping and maintenance in classrooms, laboratories, libraries, gymnasiums, offices, and rest rooms; supervision of trailer camps; insect and rodent control; fire, traffic, occupational, and radiological safety; and civil defense mobilization. The extent of these problems varies from one institution to another and the ways of coping with them depend upon local conditions, budgets, public health laws, and campus regulations.

The benefits which result from a healthful environment are twofold. There are the direct benefits from protecting the health of students and the less direct, but equally important, benefits of health education. Much education is acquired through concomitant learning. This applies particularly to learnings which accrue from being exposed to a healthful environment.

In addition to the common aspects of healthful living, other special factors are essential to the emotional and social health of students. These include counseling, recreation, and physical education activities.

College students frequently require assistance in gaining mature attitudes toward themselves, toward other people, and toward the world in which they live. They are faced with many important situations and perplexing problems which require decisions about personal, social, emotional, vocational, academic, and personal health matters. Student counseling encourages self-discipline and at the same time brings mature judgment to bear upon critical problems. The counseling program includes psychological testing services; personnel counselors to help with scheduling activities, home problems, financial difficulties, and premarriage or marital problems; vocational guidance; psychological clinics in which personality difficulties can be alleviated; "how to study" services; general orientation sessions and courses; and group study opportunities. All these specialized counseling services and many more may be found in the modern college and university in addition to the direct health counseling which is available.

Recreation is as essential for college students as good housing, sanitation, counseling, and health service. Through opportunity to rest and to relax as well as to enjoy recreational activities, one may obtain release of physical and emotional tensions, a sense of well-being, and a lift for physical and emotional fitness. The college recreation program provides ways for the student to participate in various recreational activities such as arts, crafts, dramatics, music, and sports, all of which are part of his "equipment for living."

Physical education also makes a contribution to healthful living. A worthwhile physical education program helps students develop skills in aquatics, camping and outing activities, competitive athletics, dance, gymnastics, and in individual, dual, and team sports. In addition, it may provide prescribed special exercises. Physical education affords ways to teach and demonstrate important aspects of behavior. These functional examples concern introversion and extroversion, the dangers of projection and rationalization, wholesome expression of emotions, development of poise, and social sensitivity and interaction for more harmonious adjustment. The playfield, pool, and gymnasium are rich in opportunities for guided personal development. To give the fearful confidence, the timid courage, the braggart modesty, and the handicapped satisfaction are some of the potential mental health outcomes of an intelligently conducted college physical education program.

The organic values of activity are well known. Skill, speed, stamina, strength, and organic vigor are fundamental to optimum health. They differ from the psychological and social values in that they occur in properly developed programs as byproducts of vigorous physical activity, whereas the social and psychological values have to be deliberately sought, worked for, and taught. All are important to health, and all can be promoted within an intelligently operated physical education program.

Health Service

Although college age is essentially a healthy time of life, physical handicaps, injury, and illness do occur, and satisfactory academic progress is closely related to the student's health status. Recognizing the importance of the relationship between academic achievement and the health status of the student, almost every college and university carries certain medical responsibilities for its students through a student health service, a medical office, or infirmary. Whatever the form, the functions are directed to determining student health needs and finding ways and means of meeting them.

College and university health services have evolved to their present development in the twentieth century as a distinctly novel and unique part of the American institutions of higher learning, and represent an important implementation of the philosophy which holds that education must be concerned with the "whole student." As usually organized, these services provide essential health care to students who, for a stipulated fee or on an insurance basis, may use the service for most health problems which arise. Medical, surgical, nursing, dental, and psychiatric services are included to a greater or lesser degree. Most modern health services have infirmaries or alliances with local hospitals in which students with more serious illnesses may receive appropriate care. In some ways college health services demonstrate the concept of prepaid medical care and hospitalization insurance. However, it must be realized that the accounting principles (such as allocation of overhead costs) applied to college health services, operating with a select clientele in a definite, pre-established framework, have little or no relationship with the principles needed to estimate the cost of medical care for the general public.

HEALTH EDUCATION FOR ALL STUDENTS

Even though considerable health education results from living in a healthful environment, participating in the physical education and recreation programs, receiving health and counseling services, and studying a variety of subjects in the general curriculum, all students should have direct health instruction. Most colleges and universities offer courses that touch in some degree on the principles and practices of healthful living. However, these courses are scattered through a number of departments, and the information contained in them is seldom brought to bear directly on the practical problems of personal and community health.

According to the President's Commission on Higher Education,[5]

What is needed is a course that deals specifically and explicitly with the information, attitudes, and habits the student needs to maintain and improve his own health and that of his community. An important phase of instruction to this end will be emphasis on the fact that health is more than a personal problem, that it has social implications, and that the individual owes it to society no less than to himself to keep his health and energy at their peak.

This statement is consistent with the recommendation of the Third and Fourth National Conferences on Health in Colleges:[6, 7]

Every college should provide a basic health course, preferably designated as "Personal and Community Health," which will be required of all undergraduates on the basis of need shown by pretesting; which will involve a minimum of three to four semester hours, with credit toward graduation; which will be administered autonomously and not in connection with some other course.

Course Objectives and Units

A course cannot supplant other student health education experiences, but it can serve as a means of clarifying, emphasizing, and integrating the learnings, and it also helps the student to direct his own health behavior intelligently. Briefly stated by the

[5] The President's Commission on Higher Education, *op. cit.*

[6] National Tuberculosis Association, *op. cit.*

[7] American College Health Association. *Proceedings of the Fourth National Conference on Health in Colleges.* New York: the Association, 1955. 211 p.

Third National Conference on Health in Colleges,[8] the objectives of a basic course in personal and community health are:

1. To provide a body of information concerning the functioning of all parts of the human being under varying conditions; the beneficial and detrimental factors of environment and their effect upon the body; ways in which these environmental factors may be utilized for health

2. To induce behavior which will assist the individual to attain and maintain optimal health

3. To develop attitudes which will lead the individual to cooperate with community and group programs for health protection.

These objectives are further delineated in the Report of the National Conference on College Health Education.[9] It also details the units of instruction in the course. Here are the recommended unit divisions:

Area One—Personal Health Promotion
Interpretation and promotion of health
Orientation to college life
Common health problems of college students

Area Two—Emotional and Social Health
Individual adjustment
Adjustment to group living
Preparation for family living

Area Three—Planning for Health Protection
Importance of resources for meeting health needs
Evaluation of health information, products, and facilities
Selecting medical, dental, and auxiliary services
Budgeting for medical care
Providing essential community health resources
Adequate state health resources
Understanding the functions of national and international health organizations
Health careers.

Staffing and Facilities

It is generally agreed that successful health instruction demands instructors who have specific and substantial proficiency in the content and methodology of health education. Other rec-

---

[8] National Tuberculosis Association, *op. cit.*
[9] American Association for Health, Physical Education, and Recreation. *A Forward Look in College Health Education.* Report of the National Conference on College Health Education. Washington, D.C.: the Association, a department of the National Education Association, 1956. p. 15-19.

ommendations from the National Conference on College Health Education[10] include:

Staffing of required health education should be comparable in adequacy of manpower, reasonableness of professional loads, and limitations of class size to standards prevailing in all other principal areas of the curriculum.

Classroom facilities, library resources, and instructional aids and materials should be suitable and sufficient for the effectiveness of the learning experiences meeting the objectives of the required health education in accordance with standards prevailing in other comparable areas of the curriculum.

In order to implement unity and consistency of required health education with all other phases of the college health program and with contributions through related courses, provision should be made and staff time allotted within established professional load for all staff members principally concerned to share jointly in defining the needs, establishing the objectives and scope, and planning the content, methodology, and evaluation of the required health instruction.

There should be clear and definite delegation of coordinating responsibility for the joint planning of courses and designation of operating responsibility for the conduct of the required health education.

It is doubtful that a single pattern of departmental placement for servicing the required health education could best fit all colleges and universities. It is an important consideration that the department having central responsibility possess sufficient resources of specific competence in health and health education. It must be a department in which no division of interests will detract from the importance of health education.

Contribution to General Education

Health education is basically a general education or cultural subject. It affords many opportunities for development of knowledge and appreciation of history, government, music, art, drama, cultural patterns, citizenship, family life, and ethical character, as well as of the knowledge, attitudes, and practices which are conducive to intelligent self-direction of health behavior and health conservation.

It is imperative that long-range goals be established, and that students be motivated on the basis of these long-range goals and lofty ideals. The importance of attitudes in relation to conduct has long been recognized. In view of this relationship, emphasis is best placed on the development of attitudes which will promote the conservation of health.

This does not deny the desirability of motivating the student in terms of immediate ends, such as satisfactory physical condi-

---

[10] *Ibid.*, p. 22.

tioning, alertness, preservation of teeth through proper care, and cultivating a pleasing personality. However, the nature of health is such that the main problem is conservation of health, and the most significant benefits are not always immediately apparent. Even in such matters as nutrition, rest, and sleep, the results are not always immediately evident.

Counselors are aware of the fact that long-range goals are of prime importance. "What do you want to be 1, 2, 5, and 10 years from now?" is a key question for the counselor. Research studies[11] emphasize the importance of value-oriented, long-range goals in influencing behavior. When more is learned about such things as the relationship between the hygienic care of the body in youth and disease of middle and later life, the task of motivation may be less difficult.

Other Health Instruction

It is impossible to enumerate all sources of health education available to college and university students. In addition to the basic course in personal and community health, there are scores of others. State and local departments of public health sometimes offer courses in hygiene and sanitation which are open to the general student body. There usually are important education and psychology courses in mental health and personality development. In sociology there may be courses in community health organization, the family, and sociological aspects of medical care. In home economics numerous opportunities exist for the study of nutrition, child care, and homemaking. Courses in safety education, first aid, industrial hygiene, and school health may also be found in the college curriculum. Health education for the general student population is not limited to the province of any one division or department; it is shared by many. The best type of health education takes place in those institutions which have some co-ordinating plan by which the range of student problems becomes known to all, and the total resources of the campus are brought to bear upon them.

HEALTH EDUCATION FOR PROSPECTIVE TEACHERS

One of the important responsibilities of colleges and universities is the selection and guidance of students in teacher educa-

---

[11] Allport, Gordon W. *Becoming.* New Haven, Conn.: Yale University Press, 1955. 106 p.

tion. Ideally, they encourage into the teaching profession those who have the potential for being "fit to teach." This requires, among other things, a screening process which qualifies for the teacher preparation program only those students who are physically, emotionally, socially, and morally suited for the teaching profession. Many schools and colleges of education have standards for admission which include consideration of each applicant's state of health. In addition to a careful medical examination, the prospective student is given objective tests, personality tests, and aptitude tests. Cumulative health and scholastic records from the secondary school are reviewed as well as recommendations and references from high-school administrators. These data are studied by a faculty committee as an aid in deciding for or against admission to the teacher education program.

Teacher Health Education Competencies

It is recommended that the general education of every prospective teacher include experiences which enable him to protect his own health and to understand the principles for promoting the health of individuals and groups. In addition, the person preparing to teach needs certain understandings which focus directly on helping a child to realize his potentialities. These objectives for the health education of teachers can be translated into competencies which are related to the main parts of the school health program. The following statement[12] is typical of those which have been developed in many states:

It is reasonable to expect that, in addition to knowing what constitutes an adequate school health program, every teacher at both elementary and secondary levels has competencies in:

1. *Health Instruction*—so that he can:

   a. Appreciate the importance of health education as a positive influence upon the present and future health of the child in the home, school, and community

   b. Understand how the human organism operates physically and psychologically and the means by which optimum health can be attained and maintained

   c. Keep abreast of new developments in health education and the health sciences

   d. Provide an example of healthful daily living

---

[12] Committee on Teacher Preparation in Health Education. *Health Education Competencies for All Teachers*. A Joint Report of the Wisconsin Association for Health, Physical Education, and Recreation and the Wisconsin State School Health Council. Madison, Wis.: the Committee, 1954. 4 p.

e. Identify the health interests and health needs of children and use them as a basis for health teaching

f. Organize and administer a variety of learning experiences (dramatizations, discussions, field trips, pupil committee work) which are adapted to the developmental levels of boys and girls

g. Evaluate, select, and use available teaching materials and resource personnel

h. Encourage each pupil to accept increasing responsibility for the protection and promotion of his own health and the health of others

i. Evaluate health instruction in terms of pupil health status (understanding, attitudes, interests, behavior).

These competencies require that the teacher know the basic facts of health and safety, be familiar with a wide variety of teaching materials and methods, and be acquainted with appropriate types of health instruction for various age levels.

2. *Health Services*—so that he can:

a. Help to make continuous health appraisal a learning experience for boys and girls and meaningful for parents

b. Continuously observe boys and girls for signs of fatigue, illness, emotional upset, or other health problems and follow logically desirable accepted procedures for meeting health deviations of pupils

c. Help plan and help conduct scientific screening tests of vision and hearing and make periodic growth measurements

d. Help maintain and use health records in adjusting the school program to meet individual pupil needs

e. Cooperate with physicians, dentists, public health nurses, dental hygienists, nutritionists, psychologists, and other health specialists who work with children and refer children with suspected health problems to them for further attention

f. Safeguard the confidential nature of all individual and family health information

g. Plan with pupils and their parents for meeting emergencies (illness and injury) at school

h. Render first aid when it is needed, but at no time attempt to diagnose and/or treat illness

i. Help the child with a health problem or handicap and his parent to:

(1) accept the limitations imposed by his condition;

(2) avoid further injury or impairment; and

(3) promote maximum adjustment or recovery.

These competencies require that the teacher understand what constitutes school health services and the relationships of the various health specialists in school health work. It also requires that the teacher have preparation in simple first aid.

3. *Healthful School Living*—so that he can:

a. Understand the impact of the total physical, social, and emotional environment upon the child

b. Create a pleasant classroom atmosphere through personal zest, enthusiasm, and buoyancy, and through sympathetic recognition and resolving of the individual differences among children

c. Recognize existing and potential hazards to the health and safety of school personnel and assume his role in preserving the health of school children

d. Cooperate in maintaining optimum standards of heating, lighting, ventilation, sanitation, seating, and safety at school

e. Motivate boys and girls to participate in developing and maintaining an attractive, pleasant environment in the entire school

f. Organize the school day for the benefit of pupils in regard to pupil interest span, threshold of fatigue, physical and mental abilities, and health status.

These competencies require that the teacher have a knowledge of existing standards on healthful school living—what they are, where they may be found, how they are applied in the school, and where to seek help on making environmental adjustments.

Armed with these knowledges and skills, the teacher can take an important part in the preservation and promotion of pupil health. He can participate helpfully in the school health services, develop significant health instruction, and help boys and girls to live healthfully.

How shall teachers be helped to acquire the necessary competencies in health education? No single pattern can be used by all schools and colleges of education, for their philosophies differ and their resources vary. The basic health course for all college students is merely a prerequisite to the health education courses in the professional preparation of teachers. Specific professional preparation in health education for all prospective teachers may follow a number of curricular plans.[13] For instance:

Separate courses in school health education

Units in general methods courses

Integrated courses developed through interdepartmental planning

Student observation, directed teaching, and field experiences at progressive stages of preparation

Supplemental short-term preparation for graduates of liberal arts colleges who are entering teaching without professional teaching preparation.

---

[13] American Association for Health, Physical Education, and Recreation. *Health Education for Prospective Teachers*. Report of the National Conference on College Health Education. Washington, D.C.: the Association, a department of the National Education Association, 1956. 41 p.

The following types of course are illustrative of those offered by various institutions as supplements to courses in personal and community health and for preparing the classroom teacher or "general educator."

Child health—Dealing with the mental, physical, and emotional health problems of children

School and community health problems

School health program—Presenting an over-all view of school health responsibilities, the roles of school staff members, and the ways of co-ordinating efforts of home, school, health department, and community health agencies

Methods and materials of health education—At times this course is divided into separate sections for prospective elementary and secondary teachers

Administration of school health programs—Planned particularly for principals, superintendents, supervisors, and health education specialists

Family health; first aid; home nursing; nutrition; mental health—These usually are advanced courses presenting detailed information on topics briefly covered in the basic course on personal and community health.

In-Service Education

In-service education of teachers is a joint responsibility of four groups: teachers, the employing schools, the teacher education institutions, and the state supervisory agency (the department of education or public instruction). The order in which these are mentioned gives some indication of their relative importance and responsibilities. Certainly the teacher is the one who can and does do most in this respect. Without his interest and co-operation the efforts of the others would be fruitless.

PREPARATION OF HEALTH EDUCATION SPECIALISTS

For purposes of discussing their health education needs, health educators may be divided into two groups: (a) school, college, or university health educators; and (b) community or public health educators. The latter might be grouped further according to their employing agencies as health educators serving official agencies, voluntary associations, professional societies, or industry-sponsored organizations. Although there may be significant differences in the preparation of the various types of health educators, they do have a large body of knowledge and many skills in common. All need an understanding of the health sciences (such as physiology, nutrition, and bacteriology) and the behavioral sciences (such as anthropology, sociology, and psychology). Since the major concern of this book is health education in schools and colleges, the following discussion is directed to the preparation of school and college health educators.

Competencies of the School Health Educator

The school health educator serves as a health teacher at the secondary level, or as a co-ordinator (or consultant) for the health education program of an entire school system, or in both capacities. In preparing for his work in schools, the health educator needs a broad understanding of the total school health program and the necessary skills to perform his responsibilities in that program. A report prepared by the American School Health Association[14] details the skills and abilities which the school health educator can be expected to possess beyond those recommended for all teachers. The school health educator

1. Possesses specific, scientific knowledges and understandings which help to explain the biological, social, cultural, and racial characteristics of people, and the significance and consequences of interactions of people and their environments

2. Understands and participates effectively as a leader in the methods and procedures of school and community health education activities

3. Possesses competence in *co-ordinating* the total school health program and the school and community health education activities

4. Has familiarity with and proficiency in the use of special tools, skills, and resources for stimulating action programs in health education.

The Professional Health Education Program

Satisfactory preparation of a school health educator requires at least a major emphasis at the undergraduate level and preferably additional graduate study. Because of variations in curricu-

[14] American School Health Association, Committee on Professional Preparation in Health Education. *Professional Preparation in Health Considered Essential for School Personnel in the United States.* Kent, Ohio: the Association, 1956. 31 p.

lar patterns and departmental structures, no specific course programs are recommended. However, there are certain areas of instruction which have high potential for developing and increasing competence in health education. A balance of biological (anatomy, physiology, and bateriology), physical (chemistry and physics), and social (psychology and sociology) sciences is *prerequisite* to a program for preparing health educators. It is possible that some of the background in these sciences might be achieved in part at least by other than traditional course organization. Special procedures may be developed by interdepartmental planning.

The professional program in school health education spans both the health sciences and health education, with a prominent emphasis upon the health sciences. The health sciences include personal and community health, vital statistics, epidemiology, nutrition, mental health, first aid, consumer education in health, care of the sick and injured, health problems of children and youth, rehabilitation, home and family health, environmental sanitation, accident prevention, and occupational health. Health education includes methods and materials, school health services, healthful school living, safety education, and organization and administration of school health programs.

According to a Report of the National Conference on the Undergraduate Health Education Minor Program,[15] the minimum requirement for certification in school health education is 15 to 20 semester hours (or 22 to 30 quarter hours) of course work, laboratory, and community field experiences distributed appropriately in the health sciences and health education. Student teaching experiences in health education are a vital part of the program.

RELATIONSHIP OF COLLEGE HEALTH PROGRAM TO COMMUNITY HEALTH PROGRAM

The college and university contribution to public health includes an immediate participation in the community and the long-range influence toward helping students to assume their own responsibilities throughout their lives.

---

[15] American Association for Health, Physical Education, and Recreation. *Report of the National Conference on the Undergraduate Health Education Minor Program.* Washington, D.C.: the Association, a department of the National Education Association, 1955. 36 p.

Immediate Participation

While the college or university is commonly considered a community unto itself, it is in reality an integral part of the municipal community, with its members sharing in the privileges and responsibilities of citizenship. These privileges and responsibilities are shared by individual citizens (including faculty members and students) and by the college or university as an institution. John J. Hanlon, in addressing the Pennsylvania College Health Conference, expanded on this point of view:

The dominant responsibility of the college is the provision of a significant share of participation and leadership in community health affairs through keeping currently informed, engaging in public and private discussion, promoting and participating in civic surveys and studies, serving on boards and commissions, or as consultants and advisors. Community leadership may also take the form of the provision of continued education classes, forums, seminars, and meetings. All such activities should be pursued in relation to the many voluntary health agencies as well as to the official health agency.

The position of the college and university has been similarly described by W. W. Patty (Indiana University Health Education Workshop) with the thought, "College health is public health in a special place."

Long-Range Participation

Colleges and universities serve public health goals on a long-range basis through education for citizenship and preparation of professional health personnel. Through health education of students, colleges and universities help to build an informed citizenry who will co-operate actively and intelligently in the solution of community health problems. Modern public health programs require a host of health workers, representing about 150 different occupations and professions. The nation depends upon its colleges and universities to prepare, through a variety of undergraduate and graduate programs, an ever enlarging number of young men and women who will assume health careers in neighborhoods, hospitals, health departments, voluntary health agencies, rehabilitation centers, mental health clinics, schools, industry, and research centers.

Higher education in the United States, in terms of its undergraduate programs, teacher education institutions, junior colleges, extension divisions, graduate schools, and professional schools, has a high obligation toward the present and future health education and resultant happiness of the American people.

SELECTED REFERENCES

ALLPORT, GORDON W. *Becoming.* New Haven, Conn.: Yale University Press, 1955. 106 p.

AMERICAN ASSOCIATION FOR HEALTH, PHYSICAL EDUCATION, AND RECREATION. *Fit To Teach.* Washington, D.C.: the Association, a department of the National Education Association, 1957. 249 p.

AMERICAN ASSOCIATION FOR HEALTH, PHYSICAL EDUCATION, AND RECREATION. *A Forward Look in College Health Education.* Report of the National Conference on College Health Education. Washington, D.C.: the Association, a department of the National Education Association, 1956. 50 p.

AMERICAN ASSOCIATION FOR HEALTH, PHYSICAL EDUCATION, AND RECREATION. *Health Education for Prospective Teachers.* Report of the National Conference on College Health Education. Washington, D.C.: the Association, a department of the National Education Association, 1956. 41 p.

AMERICAN ASSOCIATION FOR HEALTH, PHYSICAL EDUCATION, AND RECREATION. *Report of the National Conference on the Undergraduate Health Education Minor Program.* Washington, D.C.: the Association, a department of the National Education Association, 1955. 36 p.

AMERICAN COLLEGE HEALTH ASSOCIATION. *Teamwork in Meeting the Health Needs of College Students.* Proceedings of the Fourth National Conference on College Health. New York: the Association, 1955. 211 p.

AMERICAN SCHOOL HEALTH ASSOCIATION, COMMITTEE ON PROFESSIONAL PREPARATION IN HEALTH EDUCATION. *Professional Preparation in Health Considered Essential for School Personnel in the United States.* Kent, Ohio: the Association, 1956. 31 p.

FARNSWORTH, DANA L. "Health Services in College and University." *Encyclopedia of Educational Research.* Revised edition. (Edited by Chester W. Harris.) New York: Macmillan Co., 1960. p. 636-41.

FARNSWORTH, DANA L. *Mental Health in College and University.* Cambridge, Mass.: Harvard University Press, 1957. 244 p.

FARNSWORTH, DANA L., and THORNDIKE, AUGUSTUS. "Health in Colleges and Universities." *New England Journal of Medicine* 255: 949-55, 992-96; November 1956.

FEDERAL SECURITY AGENCY. *Conference on the Undergraduate Professional Preparation of Students Majoring in Health Education.* (Edited by H. F. Kilander.) Washington, D.C.: Superintendent of Documents, Government Printing Office, 1949. 84 p.

FUNKENSTEIN, DANIEL H., editor. *The Student and Mental Health.* Proceedings of the First International Conference on Student Mental Health. New York: World Federation for Mental Health and International Association of Universities, 1959. 495 p.

GINSBURG, ETHEL L. *The College and Student Health.* New York: National Tuberculosis Association, 1955. 102 p.

MOORE, NORMAN S., and SUMMERSKILL, JOHN. *Health Services in American Colleges and Universities.* Ithaca, N.Y.: Cornell University, 1953. 108 p.

MOSS, BERNICE. "Can Health Education Command Academic Respect?" *Journal of Health, Physical Education, Recreation* 28: 26; June 1958.

NATIONAL CONFERENCE ON GRADUATE STUDY IN HEALTH EDUCATION, PHYSICAL EDUCATION, AND RECREATION. *Report of the Conference.* Chicago: the Athletic Institute, 1950. 31 p.

NATIONAL CONFERENCE ON UNDERGRADUATE PROFESSIONAL PREPARATION IN HEALTH EDUCATION, PHYSICAL EDUCATION, AND RECREATION. *Report of the Conference.* Chicago: the Athletic Institute, 1948. 40 p.

NATIONAL TUBERCULOSIS ASSOCIATION. *A Health Program for Colleges.* Report of the Third National Conference on Health in Colleges. New York: the Association, 1948. 152 p.

RICHARDSON, CHARLES E. "Total College Health Programs." *Journal of Health, Physical Education, Recreation* 30: 23-24; March 1959.

SNYDER, RAYMOND A., and SCOTT, HARRY A. *Professional Preparation in Health, Physical Education, and Recreation.* New York: McGraw-Hill Book Co., 1954. 421 p.

U.S. DEPARTMENT OF HEALTH, EDUCATION, AND WELFARE. *Second Conference on Professional Preparation of Students Majoring in Health Education.* (Edited by H. F. Kilander.) Washington, D.C.: Superintendent of Documents, Government Printing Office, 1953. 69 p.

WORLD HEALTH ORGANIZATION. *A Study Guide on Teacher Preparation for Health Education.* Geneva, Switzerland: the Organization, 1957. 16 p.

YOUNG, MARJORIE A. C. *A Survey of College Health Programs for Prospective Teachers.* New York: National Society for the Prevention of Blindness, 1954. 131 p.

Chapter 16

Adult Health Education

Why a chapter on adult health education in this book? Because . . .

If used alone, health education in the school has little in its favor, since the "health educated" child goes back into a family atmosphere which may, through its daily living patterns, negate everything positive that the child has learned about health. It is necessary, then, that health education be conducted wherever adult education goes on. Only when the adults are kept abreast of the children in their perceptions of health can the general level of the health of the community be raised.[1]

This statement emphasizes that in any community the improvement of health conditions for boys and girls is partly dependent upon and usually reflects the interest and efforts of its adults. School health education helps to guide the behavior of children, but unless there is active home and community support the behavior learned may not be practiced beyond the door of the school. Adults, nonparents as well as parents, *are* important. Adults control the destiny of a community; they determine what the health practices and standards of their community shall be.

A most important objective of adult health education is that of gaining support for school health programs through adults' interests in their children. Adult health education has other objectives, too. It helps adults to accept responsibility for health maintenance and improvement. The health-educated adult keeps his health knowledge up to date, and he makes appropriate application of it in his personal, family, and community living. He also seeks advice from reliable sources when needed.

Health is one of the persistent interests of the adult. The desire to retain the buoyancy of healthy youth, to avoid feelings of discomfort, and to experience the joy of perfect bodily functioning is universal. Many adults seek fountains of youth and miracle cures, and they spend millions of dollars annually for nostrums—all to improve their health. The relationships between

---

[1] Koos, Earl Lomon. *The Health of Regionville.* New York: Columbia University Press, 1954. 177 p.

health, happiness, and economic security become increasingly apparent as one grows older.

THE ADULT POPULATION

The population of the United States is growing so rapidly that the number of people in this country is expected to reach 200 million sometime between 1965 and 1970. The primary reason for this great increase lies in the imbalance between the birth and death rates. Except for the 1918 influenza epidemic, the general trend of the death rate in the United States has been steadily downward and has reached a plateau in recent decades. During the 1930's the birth rate also was falling, but since 1940 a generally upward wave of births has caused the population to surge. In addition to crowded schools and bulging cities, population growth has unpredictable sociological, economic, political, nutritional, and perhaps sanitary effects.

The population of the country is not only growing *larger*, it is growing *older*. Today in the "average" American community, about two-thirds of the population are over 21 years of age, and half of these adults are 45 years of age or older. There are more adults 50 years or older than there are children of school age 5 to 15. Likewise, the number of people aged 65 or more is about equal to the number of children five years of age and under. The ratio of older people to children is steadily increasing.

Industrialization and changes in agriculture have caused a shift in the location of the population from farm to city. Approximately two-thirds of the total population of the United States now live in cities or on the fringe of cities; only about one-third are on the farm. This process is expected to continue until urban areas of one city will merge with those of its neighbors, resulting eventually in urban areas several hundred miles in length.

The aging of the population, its concentration in urban areas, and the problems of modern living in a heavily industrialized society are creating new problems with tremendous health and health education implications. What are some of these?

HEALTH PROBLEMS OF ADULTS

Mortality statistics point up some of the health problems which afflict adults. Heart disease, cancer, cerebral hemorrhage, pneumonia, influenza, accidents, arteriosclerosis, and hepatic disease are the major causes of death in the older age groups, and they also take their toll among young adults. Prevention and control of these leading causes of sickness and death are but one focal point for the health education of adults. There are other areas of concern. The case for adult health education is summarized in the following paragraphs. Each problem and each statistic represents human suffering and misery.

Disability

National health surveys reveal that each person has slightly more than two weeks of disability from all causes each year. As might be expected, the disability rates start at a low of six days for children under five, climb steadily to an average of 21 days for the age group 45 to 64, and reach a peak of 44 days for the age group over 65. Among the employed there is an annual loss of almost eight work days per person because of illness or injury.

Acute Illness

Types of acute conditions (duration of three months or less) among adults are similar to those among youth. Respiratory infections, gastrointestinal disturbances, and injuries are recurring causes of disability and absence from work. There are fewer illnesses and absences of short duration with older age groups, but the disabilities are more severe. The severity rates for each acute condition increase with age. Except for injuries, females experience a higher incidence of acute conditions than males.

Chronic Illness

Chronic illnesses present another problem. These illnesses now cause approximately two-thirds of all deaths in the United States. The basic characteristic of chronic disease is its long duration, often necessitating medical care for months and sometimes for years. Among the important chronic diseases are heart disease and allied conditions, renal disease, nervous and mental disorders, tuberculosis, cancer, diabetes, allergy, arthritis, and alcoholism. In a report of recent family interviews throughout the country, about 70 million people, or 41 percent of the population, are shown to have one or more chronic conditions, ranging from 17 percent among those 15 years of age to roughly 80 percent among those 65 years or older. Circulatory conditions account for more days of disability and work loss than any other single category of chronic conditions.

Impairments

Impairments are chronic or permanent residual effects of disease or injury involving principally the musculoskeletal system and the special senses. Such common impairments as poor vision, blindness, reduced hearing or deafness, speech difficulties, paralyses, orthopedic defects, and loss of one or more body members handicap thousands of adults. About one-third of all impairments are caused by injury. Regardless of cause, some of the impairments restrict employment opportunities for adults.

Accidents

Accidents to adults are a major killer and crippler. Accidents, exclusive of motor vehicle accidents, are among the 10 leading causes of death for each adult age group, and for the age groups 25 to 34 and 35 to 44 years, motor vehicle accidents are also among the top 10 causes of death. Next to motor vehicle accidents, falls are the most frequent cause of accidental deaths among adults.

Mental Health

Problems of mental health among adults are widespread and ill-defined. To a greater or lesser degree, millions have mental health problems varying from violent disturbances to minor personality disorders. The fast tempo of life, the competitive pressures of economic stability, and the instability of family life all affect one's mental equilibrium. The main problem is to convince people that emotional disturbances do exist, that they are a kind of sickness, and that many of them can be helped by psychiatric treatment. Because of the nature and extent of mental illness, it seriously affects both individual and community health.

Obesity

Obesity, which is defined as 20 percent above desirable weight, is a health impediment for many adults. It predisposes to hypertension, diabetes, hepatic disease, and other complications. It has a negative influence on mortality rates. Excessively overweight men and women have death rates which are 50 percent higher than the average for their ages. Obesity is invariably caused by eating food that contains more calories than the body uses in daily activity. In a few individuals low metabolism may be a contributing factor. Emotional influences, particularly boredom and loneliness, may lead to compulsive eating and obesity. The pleasure of eating may be used as an attempt at compensation. Habitual overeating may be induced by family customs, sociability, or because rich and abundant food as a symbol of success tempts the appetite too greatly.

In view of the importance of body weight to health and longevity, the findings of the Build and Blood Pressure Study, 1959, conducted by the Society of Actuaries, are of major significance. The study provides information from which new standards of desirable weight have been developed by the Statistical Bureau of the Metropolitan Life Insurance Company.[2]

Consumer Hygiene

Self-medication is one of the biggest health problems facing the American public today. The amount of money spent in self-medication far surpasses that spent for legitimately prescribed drugs. The sale of "home medicaments" in one year amounts to somewhere between 0.5 and 0.75 billion dollars. The simple and useful remedies in the home first aid cabinet represent only a small part of this cost. Most of the money goes for expensively advertised nostrums. Some of these preparations are harmless but worthless. Others are simply standard drugs packaged to sell at exorbitant prices. Some are injurious. Most people who buy proprietary medicines to treat themselves undoubtedly believe that they are saving money and saving health. In many instances they are doing just the opposite—wasting both money and health. By far the greatest hazard of self-diagnosis and self-medication is the often serious delay which it causes in obtaining professional diagnosis and treatment.

Intelligent use of medical services is a worthy objective of adult health education. There is a tendency among many people to expect either too much or too little of medical science. Some people have so much confidence in medical science that they expect it to provide or perform miracles. Others have too little confidence: if they go to a physician at all, it may be with the idea that he may be able to make a lucky guess or hit upon some remedy by chance. The discriminating and discerning person

---

[2] Metropolitan Life Insurance Company. "New Weight Standards for Men and Women." *Statistical Bulletin* 40: 1-4; November-December 1959.

expects of physicians what physicians are prepared to give— application of medical science to the welfare of the "total patient," not merely to the disease symptoms which he presents.

Obtaining medical and dental services is another problem. Despite the vast number of physicians and hospital beds, there are still unmet health needs in the population. A careful study in Michigan by Hoffer[3] revealed that almost as many people in a large population sample had symptoms untreated by a physician as had symptoms under medical care. By having a representative group of these people undergo a medical examination, it was found that the untreated symptoms deserved medical attention. This study indicates a need for greater education about the necessity for prompt medical diagnosis and treatment of symptoms. It also highlights another problem, that of budgeting in advance for these essential services.

Not only is there need to educate for wise use of medical services, but people also need help in learning how to meet the costs of medical, nursing, hospital, and rehabilitative services. Voluntary health insurance provides an orderly method of meeting the cost of medical treatment and hospital care. Its benefits will be apparent in proportion to the number of people who are informed about it and who are motivated to participate in one or more of the standard plans which are available. Here is an important responsibility of health education.

Health education for adults also includes consideration of community health resources. Inadequate distribution of public health services and of medical facilities and personnel in a state or area, particularly in rural communities, may be as serious a hazard to the health of both adults and children as are insanitary water and sewerage systems.

There are many ways of determining the existence and extent of these health problems in any given community. Some of the techniques are:

1. Analyses of the vital statistics—marriages, divorces, births, deaths, and reported diseases

2. Environmental surveys to determine the adequacy of such items as water supply, sewage and garbage disposal, food and restaurant sanitation, housing, insect and rodent control, industrial hygiene

---

[3] Hoffer, C. R.; Gibson, D. L.; Loomis, C. P.; Miller, P. A.; Schuler, E. A.; and Thadern, J. F. *Health Needs and Health Care in Michigan.* Special Bulletin 365. East Lansing: Michigan State College Agricultural Experiment Station, 1950.

3. Multiple screening tests—applying a series of approved laboratory tests and procedures to a large segment of the population on a voluntary basis to help detect physical impairments and incipient disease

4. House-to-house canvasses

5. Reports of observations by public health personnel and the health professions

6. Inventory of community health services and facilities

7. Intensive status-studies of such problems as dental health, nutritional health, mental retardation.

RESPONSIBILITY FOR ADULT HEALTH EDUCATION

No single group or agency can assume full responsibility for all adult health education activities. The wide scope of interests and the multiplicity of procedures that are a part of adult health education provide opportunities for constructive efforts by many different groups. Co-ordinated programs in which schools, health departments, voluntary health agencies, and professional associations each participate actively in planning and sharing of resources for the promotion of health education produce satisfactory results.

Schools and Health Departments

Great opportunities face the schools and the health department, the two official agencies concerned with health education, especially if they co-ordinate their efforts and work effectively with professional associations and voluntary agencies. They contribute to adult health education through such activities as:

1. Personal conferences between parents and teachers regarding the health progress or adjustment of boys and girls in school

2. Home calls of public health or school nurses and others who follow up specific health problems in the home

3. Contacts of sanitary engineers and sanitarians with proprietors and operators of restaurants, food stores, dairies, camps, resorts, beauty parlors, barber shops, and similar personal service trades, to improve standards of sanitation and personal health essential for the protection of the public

4. Services of physicians, dentists, and nurses with patients in public health facilities

5. Counseling of parents by the school medical adviser

6. Classes on home nursing, child care, first aid, nutrition, homemaking, personal health, family and community health in the adult education or "night school" program of the community

7. Lectures, forums, discussion groups, and similar type meetings to help adults

Discover community health problems and develop plans for using available resources in coping with the problems

Understand the health needs of children and how to meet them

Learn about child development

Study and understand their part in the school health program

Increase their own health knowledge

8. News releases and other appropriate items for local newspaper, radio, and television use.

Professional Associations

The health education of adults in the community is advanced by the personal services of members of the health professions, particularly physicians, nurses, and dentists. In addition to the informal education which occurs during the contacts of these practitioners with their patients, individual members of these groups give talks to teachers, civic clubs, parent organizations, and other groups of lay persons.

In many communities the county medical society has a committee relating to health education. This committee often co-operates with the school and the community health councils in planning and evaluating school and community health education and health services. It may sponsor radio and television broadcasts and informative newspaper articles. It also furnishes speakers on specific health topics of interest to lay audiences.

Voluntary Health Agencies

Adult health education is a primary concern of voluntary health agencies. Through talks, classes, study groups, conferences, printed materials, films, radio, television, and other methods of communication, millions of people are reached annually with health messages. These help to teach adults to live healthfully, inform them of health hazards, acquaint them with preventive and curative measures, and enlist their support in the solution of community health problems. Voluntary health agencies work co-operatively with schools, health departments, professional associations, and social agencies. They frequently provide printed materials, audio-visual aids, and other resources for the use of all community groups.

PRINCIPLES OF ADULT HEALTH EDUCATION

Initiative for a community adult health education program may come from schools, health departments, professional associations, or other community agencies. Those who assume major responsibility for the health education of adults need to study the community and discover:

1. The groups, organizations, and personnel resources for adult education

2. The major purposes of each of the groups and the kinds of programs they sponsor

3. The possibilities of enriching or extending these programs so that they may contribute to health education

4. The adult leaders who might help in planning for co-operation among the various groups and for better community health education.

Some General Principles

Several principles of educational planning especially pertinent to adult health education are succinctly summarized in the twentieth yearbook of the American Association of School Administrators:[4]

1. *Programs should be based on the needs and interests of people.* Adult education programs are justified only to the extent that they serve the needs of people. Adults seek further learning when they need help in solving problems of personal, family, or community living. In adult health education the focus should be on the health problems of particular individuals and groups, not on subject matter as such.

2. *Programs should reach the people wherever they are.* Most adult education is conducted on a voluntary basis. People cannot be forced to attend classes, listen to the radio, or participate in community projects. The greatest number will be served if programs are taken to people where they

---

[4] American Association of School Administrators. *Health in Schools.* Revised edition. Twentieth Yearbook. Washington, D.C.: the Association, a department of the National Education Association, 1951. 477 p.

are, as in their homes, clubs, and churches, and at times when the people are most likely to be responsive. Among the most successful programs are those on topics requested by organized groups and scheduled at times and places chosen by the groups. People not in organized groups can be reached by other means such as home visits, newspapers, and radio.

3. *The people themselves should share in program planning.* Those for whom a program is intended should have a part in deciding what the program will include. Participation of the people in program planning has a two-fold value. In the first place, the program for a particular group better fits the needs and interests of the group when members have had a chance to suggest what they want. In addition, members who have been involved at the planning level usually feel that they have a stake in the program and are more likely to take their share of responsibility for its success.

4. *Adult health education should be an integral part of the total community health program.* Health education for adults cannot function in a vacuum. Its substance comes from the health problems of individuals, families, and communities; its strength, from cooperation in community-wide efforts to meet these problems.

5. *Adult health education should be an integral part of the total adult education program of a community.* As stated before, adult education programs are directed toward helping adults solve problems of living. Health problems are inextricably related to larger problems of living and often can be treated more effectively in their broader relationships. Moreover, there is efficiency in organization when personnel and facilities which have been established to promote and carry out adult education in general are utilized in the development of adult health education.

6. *Leadership of high quality should be provided.* Health education, which is so intimately related to matters of life and death, must be in the hands of competent leaders. Those who teach adult groups must be equipped with sound health facts and must know where to turn for technical help to supplement their own background. Like all other leaders of adult groups, workers in adult health education should be skillful in group leadership.

7. *Programs of adult health education should point toward action.* Health education programs have fulfilled their purpose only when they have helped people to solve their health problems more effectively. Programs which provide for participation in problem-solving situations are more likely to succeed than those which deal only with the presentation of health facts.

Locating the Leaders

Whether one starts by attempting to arouse the community to its health needs, or by working with a group which has already started to act on a problem, an organizational plan is essential to action and involvement of people from all parts of the community. Identifying the leaders and recruiting them are the first steps in developing this plan.

A study of the community, its people, and its problems will reveal the various elements which constitute it, the racial and national groups, the sections or subneighborhoods. All groups and all areas will have leaders. They may be found in all walks of life and with varying degrees of formal education. The amount of formal schooling is not the only criterion for judging the education or leadership ability of adults. The "creative spirit" may be found among those of limited school education as well as among college graduates. Finding the leaders does not necessarily mean coming upon the so-called key people. It means finding those persons who are acceptable to an entire group, are liked and respected by them, and are closely tied to the followers as leaders. These natural leaders can help to extend the influence of adult health education into every home in the community.

Conditions for Adult Growth and Change

If a program is going to result in positive action, it has to bring about growth and change in individual and group behavior. What are the conditions for stimulating growth and change in individual and group behavior? Here are some of them:[5]

1. The individual clearly understands and fully accepts the direction and nature of the proposed growth or change.

2. The individual is free to expose or express his thoughts and behavior to himself and to others, to face up to his present behavior in relation to what he would like to do.

3. The individual can secure the necessary data to enable him to judge the discrepancy between where he is and where he would like to be.

4. The emotional climate of the learning situation is deliberately designed and constructed to reduce defensiveness and to provide the emotional support which will enable the individual to endure the awkward stage of developing and trying out new forms of behavior and new thought patterns.

5. There is opportunity to experiment with new patterns of thought and new ways of behaving so the individual can gain security in these new ways of thinking and acting.

6. The individual can develop enough skill to apply and maintain what he has learned.

---

[5] Based on: Bradford, Leland P. "Toward a Philosophy of Adult Education." *Adult Education* 7: 83-93; Winter 1957.

Presentation of Material

Regardless of the medium used, there are certain fundamentals to be observed in the presentation of materials for a community program of adult health education. Briefly enumerated, these are as follows:

1. The health education process is never ended. The receiving group—call it the audience or the public—is constantly changing. People die or leave the community; new people move in.

2. In general, ideas are presented one at a time.

3. The material arises out of the demonstrated needs and interests of the community.

4. The material is presented in a simple, understandable manner, using easily comprehended language.

5. The same material is presented repeatedly, although a new guise may be sought to give variety.

6. The material is authentic.

7. The material is practical and usable for the great majority of those to whom it applies.

8. The material is stimulating and provocative as well as useful and interesting; otherwise it will not arouse people to action.

9. There is a place for humor and sentiment in proper proportions. The best radio talk contains one laugh, one tear, and one idea. This is a good pattern for any other form of health education message.

10. Deal firmly but gently with superstition and folklore. In some instances these have turned out to be soundly based and later demonstrated to be factual. In any event, an attack upon superstitions and false beliefs is not the best way to encourage abandonment of erroneous ideas.

HEALTH EDUCATION PROCEDURES

A great variety of methods is used in transmitting health information and stimulating intelligent health behavior. Some of the more important techniques include newspapers, pamphlets, radio broadcasts, telecasts, motion pictures, exhibits, community meetings, correspondence, and individual contacts. Some of these procedures are discussed in detail in Chapter Twelve. Others are described in the following paragraphs.

Newspapers

Despite the claims that nobody reads any more, the fact is that millions of copies of newspapers are sold every day and people do read them. The newspaper still is a vital channel of communication to the public and, therefore, is an important medium of adult health education. *Health news items* of interest include:

1. Reports of the prevalence of communicable diseases
2. Reports on births and on infant deaths
3. Reports on births in relation to maternal health and mortality
4. Health anniversaries in the community, such as the passage of a given number of years or months without a death from a communicable disease or without a death from accidents, or any other significant milestone
5. New plans projected by the health department, medical society, or other health agency for better health in the community
6. The arrival of new health personnel, promotions, or other personnel changes in the agency
7. Announcements of new programs proposed by the agency
8. Comparison of local health conditions with state-wide or national corresponding rates
9. Unusual cases and incidents (with disguised identities, if necessary)
10. Recognitions or honors received
11. Indications of special deficiencies in the local public health program.

Newspapers sometimes give *editorial* support to an appropriate health project. Besides editorials and news stories, the *"letters to the editor"* column often can be used to express appreciation for co-operation by the newspaper, to answer common questions, and to correct misinterpretations or misunderstandings.

Newspapers with Sunday editions or special Saturday editions may welcome *feature stories* with pictures. It is usually best to query the editor and to work these out co-operatively. Not infrequently newspapers publish *special editions* commemorative of some event in the community's history or progress, such as a centennial or other anniversary, or the opening of a new and significant industry.

Often, a historical news summary of the health situation will fit into a special edition. A co-operative relationship with the press will result in the utilization of many opportunities to communicate with the public.

Meetings

The lecture method still has a useful place in education. Likewise, an informative *talk* given by a skillful speaker may be significant.

Despite the limits of visible audiences, the occasion of a speech or lecture has advantages not possessed by either radio or television. Even with a fairly large audience, there is opportunity for two-way communication. Questions can be asked and answered, and even the response or lack thereof of an audience to a speaker, and vice versa, is advantageous.

The modern speech is not usually an eloquent lecture. It is more helpful when it is an informal presentation in which every effort is made to establish rapport between the speaker and his audience.

Slides often accompany lectures. They may be necessary in some types of formalized presentation; but unless they are used with great skill, they are a handicap to the speaker who wishes to promote rapport with his audience. Films may be used also to supplement a speech. An effective use of films in this regard is to show a film or portion of one and then to discuss it with the audience, bringing out its salient points, and making additional points as the discussion progresses.

A talk is often a good keynote for the first part of a meeting which leads to group discussion and "buzz sessions"; frequently a summarizing talk also is advantageous. The lecture method is usually the technique chosen when visiting celebrities make contact with local audiences.

In general it is unprofitable to try to assemble an audience to hear a speech about health. Speakers are usually sent to audiences already assembled for other purposes. The luncheon clubs, chambers of commerce, women's clubs, professional groups, PTA's, and similar community organizations which hold regular meetings are eager for good speakers. On the contrary, few people will leave the comfort of the home and the attractions of television or of other diversions to go and hear a speech about health.

The *health forum* is a public meeting, but it differs from the ordinary public meeting in that it features public participation and is tied closely to intensive preliminary promotion and publicity. A health forum may be sponsored by any health agency, usually in co-operation with a newspaper, although it may be carried out in co-operation with a radio or television station. A popular subject, such as heart disease, physical fitness, diet, reducing, or dangers of atomic radiation, is selected and publicized by mass communication media; that is, newspaper, radio, and television. People are invited to send in questions in advance on the topic.

An outstanding panel of experts is drawn from the community, sometimes with the aid of visiting speakers. This panel also is widely publicized in the newspaper, by radio, television, posters, billboards, or throwaway leaflets. At the time of the forum, which is usually held in a theater or large centrally located hall, the experience has been that a sellout may be expected, although, of course, no admission is charged. In some instances, it has been necessary to set up emergency loudspeakers to take care of overflow crowds.

The subject under discussion is outlined by one or two speakers from the panel and then questions are submitted to the panel by a moderator. If time permits, spontaneous questions from the audience may be entertained. A forum takes a great deal of time and effort in preparation and, therefore, the frequency with which this type of meeting can be conducted successfully depends upon the available personnel and facilities.

To assure the success of a forum, the panelists must be willing to submit to the necessary publicity, including the publication of their pictures. For stirring community enthusiasm the combined impact of press, radio, television, posters, handbills, word-of-mouth, and, finally, the public meeting can scarcely be exceeded. It is often the topic of conversation for many weeks following.

The *conference* with working committees, or the workshop, is another of the more successful types of group discussion methods. Here the same group or shifting groups, together with resource persons, undertake to discuss various phases of a problem. Sometimes several groups may be given the same problem; sometimes each group is given a different phase. Resource persons may rotate from group to group or the groups may rotate among different resource personnel. Regardless of the mechanics, the net results can be extremely valuable in the hands of adept group chairmen and capable summarizers. By the same token, unguided group discussion is simply a waste of time.

Organized classes are another variation of the group technique, but unless these involve more than merely didactic instruction, they are not true manifestations of the group technique. Classes can also be organized by radio and television.

An *action committee* involves people not only in discussion but also in action for the solution of a problem. For example, suppose a neighborhood needs and does not have a nursery school. A group of young mothers working together can gather information, discuss it, formulate plans, and then proceed to put them into action either through the school authorities or by organizing and operating a nursery school themselves. This is education in its ultimate perfection.

Correspondence

Correspondence is not to be despised as a tool for health education. The friendly personal letter can often convey desired information and deftly include some motivating factors which will help to influence the inquirer into the desired modifications of his conduct. Letters are expensive and time consuming, but next to the personal interview, they are perhaps the best means for reaching the individual inquirer at a "teachable moment."

A few large national organizations find it possible to maintain a question-and-answer service. Once an agency has undertaken to answer questions, it assumes a tremendous responsibility. Answering questions cannot be done adequately unless the agency has a considerable source of information in a well-stocked library and can command gratis services of qualified consultants.

It is usually better to answer by mail questions which can easily be answered, and to refer others to the national agencies, such as the health agencies within the National Health Council in New York, the American Medical Association and the American Dental Association in Chicago, and the heart, cancer, tuberculosis, polio, and other specialty organizations.

Individual Contacts

Several studies show that personal contact is one of the greatest influences in health education. Individual contacts by health specialists are necessarily limited. When individual contacts are made with group leaders who, in turn, can deal with others, an ever widening circle of communication and influence can be created.

Occasionally it becomes necessary to devote time and effort to an individual who is seriously perplexed or who needs guidance. Such efforts may have repercussions far beyond what might be imagined at the time. People who have been helped through contacts with a health education agency are prone to spread the word and to create good feelings in the community. These may be far more important than can be measured.

OPPORTUNITIES FOR ADULT HEALTH EDUCATION

Every teacher and leader has opportunities for influencing the health education of adults both through individual contacts and through organized groups. Adult education is a process as old as man himself. It is an essential part of the democratic process.

Education for adults, in innumerable forms, has been in process from the beginning of our history . . . but no one talked about it. It was so inchoate and so inextricably entangled with life that, like life itself, most of it was simply taken for granted. School and college were thought of as "education," that is, as "book larnin" in an organized way. Of course you had to learn to milk a cow and to do lots of other diversified things, but these were not thought of as education. Moreover, there was another aspect of the subject. Because school, and perhaps college, alone were considered as education, and because only children and youth received it, the idea grew that education was something not intended for adults. It was even felt that they were incapable of gaining it formally, and that it was unnecessary for them anyway, and beneath their dignity.[6]

Working with Organized Groups

At the present time many organizations have adult education programs. These include the National Congress of Parents and Teachers; business and professional groups representing many interests; church, youth-serving, veteran, service, and civic groups; farm and labor organizations; fraternal orders, community councils and others—all conducting educational programs, many of which are aimed at the improvement of community or family living. Health always looms large as an interest in such enterprises.

[6] Adams, James Truslow. *Frontiers of American Culture.* New York: Charles Scribner's Sons, 1944. 364 p.

In every community groups will be found with purposes aimed toward improvement of some aspects of community living. In furthering adult health education it is wise to work through these groups, enriching their programs and helping them to achieve worthy purposes for community betterment.

Many local groups and organizations have state and national associations with platforms and recommendations which influence the direction of programs at the local level. For example, members of the National Congress of Parents and Teachers co-operate with school and public health groups in promoting continuous health care for boys and girls, with periodic health examinations and conferences for all children and youth. The platform of the National Congress also emphasizes other goals of education, such as: (a) good homes through parent and family life education; (b) safety through creation of environments free from physical hazards; (c) equalized educational opportunities; (d) constructive leisure time activities; (e) adequate school and community health programs. The objectives of the National Congress are carried through many special projects and committees, about half of which have definite health education interests. These include project committees on exceptional children, school health examinations, home and family life, juvenile protection, mental health, narcotics education, parent education, recreation, safety, and social hygiene.

Other groups which may be eager or willing to participate in health education programs are:

1. Farm organizations, including their women's auxiliaries

2. Labor unions, other worker groups, and industry

3. Civic and service groups

4. Business and professional groups

5. Public service trades such as dairies, food stores, drug stores, beauty parlors, barber shops, restaurants, ice cream parlors, taverns, and life insurance companies

6. Community councils and health committees of councils and social agencies.

Reaching Unorganized Groups

Although the easiest way to reach a large number of people in an adult health education program is by working through organized groups, such efforts will usually reach only about 40 percent of the adult population. It is urgent that methods be found for reaching the remaining three-fifths who may be more vitally in need of health information than those who have the time and energy to join a club or some other organization.

Determined effort and deliberate planning are needed to make health information easily available to every segment of the population. This means extending to the nonjoiner an opportunity to belong to a group with activities based upon his particular interests and at his educational level. New leadership will be developed within each group, but the process will be slow. In the initial stages of organization it will require much time, energy, stimulation, and careful guidance by a health educator or community worker. Co-operative planning and effort by all lay and professional leaders will make it possible for each group to participate in the total health education program of the community.

During recent years, there have been many successful experiences with this grass-roots type of community organization for health education in which the people themselves play the most important part. Real leadership has been found when on the surface none existed. People have been eager to learn and ready with ideas. Many were well aware of their health problems but needed friendly counsel or professional guidance in doing something about their problems.

SCHOOL HEALTH COUNCILS

The school health council or committee, with its participating members drawn from school personnel and pupils, parents, community physicians and dentists, representatives of local health agencies, and public health personnel, is one way of developing community understanding and co-operation in support of the school health program. It also can be an important avenue of adult health education, especially for those who participate in council activities. A school health council may serve within a school building, system, or several systems. It may be part of or closely related to a community health council, or it may be an independent unit.

The school health council is an advisory group, usually appointed by the school superintendent. Its major purpose is to assist in identifying and solving school health problems. Some guides[7] for adapting the composition and functions of the council to local interests and needs include:

1. The purposes, objectives, and policies of the council should be stated clearly and reviewed periodically.

2. The council should include representation from parents, the schools, the health department, medical, dental, and nursing societies, and community health and welfare agencies.

3. Each member agency should be given an opportunity to select its own representatives. Officers should be elected by the council for specified periods of time.

4. The council should meet at regular times and with prepared agenda.

5. Each agency should be permitted to present for council consideration any problem dealing with the health of school children. Particular attention should be given to problems requiring joint action by the schools and other community agencies and those that involve participation by two or more professional groups.

6. Use should be made of sub-committees, but these should be guided by, and report back to, the council as a whole.

7. Although long-term projects are necessary and appropriate, projects which can be completed successfully in a short period of time should also receive attention. Publicity should be given throughout the community to the council's progress and accomplishments.

8. Emphasis should be placed on solving pertinent problems rather than on organization or on routine procedures.

Some of the operating procedures of a council include:

1. Survey the entire school health program for strengths and weaknesses

2. Compile detailed data on specific school health problems

3. Analyze the various school and community resources for meeting certain health problems

4. Recommend to the school administrator a course of action for meeting each problem

5. Evaluate the influence of recommended improvements that are put into operation

6. Develop long-range plans for co-ordination of the school and community health programs.

The origin, growth, and work of the school health council in Fond du Lac, Wisconsin, is typical of school health councils in

---

[7] National Conference for Cooperation in Health Education, National Committee on School Health Policies. *Suggested School Health Policies*. Third edition. Washington, D.C. and Chicago: National Education Association and American Medical Association, 1956. 40 p.

many communities. Here is the story as told by Jane Austin Scheer,[8] a school health educator:

On the third Tuesday of the month, if you looked in at the Elks Club in Fond du Lac, you would observe the usual number of groups lunching there. However, you might also observe that one group in particular seemed to be having an especially good time.

If you looked long enough, you would notice that almost everyone of that group of fifteen had something to say. The waitress might inform you that this was the Fond du Lac School Health Council—that group which does not mind mixing weighty topics, like health examinations for school children, with lighter matters such as homemade rolls.

Our Council was organized in 1947. Its beginning was something like this. My predecessor as school health co-ordinator, Mrs. Joyce Limpert Reiss, found that many school health problems needed help from outside sources.

After talking with the superintendent and key faculty members, Mrs. Reiss met with various people to find out whether there might be interest in an informal group concerned with school health problems. The public relations chairman of the Medical Society was visited. The health officer, city dentist and nurses were asked their opinions. "Yes," they said, "let's try one meeting anyway." And so the list grew.

The first meetings were small and perhaps a little awkward. But it was amazing to see how many problems the folks had in common. The group found "Suggested School Health Policies," a report of the National Committee on School Health Policies, most helpful as a guide. Consultants from the Wisconsin Co-operative School Health Program gave invaluable encouragement and suggestions. Noon luncheon meetings were found to be the most convenient for the majority of members—especially the medical and dental representatives. During the second year a Constitution and By-Laws were adopted.

A school health council in another community might develop in quite a different way. In Fond du Lac our Council has grown to include representatives from many groups directly interested in school health. At present there are from fifteen to twenty active members. Our group is informal and everyone feels free to speak his opinion. So far we have one weakness: no student representatives.

During the first six months, the health co-ordinator acted as chairman. Realizing, however, that each member had something uniquely valuable to contribute, she asked to be relieved of the chairmanship. An elementary principal followed her as chairman. The three succeeding years found three different PTA mothers presiding. This lay leadership has greatly strengthened the group.

Perhaps I enjoy talking about the Fond du Lac Council because it has some real accomplishments. One of the early projects was a joint sponsoring between the School Health Council and the Fond du Lac County Medical Society of a series of health radio programs.

---

[8] Scheer, Jane Austin. "The Way We Do It in Fond du Lac." *The Crusader* (Wisconsin Anti-Tuberculosis Association) 43, No. 7: 3-5; September 1951.

At the request of the superintendent of schools, the Council studied the matter of health examinations for school personnel. Recommendations were made to the School Board and a program of health examinations for all public school personnel was initiated.

The Fond du Lac Health Society, from its Christmas Seal funds, paid for the X-rays that were included as part of the complete physical examinations. Now an annual check of school employees for tuberculosis is done routinely in both public and parochial schools.

Another Council project was concerned with return of children to school after illness. The old ordinance required that a child have a health permit from his family physician before he could return to school if he had been absent more than three consecutive days. A too-frequent practice for parents was to send children back to school on the third day, often before the child was fully recovered, to avoid having to go to a doctor for a permit.

After much research and discussion, the Health Council proposed—and secured adoption of—a substitute ordinance. This requires that a health permit be furnished from the family physician or the city health officer only if the illness has been communicable in nature. The Health Department and schools are very much pleased with the way the new ordinance is functioning. Teachers find that children are staying home until they are fully recovered.

At one meeting, the president of the Dental Society asked when the spring holidays were scheduled. He was anxious to know in advance so that he could keep them open for children in order to avoid taking them out of classes for dental care. As an outgrowth of the Council's interest, a school calendar was mimeographed and made available to all dentists and physicians in the community.

Besides acting as a co-ordinating and advisory body, the Fond du Lac School Health Council takes time for in-service education of its members. Members also preview films together, evaluate health textbooks, and visit school lunch programs.

If you should be in Fond du Lac sometime on a third Tuesday, why don't you stop at the Elks Club and visit us? You will be welcomed heartily. We need new ideas, and there will always be a place at the table for you.

The whole idea of health councils is sometimes surrounded with unnecessary complications and needless confusion. A health council need not be a pompous organization bogged down under operating codes, bylaws, and other impediments. The best health council depends upon the voluntary gathering together of lay and professional people with similar interests to exchange ideas, to get better acquainted, to attack mutual problems, and to become personal friends. Such a health council can be completely informal and at the same time represent a highly effective means of adult health education and of school and community health improvement.

SELECTED REFERENCES

AMERICAN ASSOCIATION FOR HEALTH, PHYSICAL EDUCATION, AND RECREATION. *Developing Democratic Human Relations*. First Yearbook. Washington, D.C.: the Association, a department of the National Education Association, 1951. 562 p.

AMERICAN ASSOCIATION OF SCHOOL ADMINISTRATORS. *Health in Schools*. Revised edition. Twentieth Yearbook. Washington, D.C.: the Association, a department of the National Education Association, 1951. 477 p. Chapter XI, "Health Aspects of Adult Education."

BIDDLE, WILLIAM W. *The Cultivation of Community Leaders: Up from the Grass Roots*. New York: Harper & Brothers, 1953. 203 p.

BUELL, BRADLEY, and OTHERS. *Community Planning for Human Services*. New York: Columbia University Press, 1952. 464 p.

COLCORD, JOANNA C. *Your Community: Its Provisions for Health, Education, Safety, and Welfare*. (Revised by Donald S. Howard.) New York: Russell Sage Foundation, 1947. 263 p.

GINSBURG, ETHEL. *Public Health Is People*. Cambridge, Mass.: Commonwealth Fund, Harvard University Press, 1950. 241 p.

HENDRICKSON, ANDREW. "Adult Education." *Encyclopedia of Educational Research*. Revised edition. (Edited by Chester W. Harris.) New York: Macmillan Co., 1960. p. 30-42.

HILLMAN, ARTHUR. *Community Organization and Planning*. New York: Macmillan Co., 1950. 378 p.

KLEINSCHMIDT, H. E., and ZIMAND, SAVEL. *Public Health Education: Its Tools and Procedures*. New York: Macmillan Co., 1953. 302 p.

KNOWLES, MALCOLM, editor. *Handbook of Adult Education in the United States*. Chicago, Ill.: Adult Education Association of the U.S.A., 1960. 624 p.

KOOS, EARL LOMON. *The Health of Regionville*. New York: Columbia University Press, 1954. 177 p.

MURRAY, JANET P., and MURRAY, CLYDE E. *Guide Lines for Group Leaders; the Why and How of Group Work*. New York: William Morrow & Co., 1954. 224 p.

NEW YORK ACADEMY OF MEDICINE. *Motivation in Health Education*. Report of the 1947 Health Education Conference. New York: Columbia University Press, 1948. 53 p.

NEW YORK ACADEMY OF MEDICINE. *Psychological Dynamics of Health Education*. Proceedings of the Eastern States Health Education Conference, April 13-14, 1950. New York: Columbia University Press, 1951. 134 p.

PATTERSON, RAYMOND S., and ROBERTS, BERYL J. *Community Health Education in Action*. St. Louis: C. V. Mosby Co., 1951. 346 p.

PATTERSON, ROBERT G. *Foundations of Community Health Education*. New York: McGraw-Hill Book Co., 1950. 288 p.

PAUL, B. D., and MILLER, W. B., editors. *Health, Culture and Community*. New York: Russell Sage Foundation, 1955. 493 p.

TURNER, CLAIR E. *Community Health Educator's Compendium of Knowledge*. St. Louis: C. V. Mosby Co., 1951. 266 p.

VERNER, COOLIE, and NEWBERRY, JOHN S., JR. "The Nature of Adult Participation." *Adult Education* 8: 208-22; Summer 1958.

CONSULTANTS

Appreciation is expressed to the following consultants for reviewing preliminary drafts of various chapters and presenting constructive suggestions for improvements.

Ross L. Allen
Director, Health, Physical Education, and Recreation
State University College of Education
Cortland, New York

Hester Beth Bland
Consultant, Health and Physical Education
Indiana State Board of Health
Indianapolis, Indiana

Leroy E. Burney, M.D.
Surgeon General
U.S. Public Health Service
Washington, D.C.

Oliver E. Byrd, M.D.
Professor of Health Education and Executive Head, Department of Health Education
Stanford University
Stanford, California

Gertrude B. Couch
Associate Professor of Health Education
University of Illinois
Urbana, Illinois

Mayhew Derryberry
Chief, Public Health Education Services
U.S. Public Health Service
Washington, D.C.

Ruth E. Grout
Professor, School of Public Health and College of Education
University of Minnesota
Minneapolis, Minnesota

Eugene H. Guthrie, M.D.
Chief Program Officer, Bureau of State Services
U.S. Public Health Service
Washington, D.C.

Marian V. Hamburg
School Health Consultant
American Heart Association
New York, New York

Ann Wilson Haynes
Chief, Bureau of Health Education
California State Department of Public Health
Berkeley, California

Patricia J. Hill
Consultant in School Health Education
California State Department of Education
Sacramento, California

H. S. Hoyman, Ed.D.
Head, Department of Health and Safety Education
University of Illinois
Urbana, Illinois

Andie L. Knutson
Lecturer in Public Health; Director, Behavioral Science Project
School of Public Health
University of California
Berkeley, California

Charlotte Leach
Consultant, Health Education
National Tuberculosis Association
New York, New York

Margaret J. McKibben
Assistant Executive Secretary
National Science Teachers Association
National Education Association
Washington, D.C.

Malcolm H. Merrill, M.D.
Director of Public Health
California Department of Public Health
Berkeley, California

409

John L. Miller
Superintendent of Schools
Great Neck, New York

Thelma S. Morris
Associate in Health Education
National Tuberculosis Association
New York, New York

Josiah G. Neal
Managing Director, Minnesota Tuberculosis and Health Association
St. Paul, Minnesota

Carl N. Neupert, M.D.
State Health Officer
Wisconsin State Board of Health
Madison, Wisconsin

Delbert Oberteuffer
Professor of Health Education
The Ohio State University
Columbus, Ohio

Norbert Reinstein
Program Director
Tuberculosis and Health Society
Detroit, Michigan

Beryl J. Roberts
Associate Professor of Health
 Education
University of California
Berkeley, California

Mabel E. Rugen
Professor of Health Education
The University of Michigan
Ann Arbor, Michigan

Perry Sandell
Director, Bureau of Dental Health
 Education
American Dental Association
Chicago, Illinois

Jerome L. Schulman, M.D.
Director, Child Guidance Clinic and
 Child Development Clinic
Children's Memorial Hospital
Chicago, Illinois

Thomas E. Shaffer, M.D.
Professor of Pediatrics and
 Preventive Medicine
College of Medicine
The Ohio State University
Columbus, Ohio

C. Morley Sellery, M.D.
Formerly, Director, Health Education and Health Services
Los Angeles City Schools
Los Angeles, Cailfornia

Elsa Schneider
Specialist in Health, Physical
 Education and Safety
U.S. Office of Education
Washington, D.C.

Margaret Stevenson
Executive Secretary, Department
 of Classroom Teachers
National Education Association
Washington, D. C.

Wilson B. Thiede
Professor of Education
University of Wisconsin
Madison, Wisconsin

Ora R. Wakefield
Health Education Coordinator
Nashville Public Schools
Nashville, Tennessee

Helen M. Wallace, M.D.
Chief of Professional Training
U.S. Children's Bureau
Washington, D.C.

Frederick A. White
Bureau of Audio-Visual Instruction
University of Wisconsin
Madison, Wisconsin

Walter A. Wittich
Professor of Education
University of Wisconsin
Madison, Wisconsin

Marjorie A. C. Young
Assistant Professor of Health
 Education
Harvard School of Public Health
Boston, Massachusetts

INDEX

411

Mortality records by ages, and curriculum planning, 127

Motion pictures (*see also* Filmstrips)
Desirable features, 291-92
Film evaluation file, 295
Film libraries, 295
Limitations of, 292
Procedure for use, 293-94
Sources, 295, 307, 308
Teacher preview, 293
Use in health teaching, 291-95, 398

Motivation
In health behavior, 97-99, 100-101, 102
In health teaching, 102, 178-79, 200-203, 235-36, 284

Muscular development, in kindergarten and primary grades, 60

Music, in correlated health program, 262-63

Narcotics
Correlated health program, secondary school, 255, 258
State education codes re, 231, 242
Temperance Movement, stimulus to instruction, 17

National Association of Secondary-School Principals, 123

National Commission on Safety Education, 172

National Conference for Cooperation in Health Education, Committee on School Health Policies, 124, 195, 204, 218, 404, 405

National Conference on College Health Education, 370, 371, 375

National Conference on Fitness of Secondary School Youth, 125

National Conference on Health in Colleges, Third, 364, 369, 370; Fourth, 369

National Conference on the Undergraduate Health Education Minor Program, 378

National Congress of Parents and Teachers, 223, 401, 402, 405

National Education Association, 2, 3, 6, 7, 18, 124, 125, 171, 172, 195, 202, 218, 309, 324, 341, 350, 370, 375, 378, 393, 404

National Health Survey (1957-58), 46

National Office of Vital Statistics, 24, 25, 26, 27, 28, 29, 30, 33, 38, 39, 40, 42

National Safety Council, 171, 333

National Society for the Prevention of Blindness, 45

National Tape Recording Catalog, 288

National Tuberculosis Association, 18, 240, 364, 369, 370

Needs, health. *See* Health needs.

Nelson, W. E., 54

Nervous disorder, chronic adult disease, 387

Newspaper, as adult health education medium, 397

Niacin, identification of, 81

Nightingale, Florence, 261

"Normality" in growth and development discussed, 58, 68, 71

Nurse, contributions of, 11, 160, 391 (*see also* School nurse)

Nursing, home, college course in, 376

Nutrition. *See* Food and nutrition.

Nutritionist, as resource person, 306

Oberteuffer, Delbert, 220

Obesity, health problem, 49, 62, 388-89

Objectives. *See* Goals and objectives.

O'Brien, Ruth, 35

Observation
Evaluation technique, 343, 346, 348, 350-51
Identification of health needs, 146-47, 169, 230

Oppenheimer, E., 56

Organizations (*see also by specific names*)
Adult health education opportunities, 401-402
Commercial, health resource materials, 311-12

Palmer, Carroll E., 35

Parents
Attitudes toward health, 348, 354
Health care responsibilities, 5
School nurse, contacts with, 322-23

Passamanick, B., 55

Passow, A. Harry, 120

Pasteur, Louis, 14, 79, 261

Patty, W. W., 379

Pediatrics, 311